BERTRAND RUSSELL: PHILOSOPHER OF THE CENTURY

BERTRAND RUSSELL
Philosopher of the Century

ESSAYS IN HIS HONOUR
EDITED BY
RALPH SCHOENMAN

A. J. AYER	VICTOR PURCELL, CMG
WERNER BLOCH	HILARY PUTNAM
MAX BORN	HERBERT READ
C. D. BROAD	HANS REICHENBACH
ERICH FROMM	MARIA REICHENBACH
ALDOUS HUXLEY	DANA SCOTT
GEORG KREISEL	REV. MICHAEL SCOTT
CONSTANCE MALLESON	I. F. STONE
LINUS PAULING	JULIAN TREVELYAN
W. V. QUINE	

An Atlantic Monthly Press Book
LITTLE, BROWN AND COMPANY · BOSTON · TORONTO

LIBRARY OF CONGRESS CATALOG CARD NO. 67-21096

Second Printing

ATLANTIC–LITTLE, BROWN BOOKS
ARE PUBLISHED BY
LITTLE, BROWN AND COMPANY
IN ASSOCIATION WITH
THE ATLANTIC MONTHLY PRESS

PRINTED IN THE UNITED STATES OF AMERICA

BERTRAND RUSSELL: PHILOSOPHER OF THE CENTURY

PREFACE

In preparing this volume I have drawn together essays which suggest Bertrand Russell's achievement. In what roles is he to be portrayed? Is it as ironist and puck, impassioned defier of cruel authority, wit, iconoclast, moral reformer, literary stylist, teller of parables and stories, educationalist, benefactor of great talents and causes, teacher, social theorist, philosopher, political activist, liberator of the abandoned, mathematician, logician or natural scientist—what is the formula for intimating his range and rarity?

I am not satisfied that this collection does what is needed. I do not disparage any of the contributions, neither as an editor nor as a critic. The essays achieve an approximation, hopefully overlapping but a little, yet leaving gaps and depending ultimately on the reader to supply a sense of unity for Russell's diversity of excellence.

I should wish to place on one side the editor's mask and speak personally. Before knowing Russell he already loomed in my mind as legendary—a man of da Vincian accomplishment, a rebel and controversialist whose fierce independence stirred me deeply. I discovered his work during my first year at Princeton University. Professor H. H. Wilson had drawn me to Princeton with his written attacks on the American witch-hunt, that 'concentration camp for the mind' then under noisy construction.

On arrival in Princeton I cornered Wilson and demanded to know if he were the H. H. Wilson who wrote for the *Nation*. Wilson asked if I had unpacked my bags. I said I had. 'Pack them', he said. He observed my shock and told me quietly: 'If you stick around: two things: (1) Maintain a sense of humour. (2) If you want to criticize orthodoxy, master it.' I was ill prepared for Princeton—its callow superiority, insularity and throw-back cruelty. I recall how I went into battle. 'You have', Wilson cautioned me later, 'an innate capacity for erecting brick walls and using your head as a battering ram.'

Russell's *Unpopular Essays* was just out in paper. It gave me more joy than I can recall receiving from anything in print. There was 'An Outline of Intellectual Rubbish' with its instance of the nun who always wore a bathrobe when bathing. Asked why since no man could see her, she replied, 'Oh, but you forget the good God'. 'Apparently', wrote Russell, 'they conceive of the Deity as a Peeping Tom whose omnipotence enables him to see through bathroom walls but who is foiled by bathrobes.'

Every turn of phrase and chosen irony gave me pure delight. I felt liberated. Days after reading the book I would smile and laugh to

1

myself, ferret it out and re-read passages. I did not share the sentences which pleased me to a point of tears. I was determined to acquire the Russell touch—to become deft and light and devastating. At Princeton there was a Chaucer specialist, Roberts, who was a fine scholar, caustic and Catholic. 'Well, Schoenman,' he said one afternoon, 'what does the liberal mind have to say? We want the lowest common denominator.' 'I'm an authoritarian, Mr Roberts', was my reply. 'I was waiting for the word of God.' I carried Russell's style in my head as best as my head could carry it. I read all I found and began to proselytize.

My friend, Godfrey Winham, and a small group agreed with conscious irony that Russell was our candidate for god. But we did worship him. He offered us that just combination of passionate rebellion and humour which saved us (we were certain) from the priggish and unrelieved simple mindedness required to do battle with America's cruelty, crassness and the impenetrable, superior manner of the chosen Princetonian.

I took up philosophy and planned to go to England for further study. Refused a passport, I lost two years before obtaining one through the courts. It was not long after arriving for post-graduate studies at the LSE that I joined in with the 'new left' and the CND. It was 1958.

Russell was President of the CND. I first saw him in the flesh at Easter in Trafalgar Square. His vigour and passion exulted me but it did not occur to me to approach him. I had no justifiable reason for doing so and I had a thing about 'seeking out' the great. It seemed to me unbecoming, fetish-making and at war with the very reasons for admiring men like Russell. Years earlier I had declined an invitation to Albert Einstein's by a friend of my parents who knew him, because it seemed to me wrong to visit a great and admired man for no better reason than the desire to see him. When I heard that Einstein, whom I revered, had made some approving comment on my Princeton activity I was elated but still determined not to see him for the sake of it. I had done some work as an assistant at the Institute for Advanced Study and met him by chance but did not pursue this. This slightly ridiculous determination to avoid the great without legitimate grounds for contact, stayed with me despite my intense sense of loss and failed opportunity when Einstein died in 1955. I placed an anonymous rose at his door on the anniversary of his death for three years running.

Although active in the CND and on its Youth Executive I did not approach Russell until April 1960. I had definite views on the future of the movement, views long discussed and carefully worked out.

2

I wanted Russell's opinions and guidance concerning these thoughts on theory and strategy of the anti-nuclear struggle; but I retained a puritanical reluctance about seeking out the great man, the better to enhance ideas which, I felt, should stand or fall on their merit.

I decided it was in order to place these thoughts before Russell and wrote him. He replied inviting me to discuss and I telephoned him to fix an appointment. I hitch-hiked to North Wales, excited and with brief fantasies flitting through my head of finding him impressed with my notions and of an ensuing relationship. I rejected these daydreams as wish-fulfilments, and prepared to speak seriously on matters which seemed then and now to be important.

I arrived late, after predictable disasters with rain, diversions and strange roads nowhere indicated on the map. The towering figure of my imagination was certain to be impatient with this unforgivable lateness and possibly caustic. I cursed myself for the incompetence and folly which led me to jeopardize so valued and serious a meeting.

To this day I retain something of the awe with which I came to that first encounter. I can not now pass a bookshop without blinking to think that it is that Bertrand Russell, that giant figure who is the same gentle warm and unassuming man I have known so intimately these seven years. I feel still a certain astonishment, an awareness which renews itself, that the lovable, unselfconsciously modest mien of Bertrand Russell corresponds to the figure who is central to our era, our history and whose accomplishment is so vast.

His welcome on that day was immediate and expansive. He remarked wryly on my soaked clothes. I was unsure whether to call him Lord Russell; or was it Earl Russell? I did not think it could be Mr Russell, but then it might have been.

'I had the same problem', he said, a few minutes after my hesitant opening, 'with the Aga Khan.' During dinner the warmth he generated dissolved the tense apprehension with which I had met him. His wife, Edith Russell, was immensely kind. I was offered a change of clothes—one of Russell's suits, an honour I declined although I wound up wearing his pyjamas that night when it was discovered that I had neglected to bring my own.

Our first conversation dwelt on the disparity between the nuclear danger we proclaimed and the methods we proposed for confronting it. There was a mélange of banter and intense pronouncement on the pity of human folly, the evident determination of men to murder and die on a larger scale than previously managed.

Our movement was telling people that men lived from moment to moment with the imminent possibility of annihilation. Rockets combed the planet, dependent upon warning systems varying from thirty seconds to fifteen minutes. The radar upon which these weapons of mass murder attended could not distinguish a goose from a cabinet minister, let alone a missile. Any insurance company dealing with commercial aircraft or automobiles on the road would set out tables for mean numbers of annual accidents and the same was applicable to the nuclear technology. With each day that passed, the probability of accident increased to a point of near certainty. Eye blink-rates were the same in the East as in the West. So was the propensity for hallucination, hysteria or electrical failure—things not dependent upon either nationality or ideology. The dangers of accidental nuclear war could be posed as a simple problem in mathematical statistics. When the accident might occur could not be said, but sooner or later, as the variables multiplied, it would come.

These were the elements of the argument concerning the imminence of nuclear war by accident; the problem we considered was what was available to us to do to stop it. It did not seem to be apathy which inhibited popular action but paralysis, that sense of powerlessness and futility which oppresses people overwhelmed with the enormity of the problem and of the society they inhabit.

The argument: 'We are in imminent danger of mass annihilation; join our annual march' seemed pathetic and we discussed the forms of struggle which had a potential of success and could be seen to be capable of achieving the end in view. Russell was eager to begin such an attempt and to start a movement quickly which would be more in keeping with the needs of the situation. He was ready to throw himself into the undertaking, heart and soul—to risk anything.

This quality is typical of the man and is in evidence as much now as then, even if the nature of the problem has altered in important respects and our struggle has taken on new aspects and theoretical bases.

He could, without any difficulty, have continued speaking and writing for the CND as its President. Above the mêlée, he could have sponsored other like bodies and restricted his role to that of honorary executive and titular head. Who could have asked more of him? Instead, at 88, he began a movement of civil disobedience, enraging the cultivators of popular-unpopular causes, those indulgent phrasemakers who plague every dissident movement with their reformist illusions and irrelevant ambition. Russell's life is distinguished by personal involvement, readiness for sacrifice and indifference to comfort and convenience. He commits all he has to what he believes. The discussion we had was intense. There was a sense of urgency which grew and plans emerged for action.

I know what he risked and what he went through. He threw in his lot with untried youngsters distinguished only by their commitment. He rebuffed blandishments and intimations of Nobel honour. He incurred venemous hostility from nominal admirers, creatures of fashion and shallow snobs who were ready for anything except personal sacrifice in struggle. There were frenzied efforts to bully him into submission. I reflect on the hours spent, the threats made, the slanders fostered, the peculiar sadism of journalists and others. His heroic determination and his role will astonish posterity as much as any earlier example of these constant qualities in his rich life.

My first meeting with Russell will remain with me. His wife, Edith Russell, is inseparable from his deepest concerns. Her knowledge and love of his past, his friends, his literary and historical interests and favourites make their partnership something moving to observe. His humour, his passions and his hates are also hers. Russell's happiness, extraordinary vitality, mental agility and involvement reflect this relationship. He is engaged and looking ahead at all moments. I think it is because he is basically content.

At times during that first meeting he would catch me staring at him. 'I attribute my longevity to controversy', he said with a smile. I had not been marvelling at his years but I was transfixed by the clarity, the precision, the warmth, the wry humour and dry wit—that permeating presence which works on the senses like ozone after a storm.

I try to remind myself of the full meaning of living and working with him: his warmth surrounding word and gesture, the small acts—the minutiae of life. Those who lay claim to the use of language inadequately prepare the imagination to grasp his achievement. Much of the writing about Russell transmits something short of the man.

I have known him six years during which our contact has been constant. The things that have happened and the pace of events strike me at the vantage of present involvement as momentous—the meetings and movements, the secret parleys and plans with heads of state, the mediation, the death-sentences commuted, the near successes in great things. He is in full command. He works and speaks to series of visitors, turning the phrase and prising up from that unfathomable memory the brief encounter which places in focus some current event. Many incidents in the on-going work can be related only at a later time. There are events and whole chapters to which my mind turns in the desire to say more of the meaning Russell holds for me and of his present activity in the Bertrand Russell Peace Foundation.

Despite the unremitting contact with the press, despite the panoply of public personages visiting, the interviews and endless television, the press carries lies about his full activity implying the opposite of the truth known to the editor or reporter concerned. Journals for whom lying is endemic and in the grain of their wood run true to character now as before. In a sense this is only grist to the mill which will grind down the malicious with their own malevolence. There is the case of the Sunday newspaper which ran an invented interview representing Russell as retired, remote, rarely seeing people and shut away from British journalists despite the fact that Russell had been seen by eight heads of state and foreign ministers, had completed two films and ten hours of television in the previous month inclusive of the period when the article was published. There is a strict counterpoint between the extent of his public activity, the degree of his personal and visible involvement and the pattern of calculated lying by newspapers which have made the truth unfamiliar.

People are surprised when these things are pointed out. The surprise is the fruit of chosen ignorance not unlike the case of American war crimes in Vietnam. People choose not to know about the gas and chemicals and the dismay shown by late discoverers is understandable but not entirely credible. Humbug, the constant object of Russellian scorn is varyingly present but unusually discernable.

The *New York Times* attacked him for accusing the Americans of chemical warfare, then published his rejoinder while excising the sentences specifying the chemicals by name and property. The paper ran an editorial censoring him for lack of evidence. Written undertakings of honourable professional conduct by newspapers and television companies are frequently broken. British film libraries contain long sequences showing Russell on demonstrations, speaking at meetings, huddled with heads of state, at press conferences and all this film is catalogued: 'Not to be shown anywhere in the United Kingdom'—fine tribute from those who are right to fear him.

The public importance of his activity during these incredible years cannot be fully developed here. In these pages I want to suggest the quality of the man in all his rich subtlety. Conversation with him is memorable and dramatic carrying the fine strands of his sensibility which catch the light and refract it like a prism. His words are used with delight and care. His talk is an entertainment in a culture where the characteristic mode of passing time is vicarious, passive and uniform. Russell's rich, varied mind exults in shaping experience through banter and dialogue, sharp anecdote, pronouncement and description. He has a quivering alertness but is at ease, always calm and vastly gentle. The qualities merge and separate. They are like a stream with tides leaving different residue and deposit on the banks of the receptive mind.

6

His writing is not a substitute for his person. He is supremely unlike the writer who astounds us by his ordinariness and for whom the written word is a release, embodying a personality born of projection. In Russell the verbal faculty is preserved and cultivated. It is fully explored and realized. He practises precisely that art of communication which seems to atrophy in people reliant upon media, who linger in that decay of intellect and sensibility which Russell's life and style deny.

His humour is a rich study. He can be mocking but it is gently done. He is derisive of pretension. He lays bare motive swiftly but it is a Socratic procedure, pointing up unseen implications or careless usage. I can not recall an instance of maliciousness in all the quips and stories, the barbed remarks and anecdotes which, taken together, comprise so unequalled a store of wisdom in wit.

He quickly discerns the beginnings of direction in remarks and he tends away from the path indicated. There are small collisions separating the components of the ideas advanced, preparing for their more excellent reconstruction. In this the humour is central. One would open: 'To be frank, I rather think . . .' 'And when you are not frank? . . .' Russell might begin, eyes sparkling. Or a long, tortuous exposition laden with latin endings will prompt: 'What you mean is you don't like it', and the expression on his face is gay.

We were preparing for a series of television interviews. Russell sensed they wanted him to be titillating and sparing of convention. He dislikes prepared talk. 'They would have me in my anecdotage', he said. His love of conversation is, perhaps, related to the age which shaped him—that world without telephone or wireless, automobile or aircraft, electric light, indoor plumbing or World War. It is a world in the fore of his mind and a canvas for the morning paper. There is no age barrier with him: Russell the ungarrulous, Russell with the pun on tongue, the wit which is clean and precise always working, Russell making art of simple moments.

We are separated by sixty-four years. His talk is studded with mention of Gladstone, Tennyson, Morris, Kropotkin, Bismarck, Lenin, Victoria, Poincaré, Mill, Browning, Wilde—people he knew or disputed. The conversation is relived and I share the first meaning. 'How close were you to Bakunin, Bertie?' 'Not all that close, but then I wasn't well acquainted with Methuselah either', and the laughter we have so often shared is with us.

His grandfather who was born during the French Revolution visited Napoleon at Elba, instituted the Reform Bill and raised Russell after the early death of his parents. Russell's maternal grandmother had visited the Pretender's widow.

'We were always brought up to feel that history stopped in 1815; after that it's gossip.'

He speaks with feeling of his parents who campaigned for birth control, free thinking, women's rights and popular education; and of his godfather, John Stuart Mill, whose style so influenced Russell. He early mastered the written word, writing out or dictating ten or thirty thousand words without a crossing-out or an alteration. If he has an article to prepare he will begin to write and when his pen falls he will have written the number of words required—no less, no more. His command of language is complete, woven into his thoughts and as effortless as the words he speaks. He can take up quickly the manner of others. His imitations of Gladstone or MacDonald are compelling. His words draw their depth from the odyssey of his life. He went up to Cambridge in 1890 with a generation which produced a plethora of exceptional men. His family pressed a political career on him and he was attached briefly to the embassy in Paris at the time of Dreyfus.

Berlin in the nineties, the forming of the Fabians, London with forty per cent at starvation, physics without quanta or Einstein, butchery in Leopold's Congo, Sir Edward Grey's deceitful war plans in 1902, the great Principia and Frege writing: 'Arithmetic totters'—the Russell years embody so many full, accomplished and extraordinary lives in the unity of his own.

The intricate memory and the wit, his passionate sense of the present, his elemental kindness—these colours are of one supremely integrated painting on which the eye may rest many times without exhaustion. At different vantages the pattern changes and surprises but the integration and beauty remain and grow. 'God bless you, my dear boy, if there be such a being; but, in any case, take care of yourself.' He said goodbye to me as I left for China, quoting Bentham's words to Owen's son.

Russell had nearly died in China. He was in a coma for a fortnight and was visited by Dewey toward the expected end. The *Manchester Guardian*, somewhat over-eager, had already published his obituary. Fifteen years later, Russell parodied an obituary he anticipated from *The Times* after a further twenty-six years, but 1962 came and *The Times* was still without its opportunity. When Russell addressed the LSE, some forty years after his inaugural lecture there, the Chairman introduced him as a Victorian fossil, a remark which Russell recalled to the students of LSE who heard him a quarter of a century later in 1961.

During Dewey's visit to a dying Russell in Peking in 1921, Russell outlined plans for ending national disputes, discussed avidly the situation in China and his debates with the leader of the Chinese Communist Party, Chen Tu-hsu, debates which had gripped China's intellectuals and which influenced the young Mao Tse-tung and Chu Teh. Dewey broke down before the passion, sense of fun and restless intelligence radiating from Russell on his presumed death-bed.

Forty years after this he addressed a large rally of the Youth CND in Birmingham without disclosing the great pain engulfing him. He had a severe case of shingles and was seriously ill. In bed and uncomfortable he completed *Has Man a Future?*, numerous articles and regaled Michael Scott and others with stories and plans for the anti-nuclear struggle. I have seen him endure people for hours, submit to a tedious interview and then do a public meeting although exhausted.

A week prior to the press conference which launched the Bertrand Russell Peace Foundation he came down with flu and ran a temperature of 104. The fever drained his energy and he became weak. Observing the anxiety in my face he told again of Voltaire's words when, on his deathbed, the bedclothes caught fire from a candle: 'Des flammes, déjà?' The day before the press conference he was up and about and no one could have detected illness or frailty during the hour that he spoke and answered questions. His quiet courage has sustained him through crises and personal suffering which few would have endured with equanimity or success.

During World War One he was banned from the coast by a Government which feared he would signal to German submarines. He lectured and spoke at meetings wherever possible. Physical danger was sometimes acute but his accounts are light and almost off-hand:

'We were attacked by drunken viragoes, wielding heavy boards with protruding rusty nails. They were hitting people over the head with these while the police stood by. One of the women with us said to a policeman, "You must save him". "Oh," said the policeman. "He's a well known philosopher." No reply. "He's an eminent mathematician." The policeman grunted. "He's a writer." Silence. "He's the brother of an earl." Then he rushed to save me.' If you question him you learn that he returned the following week and the podium from which he was speaking was set on fire.

Dismissed from Cambridge, betrayed by friends and colleagues, ostracized by the timid, he spoke, wrote, organized and gave himself in full vigour to the struggle. He was hurt above all by the behaviour of his friends and his Cambridge colleagues for he loved Cambridge intensely. His strict upbringing and fervid isolation ended in the

9

liberation he found in Cambridge, the intellectual camaraderie of brilliant companions devoted to disinterested knowledge. His love for Cambridge was such that when many of these same people ratted and acquiesced in or connived at his expulsion, it pained him too deeply to return. He finds invitations there difficult to accept and has not gone to his loved Cambridge for twenty years.

So many have benefited from Russell's instinctive largesse. His intellectual progeny cover five student generations. He was housing Eliot, comforting Conrad, guiding Wittgenstein and Lawrence, enchanting the Bloomsbury world, inspiring the Vienna Circle. The debt is indicated in Mr Apollinax. It is unstated in the Tractatus and deeply felt by Carnap for whom, when an unknown and impoverished student, Russell copied out all the definitions in Principia by hand. Russell had carried out a Copernican revolution in philosophy and in logic affecting all that followed him. Carnap, among the most profound of the logical empiricists, wrote in 1965: 'It was Bertrand Russell from whom I learned the scientific method in philosophy . . . in my philosophical thinking I learned most from (him). Passages (from *Our Knowledge of the External World*) made an especially vivid impression on me . . . I felt as if his appeal had been directed to me personally. To work in this spirit would be my task from now on!' Carnap rates Russell as indisputably the century's greatest philosopher, whose contribution to mathematical logic is unequalled since Aristotle.

Einstein and Russell intensely admired one another. They had spent many hours together at Einstein's home discussing in a small group the most abstruse and trying questions to do with mathematical physics and logic. Later, Einstein's support for Russell's initiative launched the Pugwash Movement of scientists. Russell speaks of Einstein as the most lovable and genuinely good man he has known. In 1946 Einstein wrote of Russell's *History of Western Philosophy*: 'I don't know whether one should more admire the delightful freshness and originality or the sensitivity and sympathy with distant times and remote intellects on the part of this great thinker. I regard it as fortunate that so arid and brutal a generation can claim this wise, honourable, bold and humorous man. It is a work in the highest degree pedagogical which stands outside the conflicts of parties and set opinions.'

Einstein was affected by the persecution of Russell during the New York City College drama, when he was dismissed and later faced trial. He wrote this unpublished poem in 1940:

On Russell

It keeps repeating itself
In this world fine and honest
The parson alarms the populace
The genius is executed.

It is odd that a man so true to himself should be accused of inconsistency. Those who do this are dead to the life of greatness and deaf to its death. Russell gave away his wealth and inheritance before he was thirty as he did not believe in inherited wealth. The recipients were educational and political movements he favoured; he has lived since on the earnings from his writings and lectures.

He experimented in education, applied all his brilliance to the cause of rationality in sex and wrote scathingly, with panache, about tired dogma and oppressive religion. The inevitable outrage afforded him many delightful moments and much hardship. He emphasizes the former. The Bishop of Rochester pleased him by stating that every word Russell had written was inspired by sexual lust.

Russell enjoys the surprise people provide who turn out unexpectedly. 'Arthur Balfour was reading an account of certain excesses in Serbia during the First War. "On occasion", the passage went, "priests were known to violate their cows", a pleasant misprint. Balfour had written in the margin: "Seems a case for a Papal Bull." ' He has opposed cruelty and stupidity in the full and many ways open to him for seventy-five years. Their promoters and defenders abuse him no less now than then. His words are suppressed all the while that the media seek and proclaim their grounds for supporting the napalm bombing of peasants, the gassing of villagers and the torture of revolutionaries. But he loves to reflect on the transitory nature of this speck of dust, the limitless spaces and the moment in time during which our planet makes its appearance.

His natural surroundings are essential to him. Abstraction and the world of language vibrate through Russell because he brings them close to life. For years he took walks exceeding twenty-five miles. He walked over the Alps from Innsbruck to Venice and in Wales his trained eye drinks the sun and fields. He knows most plants by sight and name.

This breadth and felt perspective permit him to treat abuse rightly as evidence that he is scoring. If he is hurt it is by those among the many who have benefited from his instinctive kindness and have then turned on him either to curry favour with the powerful or because, as he often observes, nothing is so little forgiven as a favour rendered. He has been hurt always by individuals of whom he had hopes and to whom he has given much. Russell, when all is said, values feeling and personal affection above everything.

He is 95. All the excitement remains: the energy and the élan, the passion for early Church music, the great love of poetry and the limitless recollection of cherished lines and passages, the feeling for drama, the vast knowledge of scriptures and the small ironies of old cultures—these things are with him and always shared. It is his sensibility, his passion for language, his hatred of humbug and pedantry, the great love of irony and paradox which excite every moment in his presence. This is the Bertrand Russell I cherish and whom this volume honours—the poetry of the man, the generosity of which he is unaware, the fullness of his life, his rich completion. I celebrate the beauty of Bertie for nothing touches this—not the meanness nor the smallness nor the hostility of pathetic men ridden with envy and the poison of their inadequacy. He needs no metaphor.

CONTENTS

SECTION IV: MATHEMATICIAN AND LOGICIAN

I

AN INTIMATE GLANCE

CONSTANCE MALLESON

Fifty Years: 1916–1966

The first time that I was aware of setting eyes on Russell was in the drab surroundings of Lavender Hill police station. The date was August 1916.

He was sitting at the far end of a wooden bench, and though he seemed curiously detached in mind and body, all the furies of hell raged in his eyes. H. N. Brailsford once wrote of Burke (in *Shelley, Godwin and their Circle*), that 'the evil which caused his mind to blaze was nearly always cruelty', that 'he had a nerve which twitched with a maddening sensitiveness at the sight of suffering'. Exactly the same could be said of Russell; and said even when he had caused the suffering. At Lavender Hill we were only briefly introduced and had no talk. Early in the following month, however, we found ourselves placed side by side at a political dinner—after which he walked back with me to my Bloomsbury attic. He was rather shy in those days. He seemed humble, simple, a 'real human being'. Those qualities appear, I think, in a brief letter he wrote (from Lynton, North Devon, in December 1918) to my mother:

'Dear Lady Annesley,
    I am venturing to send you a book of mine, *Mysticism and Logic*, for Christmas. I am afraid it is not very interesting, but nature designed me for a pedant so I can't help it. I wanted to let you know somehow how very much I feel your kindness to me, but it is very difficult to express things of that sort, even when one's good wishes are very strong and real.

                                        Yours very sincerely,

                                        Bertrand Russell.'

Not until several months after our first meeting did I begin to understand that he was the most complicated of men, a mass of contradictions, and often torn between reason and emotion. I was very young and inexperienced (exactly young enough to have been his daughter), so it was natural that I was at first struck by his simple and impulsive qualities, which prevented me from feeling as shy with him as I did with other—far less distinguished—personages.

Although everybody who worked with him gloried in his scintillating (and corrosive) wit, and in his immense learning and scientific fame, one frequently felt that he was a brilliant and unique diamond amongst the homespun of the rest of us. Standing on my doorstep, that September night, he said goodbye; and then walked off, a lonely figure, in the direction of his brother's house in Gordon Square.

Ten days later, on September 23rd, he was chief speaker at the N.C.F. Convention in the Portman Rooms. Though he assured me that he hated public speaking, one could never have guessed it; for he spoke fluently, distinctly, with immense sincerity and a passionate conviction which broke through his slightly pedantic pronunciation. The young N.C.F. members were intensely moved that a man of his outstanding attainments had placed himself so unreservedly at their service. They gave him a tremendous ovation. They knew that he had been prosecuted—and fined £100 with costs—for having written in defence of Everett, a school teacher of strong religious convictions, who had been handed over to the military and sentenced to serve two years' penal servitude. The consequences, for Russell, were that he was deprived of his lectureship in mathematics at Trinity College, Cambridge. As he refused to pay the fine, his belongings at Trinity were distrained upon.

After the Convention, he and I walked across the road and had supper together in the first restaurant we came to; and then walked back to my attic where we sat talking into the small hours. He, naturally, did most of the talking. Sitting very upright before a horrible little gas fire, his body rather stiff, he prodded home his words with those blunt, expressive fingers of his. 'It's not so simple as that——' The phrase cropped up again and again in his talk. Life (he said) was not simple. . . . The spirit of socialism was not likeable. . . . Freedom should be the basis of everything. There was a world of peace, and one could live in it and yet be active still over all that was bad in the world. . . . One wanted to live always open to the world. . . . One wanted personal love to be like a beacon *fire* lighting up the darkness, not a timid refuge from the cold as it often was. . . . Some of one's thoughts and feelings were just of the moment, but others were part of the eternal world, part of the real history of the universe, not only of the separate person. That was how one wanted to live, so that as much of life as possible might have that quality of eternity. Of course one didn't succeed in living like that; but it was 'the shining key to peace'. (The phrase was mine and I felt so proud hearing it from his lips.)

He went on to speak of how one felt an alien among people with whom one could not communicate in a language they could understand. . . . One lived with the pain of the world and with all the cruelty of it. . . . One felt one must know and understand and not live softly with comfortable lies. . . . One fought and battled for hope, and grew weary in the struggle. There was often more of will than anything else in the faith one lived by. . . . One could not conquer without the sternness of long effort. . . . One was strangely unhappy because the pattern of one's life was complicated. . . . The centre of one was always and eternally a terrible pain—a curious wild pain —a searching for something beyond what the world contained, something transfigured and infinite—the beatific vision. One did not find it. . . . Perhaps it was not to be found; but the love of it was one's life. It was like passionate love for a ghost. At times it filled one with rage, at times with wild despair, it was the source of gentleness and cruelty and work, it filled every passion one had, it was the actual spring of life within one. One could not explain it or make it seem anything but foolishness. . . . One had known others who had it— Joseph Conrad especially. . . . It made people's gospels often seem thin. It gave one a sense of great isolation. One sought escape from it, though perhaps one ought not to. . . . The pain and cruelty and ugliness of the world was as well worth seeing as the joy and beauty of it. One had to look into hell before one had any right to speak of heaven.

After he had gone, I stood a long time staring at a picture of Edward Carpenter which hung on my wall; and I suddenly knew that Carpenter's creed meant nothing to me any more. I had found something stronger. Everything I had believed in had fallen away. Everything I had known and loved. I felt stunted and torn, but I knew I had found myself. Nothing was any use but courage. Soft things had no place in this world. One must keep strength and love and joy alive in one, to give to all mankind.

On March 31, 1917, the Albert Hall was packed from floor to ceiling, 'to congratulate the Russian People on the Revolution'. He and I went to the meeting together and stood in the body of the hall. The spirit of hope, which inspired that meeting, was not to be quenched (for us) until late June 1920 when he came back from Russia.

Meanwhile, in the first days of June 1917, we went to the Leeds Conference, where we were hissed through the streets while the local urchins hurled stones. In the month following, at the Brotherhood Church in North London, a roaring mob, the scum of the pubs, had been recruited to storm the meeting we were attending in the church. They battered in the doors which were locked and barred. They surged down the aisles. They used iron bars to break up the pews. Russell was at one moment physically threatened and—but for a steward's intervention—might have been injured seriously. When we at last mounted a passing tram, the mob tried to pull us off again.

Shortly afterwards, on July 29, we went for a longish holiday to a remote hamlet in Shropshire. What a contrast to the Brotherhood Church! We walked enormously, read Voltaire, bathed in the Teme, and shamelessly enjoyed the good farmhouse cooking. When we lay reading in blazing sunshine out in the orchard, Russell's heathery hair seemed almost to give off sparks like a heath fire. He wore it extremely short. Gun-metal dark above the ears, it was jet black where it ended in a widow's peak at the nape of the neck. And when he threw back his head and roared with laughter, the roar of his laughter echoed almost to the distant Clee Hills.

The Shropshire farmhouse again proved a refuge just before he went into Brixton Prison in May 1918. Previously, while he was still politically active in London, a whole day of walking in the country (always on a Sunday) was about the only rest he got. He was always a splendid walker, but it was not until our first Shropshire holiday that I learnt what an expert he was at laying a good fire; and also that he knew all Shakespeare's Sonnets by heart.

Out tramping one day in wild, tempestuous weather, he delighted me by perching on a brackeny bank and reeling off the whole of Shelley's *Ode to the West Wind*. It suited him: 'tameless, and swift, and proud'. While we tramped, he often held forth on every kind of subject, at times intelligible to my mind and at times not. Earlier, on the Derbyshire moors, in the freezing depths of winter, he had introduced me to what came to be called his 'ancient puzzle about egocentric particulars'. Now, in Shropshire, he returned to that subject and became so immersed in it that he entirely forgot the direction in which we were heading; thereby adding a good eight miles to our homeward path. But it was not until the Second World War that a letter from him reached me in Finland (it had taken 'only' five weeks from America), saying: 'I have just finished the book I wrote to you about before' (the *Inquiry into Meaning and Truth*), 'and have incidentally settled, to my satisfaction, my ancient puzzle about egocentric particulars.'

From May until September 1918, while he was incarcerated in Brixton, one was only able to visit him every second or third week. He was occupied with the *Introduction to Modern Logic*; and also *The Analysis of Mind*. In an early letter from Brixton he wrote: 'I have entirely ceased to worry about the personal future. If I had to divide my life, like Shaw's plays, into two halves, pleasant and unpleasant, this time would come in the pleasant half. . . .' As time wore on, however, he became weighed down by the state of the world. His letters became profoundly gloomy; although lit, now and again, by the flash of some extraordinarily characteristic passage:

'I must, I *must*, before I die, find *some* way to say the essential thing that is in me, that I have never said yet—a thing that is not love or hate or pity or scorn, but the very breath of life, fierce and coming from far away, bringing into human life the fearful passionless force of non-human things. . . . I want to stand for life and thought—thought as adventure, clear thought because of the intrinsic delight of it, along with the other delights of life. Against worldliness, which consists in doing everything for the sake of something else, like marrying for money instead of for love. The essence of life is doing things for their own sakes. . . . I want to stand at the rim of the world, and peer into the darkness beyond, and see a little more than others have seen of the strange shapes of mystery that inhabit that unknown night. . . . I want to bring back into the world of men some little bit of new wisdom. There is a little wisdom in the world; Heraclitus, Spinoza, and a saying here and there. I want to add to it, even if only ever so little. . . .'

On his return from Russia in 1920, I met him at the station and we drove to his Battersea rooms. Not at once was he able to bring himself to speak of what he had experienced in Russia. Only later, during a visit to Lady Ottoline Morrell at Garsington, did he set down all that he had felt. It made one of the longest letters I had ever received—even from him. A part of it appears in his *The Problem of China*:

'From my window when I arrived, I looked out across the Neva to the fortress of Peter and Paul. The river gleamed in the early northern dawn; the scene was beautiful beyond all words, magical, eternal, suggestive of ancient wisdom.

'"It is wonderful", I said to the Bolshevik who stood beside me. "Yes," he replied, "Peter and Paul is now not a prison, but the Army Headquarters."

'I shook myself. I thought, "You are not here as a tourist, to sentimentalize over sunrises and sunsets and buildings starred by Baedeker; you are here as a social investigator, to study economic and political facts. Come out of your dream, forget the eternal things. The men you have come among would tell you they are only

21

the fancies of a bourgeois with too much leisure, and can you be sure they are anything more?" So I came back into the conversation, and tried to learn the mechanism for buying an umbrella at the Soviet Stores, which proved as difficult as fathoming the ultimate mysteries. . . . I was prepared for physical hardship, discomfort, dirt and hunger, to be made bearable by an atmosphere of splendid hope for mankind. Our communist comrades, no doubt rightly, did not judge us worthy of such treatment. After crossing the frontier we had two feasts and a good breakfast, several first-class cigars, and a night in a sumptuous bedroom of a palace where all the luxury of the *ancien régime* had been preserved. At the stations on the way, regiments of soldiers filled the platform, and the plebs were kept carefully out of sight. . . . It was a world of dying beauty and harsh life. One was troubled at every moment by fundamental questions, the terrible insoluble questions that wise men never ask. Empty palaces and full eating-houses, ancient splendours destroyed, or mummified into museums, while the sprawling self-confidence of returned Americanized refugees spread throughout the city. Everything was to be systematic: there was to be organization and distributive justice. The same education for all, the same kind of houses for all, the same books for all, the same creed for all—it was very just, and left no room for envy, except of the fortunate victims of injustice in other countries.

'And then I began on the other side of the argument. I remembered Dostoevski's *Crime and Punishment*, Gorki's *In the World*, Tolstoy's *Resurrection*. I reflected upon the destruction and cruelty upon which the ancient splendour was built; the poverty, drunkenness, prostitution, in which the life and health were uselessly wasted; I thought of all the lovers of freedom who suffered in Peter and Paul: I remembered the knoutings and pogroms and massacres. By hatred of the old, I became tolerant of the new; but I could not like the new on its own account.

'Yet I reproached myself for not liking it. It had all the characteristics of vigorous beginnings. It was ugly and brutal, but full of constructive energy and faith in the value of what it was creating. In creating a new machinery for social life, it had no time to think of anything beyond machinery. When the body of the new society had been built, there would be time enough to think about giving it a soul—at least so I was assured. "We have no time for a new art or a new religion", they told me with a certain impatience. I wondered whether it was possible to build a body first, and then afterwards inject the requisite amount of soul. Perhaps—but I doubted it.

'I do not find any theoretical answer to these questions, but my feelings answered with terrible insistence. I was infinitely unhappy in that atmosphere—stifled by its utilitarianism, its indifference to love and beauty and the life of impulse. I cannot give that importance to man's merely animal needs that was given there by those in power. No doubt that is because I have not spent half my life in hunger and want, as many of them have. But do hunger and want necessarily bring wisdom? Do they make men more or less capable of conceiving the ideal society that should be the inspiration of every reformer? I cannot avoid the belief that they narrow the horizon more than they enlarge it. But an uneasy doubt remains, and I am torn in two. . . .'

Shortly after writing that letter he returned from Garsington and we got off to the country. He was soon due to sail for China, to lecture for a year in the Government University of Peking. Not much time was left to us; and during the first days of August he wrote to me (I quote from memory): 'I don't know why I ever decided on China. It will be over some day.'

We were standing on the corner of Northumberland Avenue when we said goodbye; but we did not then know that it would be for ten long years. When his figure vanished from my sight, I turned and charged blindly in the direction of the river.

It was in Paris, at a small hotel in the Rue de Vaugirard, that the newspapers informed me that he had died in Peking. What I wrote then is what I still feel now:

'That news broke me. A neat job: short, sharp, permanent. Death admits no argument, anguish, or wild regret. Only the mind in its extreme agony (provided it remains intact) photographs what passes in front of it: a tall Frenchman walked down the street; he had a black beard, black frock coat, black portfolio under his arm. On his head he wore a jaunty sailor hat. A dish of red cherries stood in a café window at the Rond Point: the cherries were dark red and bright red. Those things alone were real: more real than anything that had happened before or has happened since: the sum total of life, the remains of life, photographed on your brain, cut into your brain, burnt into it in a moment of agony that lasts till the end of your days. Afterwards, you see everything quite clear. It is when you see everything quite clear that you understand the impossibility of going on. You would *not* go on if you continued to see everything quite clear: exactly as it is. You would have to be held down by force. That would not be convenient. So you become your own anaesthetist —which is called having a healthy mind.'

23

In the summer of 1930 we had a long holiday in Cornwall; but it was not until May and June 1948 that we were abroad together. The vivid interest he then took in everything—whether a runic stone beside a Soedermanland castle—or the portrait of a Scandinavian writer who had died very young—or the precision-slicing of cold ham in a provincial shop—was a constant delight. Of the precision-slicing he remarked: 'It's like a good literary style.'

One rainy evening our small white ship dropped anchor beneath Stadshuset, Oestberg's masterpiece, on Maelaren. The quay was deserted, the lamps were lit, Stadshuset's three golden crowns shone dimly above its copper dome. We stood on deck, gazing at the scene. At last he said slowly, 'I don't suppose I'll ever see this again'. I do not remember what I replied, but I remember very clearly what it was in my mind to reply: 'Oh yes you will. They'll be giving you the Nobel Prize.' In 1950 he was again in Stockholm to receive it.

In the autumn of 1948 and the spring of 1949 we were in North Wales. One particular afternoon we sat in the Ffestiniog woods, beside a rushing waterfall which plunged steeply over rocks, and swirled fiercely round granite boulders. Further away, the waters spread out—calm and smooth—broadening and broadening until, in the far distance, they merged with the ocean. '*That*,' he said, 'is how an individual human life should be.' I remembered his words when, in something he published later, I came upon this passage:

'An individual human existence should be like a river—small at first, narrowly confined within its banks, and rushing passionately past boulders and over waterfalls. Gradually the river grows wider, the banks recede, the waters flow more quietly, and in the end, without any visible break, they become merged in the sea, and painlessly lose their individual being. The man who, in old age, can see his life in this way, will not suffer from the fear of death, since the things he cares for will continue. . . . I should wish to die while still at work, knowing that others will carry on what I can no longer do, and content in the thought that what was possible has been done.'

Unable to attend the celebrations which marked his 90th birthday in May 1962, I wrote instead:

'*Russell, to some of us who were young in 1916, was the sun which lit our world. His spirit appeared indestructible; and today, after the long years, we know that it is. We hardly knew which of his qualities (frequently contradictory) we loved best. It was the whole man for whom we cared: his public spirit, courage, independence; his erudition,*

*scathing wit and instant generosity; his proper pride, humility and
modesty; his infectious gaiety, energy and triumphant vitality—quite
as much as the patience and the strength of sheer will which he put
into his best work in spite of ups and downs, in times both good and
bad. His detestation of shoddy work was absolute.*

*'To those of us who were privileged to be with him in his profoundest
despairs came the glory of the new life which rose up in him unfailingly,
releasing his love of natural beauty: of the earth, the mountains and
the sea of his fathers. "How I hope (he wrote from Brixton Prison
in 1918) that I shall live to be old! There is so much work that I want
to do."*

'Now, after the long years, we hope with all our hearts that he will.'

2

JULIAN TREVELYAN

An Old Friendship

When I try and collect my thoughts about Bertie, the image that obliterates all others in my mind is of a happy evening about 1950 when I had succeeded in bringing him together with my father, Bob Trevelyan, in my studio. There they were, these two very old friends, side by side on a sofa, and it would be difficult to imagine any two more contrasting human beings. Bertie in his neat dark suit and shock of white hair was crackling with wit and anecdote. Each sally would spring out in finely finished sentences, and he never had to hesitate or fumble for words; there was a delighted twinkle about everything he said. My father on the other hand lolled in an absurdly uncomfortable position. He wore baggy knickerbockers and country boots and his hair was white and curly. He too was happy and loquacious, but his thoughts were expressed in sentences that were no sooner begun than they had to be taken to pieces again; names were forgotten and words replaced by better words several times before the thought was made clear. 'You remember those two young ladies, Bertie, two women . . . girls, at that college, what was its name? at Cambridge—who had two bicycles, was it?' 'Ah!' took up Bertie, 'the Miss Warburtons of Girton you mean. . . .' He had probably forgotten the story for sixty years, but now he held it clear as crystal in his mind.

Backwards and forwards the ball of conversation and reminiscence was thrown between them in the delight of a long friendship that was now being chewed over and savoured once more. What then were the qualities that held these two in such mutual esteem?

My father and Bertie made friends first at Cambridge as under-graduates at Trinity in 1890. Bertie had been educated at home and at a crammer's, and needed badly the company of other young sceptical minds against which to sharpen his own. The three Trevelyan brothers, Charles, Bob, and George, soon formed with Bertie a group that included Charles Sanger, Theodore and Crompton Llewellyn Davies, Lowes Dickinson, and eventually G. E. Moore.

It was a platonic society, with arguments late into the night, and reading parties in the lake district during the vacations, and it has been well described by Leonard Woolf and by Bertie himself in his *Portraits from Memory*.

My father had little of the intellectual quickness of his friends; he lumbered along awkwardly behind them I fancy, but he had a vein of innocent drollery, a sort of Edward Lear eccentricity, which made up for his lack of cleverness. They teased him and pulled his leg till he became the sort of necessary buffoon about whom all sorts of tales circulated. He was loving and lovable and immensely awkward. Sometimes they would urge him to make speeches just to hear him fumbling for words.

And he in his turn gave them his undivided loyalty and admiration. It was not long before he had peopled his individual Pantheon with all his several friends. Roger Fry *was* Art, Donald Tovey *was* Music, while Russell and Moore had to share the honour of *being* Philosophy. There was no questioning their authority, or indeed if anyone was so bold, a thunder-clap was immediately heard and a door would soon be slammed. Yet a few minutes later a very contrite Bob would sidle in saying, 'I know I shouldn't really have said that'.

It was this awkward innocence and also a certain quality of poetic enthusiasm, an enthusiasm that must at all costs be shared, that I fancy endeared Bob to Bertie. In the other direction it was Bertie's precision of thought, his ceaseless quest for truth and for the right words with which to expound it, that fascinated my father. Also Bertie's scepticism and atheism, his Voltaire impersonation as one might say, focused all my father's latent doubts and longings. Each in fact had what the other notably lacked.

Ten years later found my father married and settled in a comfortable house in the woods of Leith Hill. In the afternoon he would stride up the hill in his big boots with a rucksack on his back—the scholar poet as Max Beerbohm described and drew him—to settle himself in a secluded corner and write, epistles to his friends, verse plays, translations from Virgil, Lucretius, or Aeschylus, or lyrics that came to him always as the light changed in the evening. His poetry, though classical in form, was shot with personal insights whether he was describing the gleaming lights on the legs of a centipede or the smell of a distant brewery wafted down a side street. His notebooks, as his speech, were filled with alternative words in brackets over which he used to scratch his head interminably, unable to choose which best expressed his meaning.

Life on Leith Hill moved at a leisurely pace; it took the best part of an hour to drive from the station in a pony trap, and friends stayed not for weekends but for weeks or even months. Desmond MacCarthy, Lowes Dickinson, Charles Sanger, and Donald Tovey were frequent visitors, and Bertie in his pre-1914 Cambridge days was often there too.

As at Cambridge there was a great deal of talk, talk of a kind that is little heard today. Lowes Dickinson's *Modern Symposium* records the mood of some of these discussions. The talk went on while they walked through the countryside, and it was only interrupted when there was music in the evenings or reading aloud. It often seems to me in retrospect that these idyllic country house friendships were cemented in my parents' case by the continuous reading aloud that went on. My father could often only be stopped by meals from reading aloud poems that had excited him, my mother read novels or other classics every evening, while in the middle of the morning a ritual was performed in the drawing room as my father shaved with a cut-throat to passages read by my mother from Boswell, Fanny Burney, or some other diarist. Between whiles books were chewed over until there seemed no more to get out of them.

In the leisurely world of books and talk Bertie was at his hilarious best. His very deep love of literature, which throughout his long life has sustained him and opened imaginative doors for so many others, here came into its own. Moreover his fantastically accurate memory for the written word brought added sparkle to the conversation; when Bertie started quoting he could never be wrong.

Bertie's belief that human affairs should be, and to a large extent were conducted on a rational basis, received a severe blow at the outbreak of the war in 1914. It was the watershed of his life. Yet he was not afraid of facing the facts. My father's first reactions were different. He hated war as much as Bertie, but he refused to contemplate the military situation out of a sort of high distaste. I remember hearing how Bertie, who was staying with him at the time of the crisis of the battle of the Marne, forced him to spread out the Sunday papers and study the maps and strategy.

During the next four years and until Bertie was finally incarcerated in Brixton prison in 1918, he was a fairly constant visitor. They were for him years of great bitterness during which he came into head-on conflict with the prevailing mood of the country at war. His letters and polemical writing of the time are all charged with deeply felt passion. Both my parents became involved with him in the activities of the No Conscription Fellowship. He was a magnificent leader, and his clarity, honesty, and acuity became the inspiration of everyone who worked with him. My father on the other hand was no politician; his passions, as we have seen, were far too easily roused. It is one thing however to slam the door in anger amongst your friends, but quite another where you are in danger of being lynched by a hostile mob. On one occasion at a meeting addressed by Bertie in a church, my father was one of many who were beaten up by local thugs on the way out, and I well remember the drama on his arrival home with broken spectacles and a black eye.

Yet the now more spartan comforts of Leith Hill somehow continued to provide a refuge for conscientious objectors and even for deserters from the army, and it was only during the last months of the war while Bertie was reading Voltaire and Chekov in Brixton that my father was finally called up. Luckily he was able to settle for work in the Quaker *Mission* in Paris where he was soon collecting books on the quays with Francis Birrell for Belgian refugees. Ever afterwards he had a habit of running blindly across streets almost under the wheels of buses and taxies. 'I avoided all danger during the war,' he would say, 'and so I take it here in Piccadilly.' (He took it once too often as a matter of fact and was run into by a taxi in the black-out of 1943, and broke his pelvis.)

It was during the war years that my own memories of Bertie begin. He was at first the magic man of numbers who could multiply six thousand five hundred and forty-eight by forty-three thousand two hundred and seventy-one, and all in a couple of seconds. Later I began to appreciate his gift of fun. The story of Noah as told by Bertie with all the naughty bits included is something one does not easily forget.

During the years between the wars my father and Bertie saw less of each other. Bob was politically passionate, but at that stage he tended to see everything in black and white. And so as Bertie and Moore had embodied for him Philosophy, and Tovey, Music, so now Clifford Allen became for him Politics and his loyalty here was complete. At a certain moment Bertie and Allen, who had worked closely together during the war, parted company, and this created a certain tension in my father's private Pantheon that he never quite resolved.

But whenever he and Bertie met one sensed that they were feeling round for a renewal of the sage–clown relationships that had brought them so close at Cambridge and afterwards. This perhaps is an over simplification, but I am certain that when they were able best to communicate, they had thrown off a lot of the encumbrances that they had acquired through their newer loyalties.

This might suggest that they were happier in the company of people of their own age, the opposite of which would be nearer the truth. Bertie in his old age has often declared that he wants to be amongst young people and not to find himself fossilized in a university high table society. 'It does not do', he says, 'to live in memories, in regrets for the good old days, or in sadness about friends who are dead. One's thoughts must be directed to the future and to things about which there is something to be done.'

My father too was always at his best with the young, showing them his latest poems and asking them for their advice in all humility, as if the boot were on the other foot. In one of his casual books I found that he had copied from Dr Johnson: 'Sir, I love the acquaintance of young people; because in the first place I don't like to think myself growing old. In the next place, young acquaintances must last longest, if they do last; and then, Sir, young men have more virtue than old men; they have more generous sentiments in every respect. I love the young dogs of this age; they have more wit and humour and knowledge than we had; but then the dogs are not so good scholars.'

In this context I would like to interpose another memory of my own, this time more recent. Somewhere in the late 1940s I had joined several young painters in a house above Taormina where we sat out a cold March waiting for a spring that seemed never to come. In the daytime we painted, and in the evenings we amused ourselves in the few bars and cafés of the town that were open. Into this arty society came Bertie for a short holiday.

The world of painting is one that has never seemed to move him greatly, though I have noticed that in fact he is a great looker, and that his eye seems to miss very little. But in Taormina he was soon at his very best, amusing the company with nonsense rhymes that he either invented or pulled out of some obscure drawer of his memory.

With the coming of warmer weather we had planned a moonlight picnic on an island, and Bertie was delighted to be one of the party. It was in a most romantic setting. Fishermen, who looked more like pirates, speared fish with acetylene flares as we approached the island. Once there, they built a fire over which they grilled the fish, while the bottles of wine stood cooling in the wet sand. The full moon cast strange shadows through the prickly pears. Bertie sat bolt upright in his neat dark suit on an upturned fishing basket saying, 'I thought that life had few new pleasures to offer me, but I find that I was wrong'. Later when we were about to leave he remarked, 'I'm as drunk as a Lord, but then I am one, so what does it matter?'

No portrait of Bertie would be complete that did not bring out the impish side of his nature. There has never been any thinker who was at times more disquieting or whose precepts and paradoxes have upset so many apple carts; to have been able to continue in this mischievous vein for sixty years or so is no mean achievement. But underlying this impishness there lies a conviction, one that was so natural to his generation that it was taken for granted by all his Cambridge friends, that man is *au fond* a rational being and will in the long run behave in rational ways. 'I am convinced', he says, 'that intelligence, patience, and eloquence can, sooner or later, lead the human race out of its self-imposed tortures provided it does not exterminate itself meanwhile.'

My father was only echoing this basic credo when in his epistle to Lowes Dickinson he wrote:

> 'Yet surely not by Nature is man evil:
> Such was your faith; therefore in Reason's truth
> And wise Persuasion's charm
> Still did you put your trust;
> Still by words calm and bold inspire our youth
> With clarity and courage to be just.'

But I would like to leave the last word to Bertie from his *Reflections on my Eightieth Birthday*:

'I may have thought the road to a world of free and happy human beings shorter than it is proving to be, but I was not wrong in thinking that such a world is possible, and that it is worth while to live with a view to bringing it nearer. I have lived in the pursuit of vision, both personal and social. Personal: to care for what is noble, for what is beautiful, for what is gentle; to allow moments of insight to give wisdom at more mundane times. Social: to see in imagination the society that is to be created, where individuals grow freely, and where hate and greed and envy die because there is nothing to nourish them. These things I believe, and the world, for all its horrors, has left me unshaken.'

3

VICTOR PURCELL

Fifty Years' Influence

Russell has excelled in so many fields that expert appraisal of his achievements must be left to the specialists. But since his thought and ideas have exercised a wide influence on three generations, an account of his impingement on a single individual, without expertise in any of Russell's chosen fields but with a special experience outside Europe, may not be without interest. To give this account, however, I shall be compelled to be to some extent autobiographical, but I will do my best to keep my own unimportant ego in its proper place as wax tablet to Russell's stylus.

I am sixty-six years of age, and for the whole of my adult life of approaching half a century I have in varying degrees been exposed to Russell's influence. I first became remotely aware of his existence during the first war when I was serving in the infantry and Russell was (to all appearances) a pacifist. In those days the vital issues had a definition and simplicity which they did not reassume until the Second War. Being only a youth in 1914 when I became a 'temporary gentleman', and knowing little of the history of power politics and caring rather less, I was satisfied with the simple belief that either we must beat the Germans or submit to the intolerable tyranny of a German-dominated world.

If one adopted this point of view, the only consistent course for a fit adult male was to take the fullest part in the fighting that his courage, endurance, and opportunities would allow. If one did not accept the war as necessary, the only logical alternative to fighting was to become a militant pacifist and do one's best to stop it. The strain of front-line fighting, however, was so great that for the individual it had to be discontinuous since, indefinitely prolonged, it could end only in insanity. (Having the great good fortune personally to be severely wounded twice and taken prisoner by the Germans on the second occasion, I was saved the necessity of running away.) The appalling slaughter of the Somme and Passchendaele made me feel that some compromise peace ought to be possible, but I could see no chance of one being arranged (even after the Lansdowne Letter).

When the war broke out in 1914, Russell was 42 years of age; when conscription was introduced in March 1916, he was nearly 44, and, had he accepted the calling-up, he would inevitably, with his qualifications, have become a staff-officer at the War Office or St Omer and have duly been decorated with the D.S.O. But, whatever his age, Russell, as we know from his record of fearless integrity, would have acted as he did and needs no defence for his action. He tried to stop the war and to end the horrible shambles, since being blessed (or cursed) with an unusual capacity to visualize and share the sufferings of others, he found the slaughter and maiming unendurable. Even so, his logical mind refused to be trapped into the difficult position of opposing war in *all* circumstances, and it is reported that in answering the question of a court or tribunal, 'We understand that you are opposed to war, Mr Russell?', he replied, 'Not *all* war; only *this* war'. Thus when in the second war he decided that Hitler must be fought to a finish, he was not guilty of inconsistency. So while I could not share Russell's attitude towards the first war, I could at least comprehend that it was based on hard logic and inspired by disinterested motives.

Was this particular victory worth all the murder and maiming that it involved? W. H. Auden wrote an *Epitaph for the Unknown Soldier* which runs:

> To save your world you asked this man to die;
> Would this man, could he see you now, ask why?

Just because one had happened to survive oneself did this give one the right to say that the death of the million who had not was 'worth while'?

Russell himself admits that if Britain had been neutral Germany would have won, and this would have probably meant that when war eventually came Britain and her allies (if any) would have been defeated. But to explore the 'ifs' of history is rarely profitable, and to put the matter mystically (though not theologically) one can say that the answer can be given only *sub specie aeternitatis*.

Russell next impinged on my horizon early in 1922, shortly after I reached Canton as a Cadet in the Malayan Civil Service to study Chinese. His book, *The Problem of China*, had just been published, and I read it. I must confess that few of its conclusions were to my taste. For example Russell wrote: 'The Chinese have discovered, and have practised for many centuries, a way of life which, if it could be adopted by all the world, would make all the world happy.'[1] Now, this conclusion was in direct opposition to my own observation. Most of China was now split up into fragments under the 'warlords'; Canton, intermittently under Sun Yat-sen's control, had

[1] *The Problem of China*, 1922, p. 17.

two revolutions whilst I was there, the people were mostly living in poverty and misery, and the city was a kind of termites' nest of dark cells and tortuous narrow alley-ways pierced here and there by the new thoroughfares, and so poor that for the masses existence was drab and featureless. Their 'way of life' did not seem to have made the Chinese very happy.

Again Russell wrote:

'Our prosperity, and most of what we endeavour to secure for ourselves, can only be obtained by widespread oppression and exploitation of weaker nations, while the Chinese are not strong enough to injure other countries, and secure whatever they enjoy by means of their own merits and exertions alone.'[1]

In contradiction of this view nearly all that was worth while in China, and especially in Hong Kong and the Treaty Ports, seemed to derive from the West. The West had introduced law, order, hygiene, efficiency, and security to remedy the lack of these things in China. At this period I shared most of the conventional prejudices of the 'China Coast' European, and it must be remembered, too, that I was a Colonial Civil Servant who had already spent six months in Malaya and had been greatly impressed by what I had seen of the British achievement there.

It was only very gradually that Canton and South China revealed to me their well hidden attractions, but when I went to Peking in 1923 I was confronted by the full beauty of the Chinese civilization and I responded with surprise and joy. As the years went on this appreciation, assisted by study, increased and I began to understand what Russell had seen when he visited China. But in my own defence it must be borne in mind that Russell, by virtue of his intellectual eminence, had been admitted at once to the society of the Chinese scholars and intelligentsia, mainly in Peking, whereas I had to flounder for long in a cruder environment.

In the matter of 'oppression' and 'exploitation' again I was imperfectly informed. It seemed to me then that the West had conferred little but benefit on the Chinese, and even now I am satisfied that it did perform an indispensable office in introducing China to the international world. But it was only by dint of study that I began to realize that the European Powers (*and*, later, Japan) had treated the weak and technically backward 'Middle Kingdom' with rapacious barbarity, from the Opium War to the Boxer Uprising and beyond. I observed, too, that the foreigner exercised 'extra-

[1] *The Problem of China*, 1922, p. 12.

territorial' powers in the country, that he controlled the Chinese Customs, river conservancy, and the salt gabelle, and that his gunboats patrolled the Chinese rivers far into the interior and I reflected to myself that an ancient and civilized people such as the Chinese were could not be expected indefinitely to tolerate such a state of affairs.

In the meantime I was engaged for years in Malaya in helping to counter the claims of Chinese Nationalism when it began to develop under the Kuomintang and aimed to establish an *imperium in imperio* in Southeast Asia by applying its nationality law, which amounted to 'once a Chinese always a Chinese' with the corollary 'where there are Chinese, there is China'. So I thus experienced something of what Russell had feared, namely that the Chinese might, in copying the West, adopt an 'imperialism' of their own devising. In such circumstances a sympathy with the aspirations of the Chinese people was slow in growing in my mind. Nevertheless I understood as the years went on that Russell, with his superior perception, had grasped intuitively certain essential facts regarding China which had eluded me in my early years.

Yet, by a strange irony, I have been led to feel a sympathy for the Communist Revolution in China which Russell, because of his dislike of Communism as a system, is still seemingly unable to share. For many years, in the case of my duties as Protector of Chinese in Malaya I had to interest myself in the politics and policies of Nationalist China and formed an increasingly unfavourable impression of the cynical indifference of the Kuomintang to China's needs at home and of its aggressive nationalism in Southeast Asia. Successive visits to China, both in peacetime and wartime, confirmed me in these opinions, and I have become convinced that the task of bridging the time-lag of centuries consequent on her having missed the Scientific Renaissance (although previously far ahead of Europe technologically) could never be accomplished within the framework of Western Capitalism and under the selfish monopoly of the 'Four Families' of the Kuomintang. A fundamental revolution became inevitable. So whilst (like Russell) I was repelled by Communism as such, I was prepared to believe that only by submitting themselves to a totalitarian régime could the Chinese people enter the modern world. Even so, I was not prepared for the enormous improvement in every sphere which I eventually saw when I penetrated behind the 'Bamboo Curtain'. Nor have subsequent setbacks in agriculture and crises in planning changed my views on the subject. I feel, moreover, that if Russell's contacts with China, like mine, had been continuous from the early 'twenties onwards he too would have been brought to believe that whatever its unsuitability as a system for the technically advanced Western world, as a means of solving China's unique problems—at least on a short-term basis—Communism, as adapted to the Chinese ethos (which Russell so greatly approved in 1920), may serve the purpose.

A civil servant living in the intellectual isolation of a British colony in the Far East (though it was nothing like as intellectually isolated or 'suburbanite' as Mr Somerset Maugham would have us believe) was bound to rely exclusively on reading to acquaint himself with Russell, the philosopher, and, even so, could do this only within the limitations of his own intellectual and scholastic equipment. But it was as sociologist and reformer and practical experimenter in education that Russell was known to the public at this period. And it happened that at the time when he was running his Beacon Hill School, attracting a good deal of newspaper publicity, I found myself in charge of some hundreds of Chinese Schools in the Straits Settlements as Assistant Director of Education (Chinese).

Mine was primarily a political job concerned with preventing these schools being used for 'subversion'—i.e. spreading the Chauvinistic doctrine of 'where there are Chinese, there is China'—which was objected to not only by the British Colonial Government but by the Malays and other communities as well. But the job offered opportunities for improving education and I became very interested in educational theory. Russell's emphasis was on freedom and the avoidance of repressions. He felt that theories which justified cruelty almost always had their source in some desire diverted by the will from the natural channel, driven underground, and at last emerging. By contrast (he felt) the secret of modern moral education was to make behaviour a matter of *habit*, not of *self-control*. Hence at Beacon Hill School the children were given great freedom—their lessons were not compulsory, they were allowed to use bad language when they felt like it, and were at liberty to call their teachers fools.

The Russell system, of course, was intended mainly for younger children, but it had considerable appeal to one who (like myself) had suffered from the public school system with its mass production of stereotypes, its impracticable and undesirable moral code, and its compulsory chapel and games but our problem in Malaya was rather a different one from that which Russell had to face in ironing out maladjustments in a sophisticated industrialized society. What we were confronted with was a 'plural' society, namely one consisting of three main communities (Malays, Chinese and Indians) which lived side by side without intermarrying and had different standards

37

of living, at a very much less advanced state of development than our own. There was a cultural gulf between the English-educated and the Chinese-educated and this we had to try to bridge. The question of how to teach English to the Chinese in Chinese schools in which Mandarin was the medium of instruction was one which also occupied me and led to experiments with Basic English and to membership of a committee in China advising the Chinese Ministry of Education on the teaching of English in Chinese Secondary Schools. But this is another story whose telling would take me far away from my recollection of Russell's influence on me.

Russell, as I have said, worked out his theories in a very different setting from the one I found myself in in Malaya, but no one concerned with schools could afford to ignore his book *On Education*, which, in principle, applied to all humanity. He was concerned with the transition from a traditional to a modern system, and so were we. In Malaya, in 1924, when I became Inspector of Chinese Schools, there were still many old-type schools in existence in which the pupils 'backed' their lesson, learning the 'Four Books' by heart and chanting out extracts from them independently (there were as many 'classes' as there were pupils) with their backs to their teacher. But most of the schools were now new and modern, using 'Mandarin' as their medium, and producing a new system in which science and nationalism were uncomfortably blended. What Russell had to say on Chinese education then 'controlled by missionaries and conservative white men' (as well as on Dr Arnold, Nietzsche, and Uriah Heep) was very much to the point. The Chinese, he saw, had to work out their own salvation.

I should mention before I leave the subject of education that Chinese children, both in China itself and Malaya, seem to suffer from few of the repressions, maladjustments and Freudian complexes which plague modern children and their teachers; they are nearly always ductile, obedient, and well adjusted. In the girls' home ('Preserve the Virtuous Establishment' as it was called in Chinese) for which I was responsible as 'Protector' of Chinese, there were indeed cases of girls who were 'problems' on account of the ill-treatment they had received—but these were exceptional. I can remember only one girl who smashed the crockery (which was part of the curriculum, the papers said, at Beacon Hill).

Another aspect of Russell's multifarious theorizing was his Socialism. This I felt was the kind of Socialism with which I could sympathize. It had no specious egalitarianism about it; Russell, although a genuine democrat, was consistently opposed to any 'levelling down'. Yet the desire for equality is perhaps the strongest force in shaping our modern democracies, either 'free' or 'people's'. Russell says:

'A good deal of needless pain and friction would be saved to clever children if they were not compelled to associate intimately with stupid contemporaries. There is an idea that rubbing up against all and sundry in youth is a good preparation for life. This appears to me to be rubbish. No one, in later life, associates with all and sundry. Bookmakers are not obliged to live among clergymen, nor clergymen among bookmakers.'[1]

It will be noticed that Russell chooses 'clergymen' and 'bookmakers' as antitheses, not, one may suppose, because he regards clergymen as an especially exalted form of life or bookmakers as an especially low one, but because he feels that classes such as these with their separate interests and specialist jargon could not be expected to have much in common (that clergymen *ought* to live among bookmakers to save them from damnation is a doctrinal point, not a social one).

The common insistence both in Western democracy and Eastern communism is on 'levelling down'. Thus a youth who 'works his way' through college by working in a laundry is admired in America as a brain worker who is not ashamed of manual labour, while in Communist China a Minister is called upon to work in the fields or building a dam for a certain period of the year to demonstrate that there is no class distinction between Ministers and labourers. Bernard Shaw argued on these lines incessantly, pointing out that surgeons worked with their hands without losing caste, but it does not seem that he backed up his theories by labour with pickaxe or hoe.

Russell's inegalitarianism is also demonstrated in his attitude towards the linguistic philosophers. He is unable to accept the view that the language of daily life, with 'words used in their ordinary meanings, suffices for philosophy'.[2]

To counter the 'levelling down' theory it is not necessary to argue that one function is superior to another, but to insist that the 'division of labour' was one of the most important revolutions in the advance of civilization since it marked the point when production of foodstuffs first became sufficiently great to permit of a section of the community occupying itself with cultural activities instead of engaging in subsistence agriculture with the rest. The fact is that the

[1] *Education and the Social Order*, quoted by Alan Wood, *op. cit.*, p. 165.
[2] *Portraits from Memory*, p. 154.

satisfactory performance of any intellectual task demands that an individual shall devote all his working hours to it. This is not to argue that a scientist or a historian should not, especially in their youth, gain some knowledge of manual labour by engaging in it, but it is a waste of his expertise for an intellectual to masquerade as a 'manual worker' (the real workers, in any case, would probably regard his unskilled efforts as a hindrance to them rather than a help).

Nevertheless it is clear that in Russell's ideal state, with its '. . . degree, priority, and place, insisture, course, proportion, season, form, office, and custom, in all line of order' is an organism in which the intellectuals and manual workers operate in perfect collaboration for a common end. It has no resemblance to our existing society in which the intelligentsia are ground between the upper and nether millstones of finance and organized labour. In Russell's state the intelligentsia rule by example, not by military command. It is in this sense 'aristocratic'.

Russell's ideas on government had an especial interest for me in the situation in which I found myself. It would be absurd to pretend that colonial Malaya was an 'ideal state' or anything like it. Rubber and tin were the presiding deities, and Whitehall gave them proper reverence. By Russell's principles our colonial system was one of 'exploitation', though without the revenues from rubber and tin it would have been impossible to pay the labour force to redeem the country from jungle and swamp, or to develop hygiene or education. The Malay States were governed by British 'advice' to the Rulers under the treaties, but in practice this 'advice' was not tendered unless it had been previously ascertained that it would be acceptable. Moreover, legislation was in the hands of the Federal and State Councils, and although on these councils there was a small official majority, it was very rarely used. If a proposed measure was unpopular with the unofficials (Malays, a Chinese or Indians), it was dropped. The system, therefore, was one of calculated compromise.

Since there were no domestic political parties to direct or harass us, we of the Civil Service (the 'heaven-born') enjoyed a considerable discretion in carrying out our duties. In many matters we had no guidance except that of our own judgment as to what was likely to be in the best interests of the people and the country. And what my service was able to accomplish was far more through prestige and personal influence than by word of command. The system was certainly not 'democratic', but it had advantages which are difficult to reproduce under a democracy. I feel somehow that Russell would have approved of the spirit in which administration was approached in Malaya, if not of the capitalistic framework in which we had to operate.

It was in these decades, the 'twenties and 'thirties, that I first began to have some real appreciation of the significance of Russell in the intellectual climate of the time. I had grown up in England during a period of great economic stringency for the many (among whom my family was numbered) but of great optimism. The popular prophets of the Left between 1900 and 1914 were Shaw and Wells, and the bright vistas they unrolled of a socialist future far outshone in attraction the fabulous 'Middle Ages' to which Belloc and Chesterton exhorted Britain to revert. The first war put an end to this optimistic phase, and though Shaw and Wells lived on to bridge the wars, the trumpet of their prophecy was muted. Then after the second war and the advent of the atom-bomb, the question whether there could be a workable utopia was given second place to the question whether, in the long run, civilization itself could survive.

During this extended period (a half century and more) Russell had also been a prophet, but only to the few, and he never had the popular appeal of Shaw or Wells. In *My Philosophical Development* he has himself traced the evolution of his thought in a way no one else could do—his excursion into idealism, his revolt into pluralism, and his investigation (with Whitehead) of the nature of mathematics (that he could eventually conclude that mathematics, instead of being mystical and absolute, were tautological is the perfect example of Russell's secular mind at work, for he thus surrendered the opportunity to turn mathematics into a religion with himself as high-priest). But side by side with his adventures in pure thought he occupied himself with social questions, and since he wrote prolifically about his ideas and experiences, it was not hard, even for lay exiles *in partibus* such as myself, to keep in touch with his general progress.

I now come to Russell's views on religion which I find more congenial than those of any other individual, but to make it clear why I do so I must first outline the developments in this sphere in Britain as I saw them.

There had been a widespread loss of faith among the intelligentsia in the second half of the nineteenth century when the historicity of Genesis had been destroyed by the geology of Lyell and the Natural Selection of Darwin. To many who accepted the new interpretations it seemed logical that they must therefore dispense with their faith. But a majority of the newly faithless had strong emotional attachments to the religion of their forefathers, based on habit and filial piety, and these found themselves in the uncomfortable position of being Christians without faith. The educated, therefore, tended either to be Christian agnostics or agnostic Christians.

Christian apologetics, however, soon rallied from the setback, explaining that Genesis was 'allegorical' or 'Symbolic' rather than literal (though what it was symbolic *of* was not quite clear). It went on to claim that theology itself had 'evolved' and was still 'evolving' (though what Genesis was symbolic *of* was not quite clear). Which was sufficient to console (if not to satisfy intellectually) those who wished to believe without resorting to fundamentalism. In the long run, the retreat from church attendance was not halted, but thousands who continued to adhere to the churches found it sufficient to conform for baptismal or burial purposes with maybe an occasional church attendance when the boredom of platitude was mitigated by the soporific of the liturgy.

Among those who remained true to orthodoxy, established or non-conformist, a revival began during and after the first war which has continued ever since. To reconcile even the old science with literal faith involved a great deal of intellectual contortionism, but when in the 'thirties the new science bounded forth simultaneously into the macrocosm and the microcosm, the reduction of the sun to the position of a minor star of a galaxy among a myriad galaxies and the resolution of the solid atomic cannon ball into a mere series of events, the feat of interpreting the Scriptures symbolically or 'allegorically' to meet these theories was beyond the skill even of the most subtle apologist. The stratagem was then adopted of allotting the scientific and religious functions of the brain to two separate divisions of the cortex without intercommunication. Denis Johnston, the Irish playwright, put the orthodox position in a nutshell when he declared, 'I *believe* the world was created in six days, but I *know* it wasn't'.

Thus, as science advanced, opening up new vistas to the imagination, religion retreated further and further from the realm of knowledge, confining itself increasingly to ritual, the moral supervision of society (maintaining rigidly its traditional precepts in face of an almost universal disregard of them), and, above all, on the consolidation of its political and social power through its churches, sects, societies, and pressure groups. By virtue of its alliance with vested interest, it enjoyed a monopoly of the press and other mass media. Although the union of the Churches still seemed remote (and reconciliation with the Roman Catholic Church by definition impossible), there was a great rationalization of religious government, and religious tests were as far as possible enforced for all appointments controlled by the Establishment. Professed disbelievers were isolated and tacitly labelled to prevent them contaminating those disbelievers who conformed. A non-Christian (Muslim, Buddhist, Hindu, or agnostic) could not take part in an ex-service reunion or the procession of an Order that was not sanctified and supervised by the Church. Fear of Communism gave a further impetus to the religious revival, though sometimes even the orthodox were troubled by the apprehension lest anti-Communism might adopt the methods of its godless enemy.

Since the new enthusiasm for religion was unaccompanied by any new inspiration or original ideas, and the moral code of the Churches fashioned for use in vanished circumstances accorded less and less with the mores of the age, the sceptical observer might be excused for believing that Britain was now entering on a condition comparable to that of Rome under Theodoric the Ostrogoth. The invasion of the country by heretical sects, such as MRA or Jehovah's Witnesses, recalled that of Rome by the Ebionites, Nazarines, Gnostics, and Nestorians in the fifth and sixth centuries and added colour to this belief.

The state of poetry is a sure index to the spiritual health of a society ('spiritual' being used here, of course, in a special sense). Poetry which had abandoned its emancipating role on the death of Shelley, nevertheless continued its hopeful message through the medium of a few lyric poets piping out manfully from their ivory towers. But after the first war it took a headlong plunge into the quagmire of mysticism and credulity. Instead of confirming the salvation of mankind from the superstitions which had oppressed its soul for centuries, it fed them on dirges and incantations and attempted to revive the dying embers of hell-fire. Yet the arch-poet (or arch-priest?) of this new 'Main Stream' poetry, Mr T. S. Eliot, quaintly attributed the onset of the new 'Dark Ages', not to the *revival* of 'faith' but to the *decay* of it!

Science, of course, constituted a perpetual challenge to religion, but since it seemed indifferently dedicated to mankind's welfare and destruction, it had little chance of becoming a popular faith on its own account. A number of scientific theories, however, lent themselves to religious exploitation. The astronomy of Jeans and Eddington, for example, left the field open for transcendental speculation, and Heisenberg's 'uncertainty principle' was invoked to discredit causality. Wittgenstein's philosophy was a god-send to the irrationalists, for quite apart from the great obscurity of the *Tractatus*, his constant change of front made it possible whenever desired to re-interpret him 'nearer to the heart's desire'. Moreover, the dogmatic form of his discourses was congenial to the religious mind. There was Jung, too, whose opinions could always be invoked to justify irrationality.

As time went on a new generation of apologists defended orthodoxy with adapted arguments. Prominent among them was Herbert Butterfield who held that since science makes mistakes, theology must be allowed to make its mistakes too. This was to suggest that the methods of science and theology were similar and that therefore (by analogy) what science did was to stretch, dismember, or otherwise mutilate the facts to fit them into the Procrustean bed of authority. Russell, however, holds that 'science is seldom entirely wrong', which would scarcely be true if Professor Butterfield is right about its methods. The latter's final counsel is, 'Hold to Christ, and for the rest be totally uncommitted'. Since, however, it is clear from the context that 'holding to Christ' entails the membership of a church and submission to its discipline, whoever accepts this counsel is about as 'uncommitted' as Laocoön.

But the strange thing is that the really serious undermining of the rationalist position came from the sceptical side of the fence. Wells had dabbled in theology long ago in his *God, the Invisible King*; Aldous Huxley forsook the rationalism of his grandfather for oriental mysticism; his brother, Julian, attempted to elevate (or depress) science, and especially evolution, into a religion; even Shaw's Bergsonism had a strongly mystical character. Nor could the orthodox atheists, agnostics, and humanists be relied on to be true to their principles. A notable example was Joad who, after spending a lifetime denouncing the Christian religion, was converted to it by travelling without a ticket on the railway, and who then had the impudence to attack Russell for 'destroying the authority of traditional religion and morality which could have important effects on people's conduct'. (As Russell remarked, 'Joad found his God after he had lost his railway ticket'. One wonders whether he had ever really lost him.)

One of the most subtle arguments undermining the rationalist position to come from the sceptical side of the fence was that of Noel Annan in his book on Leslie Stephen. He says, in summing up:

'When Stephen said that theology was unreal and had no right to exist, he confused an ethical reflection (that theology is a waste of time) with a logical inference (that theology is logically improper). Theology, however, is a mode of reasoning as valid as other modes of reasoning; as a human activity it is no more unreal, nor are its rules dissimilar from those which govern other activities, such as jurisprudence, and there is no *logical* reason why men should not use this mode of reasoning if they please. Yet Stephen was arguing only as his Christian opponents argued when they declared in ethics that the ultimate justification for preferring one course of action to another was that the former accorded with the will of God.'[1]

Logic, as now understood, has of course changed greatly since Stephen's time (largely owing to Russell) and what purports to be a form of it is often used in arguing theological propositions. But theology is not in itself a method of reasoning, but the application of reasoning to a predetermined end. What Russell says of the philosophy of St Thomas Aquinas might equally be said of theology: 'The finding of arguments for a conclusion given in advance is not philosophy, but special pleading.' In science, if a theory does not work out in practice, it is abandoned, whereas the first axiom of theology is that arguments which refute dogma are *ipso facto* false. As for jurisprudence, the fact that its methods are theological rather than rational is sufficient to account for the unreformed state of so much English law.

It was clear that when Englishmen lost one faith they immediately began to search for another one to replace it. One which attracted many between the wars and after was the cult of D. H. Lawrence. The Lawrence creed, however, with its rejection of the intellect and call to reversion to the irrational, the superstitious, and the rudimentary in man, could have little attraction for those whose hopes still lay in reason, while the exhaltation of sex (without reference to the rights of the parties concerned to have any) seemed to two generations of warriors as a reflex of sterility or impotence. Russell vehemently rejected the mystical philosophy of 'thinking with the blood', and after the second war he characterized it as a doctrine which 'led straight to Auschwitz'.[2] Nevertheless Russell must have been one of those who acclaimed the outcome of the *Lady Chatterley* case as a victory for cultural freedom.

What was the reason for this persistence of the West for its search for religion? Dissatisfaction with *this* life, no doubt, was a main reason for the yearning for a *future* one, and the Freudian desire for parental authority made a 'heavenly Father' acceptable. But now that the scourge of eternal punishment had receded into the realm of the visible, the carrot of the life everlasting had become a very shadowy vegetable. It seems to me to derive from the Western dichotomy of reality into 'body' and 'spirit'. Orientals in general are incapable of effecting this dichotomy and the Chinese definitely reject it. Of an individual 'soul' there was no clear conviction in any

---

[1] *Leslie Stephen*, 1951, p. 285.   [2] *Portraits from Memory*, p. 107.

of the Three Doctrines (Confucianism, Taoism, and Buddhism). Confucianism has always declined to discuss personal survival in the explicit interest of high social morality here and now, whilst to Buddhist philosophy the belief in the individual persisting soul was positive heresy. The Taoists recognized a considerable number of spiritual essences, even godlings, in the human body–soul complex, almost as many indeed as the limbs and viscera of the human organism itself, but there was no other place than earth for them to inhabit as a coherent entity, and after death they simply dispersed, some rising to join the pneuma (*ch'i*) of the heavens, some sinking to mingle with that of the earth, and others disappearing altogether. The Chinese also regarded the happenings in the universe as arising from internal necessity, the interaction of parts of a whole, not as the operation of 'laws' of a patriarchal law-giver, as in the West from the Decalogue to Newton's *Principia* and beyond.

(But who in the West cared a damn what the Chinese thought— so long as they did not possess the atom-bomb?)

Russell's position, however, was not very far from that of the Chinese. He pointed out that Plato, reinforced by religion, has led mankind to accept the division of the known world into two cate- gories—body and mind. Physics and psychology alike had begun to throw doubt on this dichotomy.[1] He then proceeds to give reasons for believing that the supposed problem of the relations of mind and matter arises only through mistakenly treating both as 'things' and not as groups of events.

Yet in Britain only a small minority were satisfied with a unitary universe. Although the infinite vistas of macro- and microcosm were available as a palaestra for the most ambitious imagination, the many still hankered after the ineffable. The consequence was that in competition or collaboration with the official religion, the field was open to the Moral Rearmers, the magicians, and the witch-doctors. The non-spiritual religions, such as Communism, were also hier- archically organized and were, like the spiritual religions, engaged night and day in heresy-hunting. Had not Russell equated Dialectical Materialism with Yahweh, Marx with the Messiah, Proletarians with the Elect, the Communist Party with the Church, the Revolution with the Second Coming, the Punishment of Capitalists with Hell, and the Communist Commonwealth with the Millennium?[2] Kathleen Nott (herself a humanist) has said, 'This is a *secular* century'. On the contrary, alas, it is a highly *religious* one.

Meanwhile I was only vaguely aware of the English religious scene

[1] *Portraits from Memory*, p. 135.
[2] *History of Western Philosophy*, p. 383.

in the course of my visits home on leave. Most of the time I lived among Malays, Chinese, Indians, and other Asians, whose entire outlook had nothing in common with that of Britain or the West. The Malays, of course, were Muslims, but not of a fanatical kind, and their monotheistic and exclusive religion did not impinge on the non-Muslims; the Indians, mostly Hindus, also kept their observances to themselves; while the Chinese, whether Buddhist, Confucian, or Taoist (often all three simultaneously) or merely indifferent to religion had no proselytizing zeal whatsoever. None of these communities were organized for evangelism so that Europeans resident in their midst were completely free from external religious pressures. Within the European community there were indeed attempts by the churches or sects to regiment their small congregations and to reduce the non-conformer to conformity, but the fewness and wide distribution of the Europeans had rendered the attempt largely ineffectual. It was a shock, therefore, when I was once again living permanently among my own people to discover that under the surface of urbane, secular, and friendly social intercourse, the spirit of the Covenanters and of the Occasional Conformity Act was still very much alive, and if the fires of Smithfield were not yet relit, it was not due to the lack of matches or dry faggots ready at hand to relight them.

While to affirm or deny religious faith was a gaffe in polite society, much latitude was allowed in conversation. (Only the other day I heard a lady of otherwise impeccable orthodoxy remark of the characters of the Old Testament, 'They were a *dreadful* lot, *weren't they?*') But, behind the scenes, organized religion was very active. The political parties felt it expedient to lean over backwards to gain favour with the Churches, and it was a common sight to see an agnostic M.P. taking round the plate or reading the lesson. The entire press, except for one or two humanist or freethinking journals, was the monoply of religion, while the BBC invariably inserted a hymn *after* the time-signal on holy days as forcible spiritual feeding for the ungodly. What was worse, the Churches had mobilized all their pretty girls to terrorize freethinking males with the weapon of 'Lysistra'.

This picture may seem a trifle exaggerated to the practising sceptic resident in Britain, but it was how things appeared to be to an exile in his return home from abroad. He had dreamt that he was living in the *twentieth* century, and had come home to find himself in the *sixth*!

In a situation such as this a person like myself could not help feeling somewhat isolated. To whom could I turn for moral support? The answer could only be—to Russell.

47

Russell is aware that there is no certain way of proving or disproving revelation, or, for that matter, anything else. He recognizes that belief or disbelief is mainly a matter of emotion arising from experience or predisposition. 'God' certainly exists, however, whether in the visions of St John of the Cross or as the unseen authorizer of persecution. Personally I incline to see 'Him' as the projection of the hopes, fears, and hatreds of millions of semi-barbarious people through thousands of years and therefore as a cruel, absurd, and ugly monster—above everything an *ugly* one. God's crime is essentially aesthetic. Russell, however, with his scrupulous fairness, would no doubt be able to detect an element of love in Yahweh's make-up.[1]

While sceptics have on the whole felt constrained to concede the perfection of Christ's character, Russell saw no necessity for this. He admits the merits of Christ's teaching, though pointing out that the precept of returning good for evil is found long before Christ in Buddha and Lao Tzu. But since the precept is so rarely followed by Christians or by any one else, he finds it irrelevant. But against the good points, Russell cites the vindictiveness or lack of consideration on the part of Christ in the case of the 'generation of vipers', the fig-tree, and the Gadarine Swine.

These propositions I find acceptable, but I do not propose to repeat Russell's opinion of Christianity which he has stated so adequately himself in *Why I am not a Christian* and elsewhere. What I would ask leave to do, however, is to add a reflection of my own on the international implication of the claims of Christianity. It shares with Judaism and Marxism the quality of being monopolistic. It will receive any convert to its creed, irrespective of race, but on condition of the exclusive possession of his mind. In the words of *Revelation* (xi, 15) 'all the nations of the world' are 'to become the Kingdoms of the Lord'. A Chinese might be a Confucian, Buddhist and a Taoist simultaneously (however conflicting their doctrines might seem), but he could not be a Christian as well—Christianity would not permit it. As an American writer has said:

'Christianity has the misfortune in every alien land of running counter to almost all cherished local institutions. It offends every one; it antagonizes every creed; it mingles with none, because its fundamental tenets deny the co-existence of any other faith or standard of morality.'[2]

[1] Adolf Eichmann was executed on May 31, 1962, declaring himself 'a lifelong believer in God'.

[2] Paul A. Clements, *The Boxer Rebellion*, 1915, p. 74.

This exclusiveness was as much the cause of the Roman persecutions as it was of the Boxer Rebellion.

Because he rejects Christianity, Russell has been accused of turning his back on mystery and the imagination. This is not so. Throughout his writings he has paid the sincerest tribute to creative art and the writings themselves are sprinkled with poetic passages of a high order, but his own function he realizes to be the pursuit of objective truth. Shaw agreed with Samuel Butler that Darwin had 'taken mind out of the universe' and proceeded to try to put it back again (invoking Bergson' help in doing it). Russell will have none of this. If mind is not in the universe, it cannot be artificially injected into it. As Colin Wilson says, 'Russell prefers the discomforts of scepticism to wild guesses and assertions that seem to be born of wishful thinking'. 'Unfortunately (Wilson adds) most creative artists and thinkers cannot live happily in Lord Russell's state of stoical agnosticism.'[1]

Russell would deny that his agnosticism *is* 'stoical' (in fact, he questions the bona fides of the Stoics[2]), and on the contrary believes in the 'pursuit of happiness'. But it is not the case that agnosticism is incompatible with creative art or thought. Among creators who were agnostics—or at least non-Christians—can be counted (quite at random) Conrad, Hardy, Bizet, Rémy de Gourmont, Ibsen, Berloiz, Brahms, Goethe, Schiller, Shelley, Keats, Leconte de Lisle, Flaubert, Tchaikowsky, Tchekov, Turgeniev, and Rodin among scores of others, and in contemporary creative writing the great majority of the personalities of the first rank, from Robert Graves to Sartre, are non-Christians. The outstanding writers on the other hand are of the stature (almost) of Eliot, Evelyn Waugh, and Graham Greene. Non-Christians meanwhile are not united (in the nature of things they could have no discipline of dogma) or even organized for their own protection.

The death of faith is the birth of the imagination. Until liberated from the toils of a savage fancy and primitive morals the progressive instinct cannot function. The faithful are not allowed even to *imagine* that the Atonement is an invention. Dante's intellect and humanity were immobilized by piety, and the wings of his poesy pinioned to his sides by the strait-jacket of Aquinas' cosmogony.

Believing this, I came to regard Russell as the great emancipator from the appalling thraldom of the mind which produced the religious misery of Samuel Johnson, the unctuous 'Truth' of 'Soapy Sam' and the whole of his generation (of which Mr Chadband's

[1] *The Strength to Dream*, pp. 19, 20.
[2] *History of Western Philosophy*, Chapter XXVI.

'Ter-uth' was only a logical extension), the anti-humanism of
Cardinal Newman, and the furtive Thomism and fashionable
'despair' of T. S. Eliot. It was Russell who formulated the common-
sense doctrine which, if adopted, would bring all the religions
toppling to the ground, namely that 'it is undesirable to believe a
proposition when there is no ground whatever for supposing it to
be true'.[1]

To describe the sense of the splendour of life and reality and the
aspiration of the individual towards some noble end, another word
than 'religion' will have to be found, 'Religion' is so associated with
wickedness, oppression, credulity, cant, and all that is ignoble that
it has become a 'dirty' word, suggesting the very opposite what many
excellent people would like it to mean.

There may have been a moment in history when Christianity had
a chance of becoming the world religion. That moment, however,
if it ever existed, has long since passed. Christianity advanced in the
world behind the spearhead of Western military power and unless
the West is able once again to exert this power, the hopes for the
extension of Christianity must be very modest indeed. It is an
expression of Western nationalism, and its greatest hopes lie in the
rebirth of imperialism; but its monopolistic claims will always be
resisted by the greater proportion of the world's inhabitants. This
is a fact that should be borne in mind in international politics,
whatever the present consolidation of Christian power in Europe or
America.

In stating these forthright personal views in the course of describing Russell's influence on me there is a danger of my misrepresenting
his attitude by implication. He is constitutionally compelled to see
what is good or valid in his opponent's point of view. Thus he is
never to be found uttering anathemas, copying the abuse by Milton
of Salmasius, or being unfair to religious enthusiasts as Voltaire
was unfair to Joan of Arc. One can visualize him in Elysium listening
patiently to the oratory of Marx, Hitler, or God and, when they
have talked themselves into silence, remarking, 'I regret that I find
myself unable to subscribe to your point of view'.

In the necessity he felt for fairness to someone he did not otherwise approve, Russell greatly resembles Gibbon. And the two are
alike in some other respects. Both of them see little merit in the
Christian religion. Gibbon undoubtedly regarded the adoption of
Christianity by Constantine as the state religion of Rome as a great
misfortune both to the Empire and the cause of civilization. Yet he
gives full weight to Constantine's virtues (approving, for example,

[1] *Sceptical Essays*, p. 11.

his 'chastity and temperance'). He might have been expected to make a hero of Julian, but of him he says, 'When we inspect with minute, or perhaps malevolent attention, the portrait of Julian, something seems wanting to the grace and perfection of the whole figure'. Similarly Russell, in his *History of Western Philosophy*, though he has very little good to say of the Franciscans, calls St Francis 'one of the most lovable men known to history', and the pantheist, Spinoza, he refers to as 'the noblest and most lovable of the great philosophers'. On the other hand, he holds no brief for the pagan Socrates, likening him to a 'bad type of cleric' (not, be it noted, *any* type of cleric).

It is instructive to compare the treatment the two men received from the Establishment. Gibbon, in his *Autobiography*, records:

'Let me frankly own that I was startled at the first discharge of the ecclesiastical ordinance; but as soon as I found that the empty noise was mischievous only in intention, my fear was converted into indignation or curiosity has long since subsided in pure and placid indifference.'

When Russell received the full blast of the Establishment's displeasure it was in a much less civilized setting than that in which Gibbon had found himself, and when a case was fabricated in the New York courts to prevent him from earning a living, he was showered with abuse from Anglican bishops and Jesuit magazines accusing him of atheism and other crimes, and the judge trying the case denounced his 'immoral and salacious doctrines', but although Russell might well have decided that any state of society was preferable to that represented by Judge McGeehan, he was still not attracted to Communism.

In some respects, of course, Gibbon and Russell were very different (for example as regards the part sex played in their outlook), but both great men belonged to the Enlightenment which was not, as represented by the orthodox historians, merely a period in the eighteenth century when it was fashionable to rely on the unassisted reason, but a serene, philosophic, and civilized state of mind which has persisted in varying degrees and in limited circles since the time of the Greeks.

All the above was, of course, the public Russell whose companionship was open to anyone who read his books. My knowledge of the private, more intimate Russell was confined to occasional glimpses. It is only in very recent years that I have had any personal contact at all with him, but my long friendship with his sister-in-law,

'Elizabeth' (author of *Elizabeth and Her German Garden*), kept me in touch, at second-hand, with his personality and vicissitudes. I learnt something of the human being, Bertrand Russell, and I felt that in respect of freedom from vanity he was superior to the other prominent personalities of the age with whom I had had any contacts. I have corresponded with Shaw and have to admit that in spite of his greatness he was indisputably vain and opinionated (especially on points on which he was demonstrably wrong—English usage and pronunciation, for example); Wells, when I met him, I found very friendly but absurdly irascible, going up in flames like a spoilt child at the slightest provocation. The only other personality of comparable calibre I have known was Gilbert Murray who in his last years, it seemed to me, tended to become rather set in his ideas, whereas Russell has retained his mental flexibility in old age to a quite extraordinary degree. The remaining personality of note with whom I was brought once or twice into close association was Hilaire Belloc, though I scarcely feel that he can be classed with these others since apart from his unrealistic cures for social ills he seemed incapable of compassion, and this alone has sufficed to place his reputation in eclipse. In Russell, on the contrary, compassion is his outstanding quality.

It was, however, a private venture of my own which brought me to Russell's notice and earned me (I am happy to believe) a measure of his personal regard. I had all my life written verse as a relaxation and on my return to live in England I was so exasperated by what seemed to me to be the artificially inflated reputations of the 'Main Stream' poets, especially of their patron saint, that my *alter ego*, 'Myra Buttle' ('My Rebuttal' of the claims of the 'Main Stream') was inspired to write 'The Sweeniad'. I did not expect that the identity of Myra Buttle would permanently remain a mystery, and it was eventually revealed by accident. Russell at first took Myra for a woman and applauded her efforts with warm but courteous chivalry, but his approval continued even when Myra's real sex was revealed, and he seemed to find equal satisfaction in the two successors to 'The Sweeniad', namely 'Toynbee in Elysium' and 'The Bitches' Brew', or 'The Plot Against Bertrand Russell'. 'The Sweeniad' did well, especially in America, and has 'made' the anthologies; the other two have so far enjoyed little more than a *succès d'estime*, but Myra's warm and flattering reception by a score of distinguished persons as well as by her own friends has been a great comfort to her unpoetical colleague.

Since Russell is now ninety, it is instructive to enquire what was the situation of other eminent philosophers who succeeded in becoming nonagenarians. There have been extremely few of them. Hobbes (1588–1679) springs to mind as one, though with all his influence on English political thought and institutions he did not, I feel, approach Russell in achievement. Hobbes's eighth decade (unlike Russell's) was placid and uneventful and he spent his time translating the *Iliad* and *Odyssey* and writing his autobiography in verse (I wish Russell would do the same). Shaw, as we know, reached the age of 94, and died, if not in the 'odour of sanctity', in something very like it. John Dewey (1859–1952) was 93 when he died; Santa-yana (1863–1952) just missed his ninetieth birthday. The dates of the ancients are uncertain, but I cannot think of any other philo-sophers off hand who attained their tenth decade. But none of those who lived to a great age were engaged in active political life and controversy in their last years as Russell was on his ninetieth birthday.

Had Russell died twenty years ago, or even ten, it is likely that he would have been buried in Westminster Abbey (unless he had provided against such a contingency in his will) and his name would have been revered almost universally by the British nation. As it is, he is the centre of a bitter controversy, a public figure who is regarded by his supporters as the greatest living Englishman, but who is denigrated by his opponents as an ally of the Communists and sentenced to prison by the law as a criminal. Yet when the issue between the two sides is carefully examined it will be found that on this occasion it is not so much one of fundamental doctrine as of ends and means. Philosophically speaking, it is epistemological rather than teleological.

Russell's part in the Campaign for Nuclear Disarmament is in keeping with his character and record. It is inspired by a spirit of passionate altruism deriving from the belief that in the universe so far explored human civilization offers the only promise for the expansion of rational consciousness. If sometimes his action seems quixotic, the same is true of the action of all the great prophets and reformers. Throughout his career, moreover, his principles have shown a remarkable consistency.

In concluding this article, I ask myself from my half century of experience of Russell what he stands for that is positive, valuable, creative, and likely to be enduring.

To begin with he has revolutionized both our logic and our language. We use his words and methods in our daily talk without realizing it. Says Alan Wood:

'I have come across few present-day critics of Russell who do not either unwittingly repeat points he himself has made, or else show ignorance of his true views. (It must be remembered that his books are already becoming classics, and a classic may be defined as a book which people think they know about without having read it.)'[1]

Russell has examined and criticized accepted values in such a way that our attitude towards politics, morality, marriage, etc., have been insensibly influenced and prepared for change. In an age which is resorting increasingly to mystagoguery, ritualism, and sacerdotalism (both religious and lay), he has provided those of us who find the process abhorrent and intolerable with new philosophic weapons wherewith to fight for our rational survival. He has for long been a beacon of hope in a darkening world.

Yet, Russell's very solitariness in our age prompts us once again to wonder whether he is not a survival from a past age rather than just one other in a long line of eminent men. He so emphatically belongs to the 'Enlightenment' and not to the present 'Muddiment'. It seems absurd on the face of it to compare Britain in the twentieth century with Rome in the sixth century (as described by Gibbon). There is so little superficial resemblance. Whereas Rome was 'a dreary wilderness, in which the land is barren, the waters are impure, and the air is infectious', science yearly improves our own material situation; whereas 'the far greater part of the Romans was condemned to hopeless indigence and celebacy, the depopulation was constant and visible, and the gloomy enthusiast might expect the approaching end of the human race', our own population mates and reproduces to an extent which many authorities consider dangerous; in the sixth century 'the number of citizens still exceeded the measure of subsistence', while we, in spite of our overbrimming population, are still able to grow and import enough to feed ourselves. Notwithstanding our de-intellectualized press and TV, our literature and art are still vigorous and experimenting, and it is at least premature to say (as Gibbon said of sixth century Rome) that 'curiosity and ambition no longer attracted the nations to the [a] capital of the world'. Nevertheless there are some ominous similarities in our respective conditions. In place of disease and hunger, we have the menace of the atom-bomb which may at any moment reduce our country to a state compared to which the 'dreary wilderness of the Campagna of Rome' would be a fruitful paradise. True, we have no Pope Gregory with sufficient power to mutilate our statues, to reduce the British Museum (as Gregory did the Palatine Library) to ashes, or to forbid the teaching of grammar as profane. But the *will* to do

[1] 'Russell's Philosophy; a study in its development', by Alan Wood, in Russell, *My Philosophical Development*, p. 258.

these things is still there (as our ecclesiastically expurgated encyclo-paedias show). It is only at the price of eternal vigilance and militant broadmindedness that we can hold on to what, in the last four centuries, we have gained.

It is therefore not stretching analogy or the imagination too greatly for the 'gloomy enthusiast' to visualize Russell as another Boethius. Boethius, Gibbon said, was 'the last of the Romans whom Cato or Tully could have acknowledged as their countryman', and in the message I was privileged to contribute to the programme of the concert in honour of Russell's ninetieth birthday I adapted to this to suit Russell in the form of 'the last of the Europeans whom Socrates or Spinoza could have acknowledged as their countryman'.[1] But, needless to say, such a despairing guess was not intended as a prophecy: it was the oblique expression of a hope, reinforced by a secret faith, that Russell would yet prove to be harbinger of an age of security and of a return to reason.

[1] In the message, *auspex* was misprinted *suspex*! The work of an enemy gremlin?

4

I. F. STONE

To Oppose the Stream

All over the world there are people who love Bertrand Russell. Love is the only word for it, a filial love as for a wise father. The Polish writer Czeslaw Milosz, in his novel, *The Seizure of Power*, about the Polish underground in World War II, describes one of them, a resistance fighter. This man had taken the name Bertrand as his '*nom de guerre*, in honour of Bertrand Russell. After the war he wanted to devote himself exclusively', so Milosz describes him, 'to mathematical logic.' But it was more than admiration for the *Principia Mathematica* which explained why a man in the Polish underground took the name of the British philosopher. 'Bertrand', as Milosz pictures him, was somehow different. 'It was difficult', he writes, 'to find fault with him because he was an exceptionally good shot.' Yet in the eyes of the underground group leader, 'Bertrand' had 'many failings'. He 'made no secret of his contempt for the army and for war'. His 'companions in the battalion scornfully called him a pacifist'. It is when we come to the final touch of his portrait that we fully understand his identification with Bertrand Russell. 'One day', Milosz relates, 'he had brought a wounded German to safety under fire.' It was this survival of an objective of humanity, and this willingness to take risks on its behalf, which marked 'Bertrand' as one of Russell's brood.

I remember the night I joined it. One night several summers ago, after going to press, I was walking, rather lonely, around Washington and wandered for lack of anything else to do into the Public Library. There on a shelf a title caught my eye. The letters were old and faded but the words urgent, *Why Men Fight*. It was a book Russell wrote in 1916 during the first World War, published originally in England as *Principles of Social Reconstruction*. Almost at once, as I began to read, I came on words which though written 40 years before seemed terribly relevant and deeply comforting to one who felt an outcast in cold war Washington, as Russell felt an outcast in that earlier England which had made 'hate the Hun' its motto. 'To one who stands outside the cycle of beliefs and passions which make the war seem necessary,' Russell had written, 'an isolation, an almost unbearable separation from the general activity, becomes unavoidable. At the very moment when the universal disaster raises compassion to the highest degree, compassion itself compels aloofness from the impulse to self-destruction which has swept over Europe.'

I read on, like someone on a deserted island who has suddenly found a note which indicates that others had lived and suffered there before him. 'The helpless longing to save men from the ruin towards which they are hastening', Russell continued, 'makes it necessary to oppose the stream, to incur hostility, to be thought unfeeling, to lose for the moment the power of winning belief.' *To lose for a moment the power of winning belief*—how presciently this seemed to express the feelings of a maverick journalist, trying in a minuscule publication of his own to buck the hateful tide toward war. Then came the healing message, as if in a father's testament, leaving a heritage of courage. 'It is impossible', Russell went on, 'to prevent others from feeling hostile but it is possible to avoid any reciprocal hostility on one's own part, by imaginative understanding and the sympathy which grows out of it. And without understanding and sympathy', he concluded, 'it is impossible to find a cure for the evil from which the world is suffering.' What Russell meant to 'Bertrand' in the Polish underground in the 40s, Russell meant to me in the American cold war of the 50s.

Russell has taught us all by word and by example. His first test came in the Boer War, which split the Fabian Society; the Webbs wavered, even George Bernard Shaw wrote nonsense but Russell opposed the war. When the first World War came, he went to prison as a conscientious objector. The Appeal to the Intellectuals of Europe which he wrote in 1915 is as relevant now as it was then. 'Men of learning,' he wrote, 'who should be accustomed to the pursuit of truth in their daily work, might have attempted at this time to make themselves the mouthpiece of truth, to see what was false on their own side, what was valid on the side of their enemies. They might have used their reputation and their freedom from political entanglements to mitigate the abhorrence with which the nations have come to regard each other, to help toward mutual understanding, to make the peace, when it comes, not a mere cessation due to weariness but a fraternal reconciliation, springing from realization that the strife has been a folly of blindness. They have chosen to do nothing of all this. Allegiance to country has swept away allegiance to truth.' The reproach is freshly applicable in these days of emotional and ideological mobilization for a new war. So is his observation, 'oddly enough, those who most bitterly hate democracy at home are the most ferocious in defending it against

1 It may be found in *Justice in War-Time*, 1916.

Germany'. In America, too, a generation later, those least concerned for a genuine freedom at home have been the most clamorous for a new war in its supposed defence abroad.

Russell, a lifelong Socialist of a non-dogmatic variety, did not have to wait for Khrushchev's secret speech at the Twentieth Congress to see the evils of Stalinism. His *Practice and Theory of Bolshevism*, published in 1920 after a visit to Russia, anticipates the criticism and the confessions to come 35 years later. He foresaw 'the establishment of a bureaucratic aristocracy, concentrating authority in its own hands, and creating a régime just as oppressive and cruel as that of capitalism'. That early he wrote, 'The necessity of inculcating Communism produces a hot-house condition, where every breath of fresh air must be excluded: people are to be taught to think in a certain way, all free intelligence becomes taboo. The country comes to resemble an immensely magnified Jesuit College. Every kind of liberty is banned as being "bourgeois" . . .' This is how the best youth of the Soviet bloc feels about it today. It was because Russell felt so deeply that 'the civilized world seems almost certain, sooner or later, to follow the example of Russia in attempting a Socialist organization of society' that he also felt it a duty to call attention to the problems of the transition period and the danger of following the Bolshevik pattern in the West. 'For this reason, if for no other,' Russell wrote, 'I cannot enter into the conspiracy of concealment which many Western Socialists who have visited Russia consider necessary.' Here again, as in the Boer War, he met a test failed by the Webbs whose monumental work on the Soviet Union now seems monumentally naïve. But long before the cold war he also warned, with that humanity which is his characteristic:

'Life in Russia has always been fierce and cruel, to a far greater degree than with us, and out of the war has come a danger that this fierceness and cruelty may become universal. I have hopes that in England this may be avoided through the moderation of both sides. But it is essential to a happy issue that melodrama should no longer determine our views of the Bolsheviks: they are neither angels to be worshipped nor devils to be exterminated, but merely bold and able men attempting with great skill an almost impossible task.'

As early as 1928, in his *Sceptical Essays*, writing on 'The Danger of Creed Wars', Russell foresaw a gigantic struggle coming between America and Russia and wrote, 'For my part, I look upon the coming strife as Erasmus did, without the ability to join wholeheartedly with either party. No doubt I agree with the Bolsheviks,' he continued, 'on many more points than with the American magnates, but I cannot believe that their philosophy is ultimately true or capable of producing a happy world.' He foresaw the torrent of propaganda from both sides. 'One may expect', he predicted, 'that on both sides there will be cruelty on a large scale, and that propaganda will cause each side to know the cruelties of the other, but not its own. Very few Americans, for example, know the truth about Sacco and Vanzetti' though this had been well publicized in Soviet Russia 'to produce an unfavourable opinion as to capitalistic justice. Similarly the Russian trials of Patriarchs and Social Revolutionaries are known in America. Thus each side acquires abundant evidence to prove the other side wicked, but remains ignorant of its own wickedness.'

Even more perceptive, if despairing, for those who try to see the struggle objectively and to find means of moderating and avoiding it was his conclusion to that same essay:

'The fundamental delusion of our time, in my opinion, is the excessive emphasis upon the economic aspects of life, and I do not expect the strife between Capitalism and Communism as philosophies to cease until it is recognized that both are inadequate through their failure to recognize biological needs.

'As to the methods of diminishing the ferocity of the struggle, I do not know of anything better than the old Liberal watchwords. What is needed is freedom of opinion, and opportunity for the spread of opinion. It is the latter particularly that causes the difficulty. The mechanism for the effective and widespread diffusion of an opinion must necessarily be in the hands either of the State or of great capitalistic concerns. Before the introduction of democracy and education this was much less true: effective opinion was confined to a small minority, who could be reached without all the expensive apparatus of modern propaganda. But it can hardly be expected that either the State or a great capitalist organization will devote money and energy to the propagation of opinions which it considers dangerous and subversive, and contrary to true morality. The State, no less than the capitalist organization, is in practice a stupid elderly man accustomed to flattery, ossified in his prejudices, and wholly unaware of all that is vital in the thought of his time. No novelty can be effectively advocated until it has passed the censorship of some such old fogy. It is true that hole-and-corner publicity is possible, but this only obtains hold-and-corner readers.'

To browse through Russell's works, reading here and re-reading there, is to see that his life has been one continuous and consistent effort to liberate man by intelligence and by love from his self-destructive illusions and hates. No philosopher in history has so descended into the arena of events, seeking by preachment, homily, wit and exhortation to bring about a world without injustice and war. Long before Sartre's existentialism, Russell in his 'A Free Man's Worship', saw that a new and enduring faith could be erected 'only on the firm foundation of unyielding despair'.

As the weapons grow more terrible, Russell's message has grown more urgent, his vision of a World State more necessary. The awe felt for his learning, his esoteric achievements in mathematical logic and his great age have given him a weapon he wields for peace. This has earned him as much aspersion as gratitude, but did not he himself once write, 'I do not know of any country where a man who has a genuine love for his neighbour can long avoid obloquy'? Like Einstein, his great comrade-in-arms, he combines a deep pessimism with a fresh and almost child-like joy in the beauties of the world he would save. His scepticism is only a deeper faith. Every truth, once organized, becomes a lie; every liberation, a new enslavement. Russell teaches us to be eternally sceptical in order to stay eternally humane.

[1] Reprinted in *Mysticism and Logic*.

II

THE PUBLIC MAN

5

MICHAEL SCOTT

Civil Disobedience and Morals

It is impossible to write about Bertrand Russell without offending somebody, possibly everybody, probably Bertrand Russell. To me he appears as a giant among mental and spiritual dwarfs, who are hecticly engaged in erecting frankenstein monsters having their own spiritual limitations, powers of perception, scales of value, and sense of proportion.

I have not been asked to write about Russell and Religion or his Philosophy mainly because I am known not to be an expert in either of these. In fact I have not often discussed the subject of religion with him for all the hours and days I have spent with him, perhaps for fear of his wit and wisdom in the presence of which I know myself to be decidedly one of the dwarfs.

Perhaps it is only through a succession of unusual experiences in life which have enabled me, as they would anyone who had shared them, to sense some of the truly great proportions of Russell which are enhanced rather than diminished by his admitted frailties.

A common failing of preachers is to represent God as like ourselves only bigger. This is also true of the character and personality of Jesus who often acquires as many of the characteristics of the preacher as the preacher does those of Jesus. If we look at the history of the Christian Church we may be appalled at the discrepancy between the Jesus of the pulpits and platforms and the Jesus of history as in the agony of the last throes of a death sentence under Roman-jewish law for one deliberately guilty of treason and blasphemy muttering, audibly enough to be overheard by the guard, 'Father forgive them. They don't know what they are doing.'

It is that discrepancy and the hideous consequences that have resulted from it, not only in the dwarfing of human minds but the dwarfing of the whole scale of human achievements and sense of values that are difficult to explain.

Russell's explanation of this does not seem adequate any more than his explanation of his contemporary world's rejection of many of his own ideas and actions. The dwarfs around him he is always accustomed to treat as his equals until they do something outrageous and then more than likely it will be his wit rather than his wisdom that is exercised on them.

There is no greatness in sitting in the road outside the Ministry of Defence, even if you are philosopher. It might be exhibitionism, frustration, resentment against lack of recognition, any of the things that journalists have made so free with in their superficial descriptions and analyses. The quality of greatness lies in the reasons, judgments, valuations of relevant factors, appraisal of the consequences for the self and society, etc.

Socrates voluntarily rejected civil disobedience as wrong for him and his society. But the circumstances for him were not the same as for Russell in so far as respect for the law was concerned. Socrates considered that he owed it to society not to escape death but to embrace it. But Greek society existed only very precariously surrounded by a sea of barbarism and rested in part on a legal foundation of slavery which made civil disobedience an imminent threat to civilization as it was then conceived and as Socrates conceived it.

Bertrand Russell lives in an era of increasing state power merging in totalitarianism and its opposite number, as politicians conceive opposition, namely the Warfare State. Jesus took passive resistance further than Socrates or Russell. He defied both the religious and secular authority of his time in blasphemously claiming sonship with God and interfering with the perquisites of the priests and traders in the Temple precincts.

There is a revealing passage in Russell's *Authority and the Individual*: 'All these moral gains, it must be admitted, have been jeopardized by a recrudescence of ferocity. But I do not think that in the end the moral advance which they have represented will be lost to mankind. The prophets and sages who inaugurated this moral advance, although for the most part they were not honoured in their own day, were nevertheless not prevented from doing their work. In a modern totalitarian state matters are worse than they were in the time of Socrates or in the time of the Gospels. In a totalitarian State an innovator whose ideas are disliked by the Government is not merely put to death, which is a matter to which a brave man may remain indifferent, but is totally prevented from causing his doctrine to be known. Innovations in such a community can come only from the Government. And the government now, as in the past is not likely to approve anything contrary to its own immediate interests. In a totalitarian State such events as the rise of Buddhism or Christianity are scarcely possible and not even by the greatest heroism can a moral reformer acquire any influence whatever. This is a new fact in human history, brought about by the much increased power over individuals which the modern technique of government has made possible. It is a very grave fact and one which shows how fatal a totalitarian régime must be to every kind of moral progress.

'In our own day an individual of exceptional powers can hardly hope to have so great a career or so great a social influence as in former times, if he devotes himself to art or religious and moral reform. There are however still four careers which are open to him: he may become a great political leader like Lenin; he may acquire vast industrial power like Rockefeller; he may transform the world by scientific discoveries, as is being done by the atomic physicists; or finally, if he has not the capacities for any of these careers, or if opportunity is lacking, his energy in default of other outlet may drive him into a life of crime. Criminals in the legal sense, seldom have much influence upon the course of history, and therefore a man of overweening ambition will choose some other career if it is open to him.

'The rise of men of science to great eminence in the State is a modern phenomenon. Scientists, like other innovators, had to fight for recognition: some were banished; some were burnt; some were kept in dungeons; others merely had their books burnt. But gradually it came to be realized that they could put power into the hands of the State. The French revolutionaries, after mistakenly guillotining Lavoisier, employed his surviving colleagues in the manufacture of explosives. In modern war the scientists are recognized by all civilized governments as the most useful citizens, provided they can be tamed and induced to place their services at the disposal of a single government rather than of mankind.'[1]

Such is the dilemma as Russell sees it. It is against this historical background that he must be seen sitting on the pavement in Parliament Square. No one can suppose that with his sense of humour he would not have foreseen the caricatures of his action that would appear in the press of the world and the travesty of his attitude which represents this as anti-parliamentarian. He would appreciate the irony of this criticism, when all he is doing is asking people to think for themselves and act in accordance with their own reasons not those someone else has imposed, whether through force, or the distortion or denial of information. It is tragic evidence of the trend he is trying to warn the world to heed, that the press of a free country should so misrepresent his protest against the acquisition of power by governments and the caucuses which influence it, at a time when governments have the power to utterly destroy civilization, and perhaps all life on this planet. At present, at every moment of time,

---

[1] Reith Lectures, 1948–49. *Authority and the Individual*, p. 51 *seq.*

there is nothing in the organization of man to prevent this happening. That is why Bertrand Russell sat on the pavement in Parliament Square, to be ridiculed by every daily newspaper in Britain.

Nor has there yet been any serious attempt to evaluate a movement in which thousands, some elderly but mostly young, many with young families, many with no party political interests or affiliations, most of them liking life and wanting to enjoy it, deliberately break a law and court a term in gaol. They know, especially the students, that they are risking their whole careers. Many in employment stand to lose their jobs or will have to make other provision for their families, many old ladies and young mothers feared they might be batoned by the police or trampled by a stampeding crowd. But there they sit. Politics and the press who today almost monopolize the sources of information and so can poison the springs of thought, could not find time or space for even that little generosity needed to allow a proper evaluation of these happenings at a period in which they frequently bewail the declining moral sense and growing delinquency of the younger generation.

When two silly people, unable to see any difference between people disagreeing with one another and Russell's form of argument with the State, sat on his drawing room floor and refused to move or let him get on with his work they were surprised when he called up the police and asked that they be removed in the name of the law. The newspapers all over the country made great play with this and so did some of his erstwhile colleagues on the Executive of the Campaign for Nuclear Disarmament.

While not suffering such foolishness kindly, Russell is one of the most kindly and tolerant of men. But his tolerance is not an easy going indulgence or acquiescence in things which he believes to be wrong. His belief is his point of view and it may be wrong. His tolerance is rather a positive delight in variety and in the conflict which this inevitably implies in the whole order of things. The art of civilization is the pursuit of these conflicts in a rational and civilized manner, not either by deceit and trickery or the mere use of *force majeur*. Hence his opposition to all forms of bigotry or dogmatism including that sometimes exhibited by rationalists and atheists, secularists and materialists.

Perhaps it would be true of Russell to say that there is nothing which he fears except Nothing. Nothing in the heart of man and in the mind and soul of man. That is what threatens death to humanity. That today is the threat to life and to the Universe. And it is this that he has inspired human beings to resist with all the strength they can muster—the organisation of Man into Nothing.

6

ERICH FROMM

Prophets and Priests

I

It can be said without exaggeration that never was the knowledge of the great ideas produced by the human race as widespread in the world as it is today, and never were these ideas less effective than they are today. The ideas of Plato and Aristotle, of the Prophets and of Christ, of Spinoza and Kant, are known to millions among the educated classes in Europe and America. They are taught at thousands of institutions of higher learning, and some of them are preached in the churches of all denominations everywhere. And all this in a world which follows the principles of unrestricted egotism, which breeds hysterical nationalism, and which is preparing for an insane mass slaughter. How can one explain this discrepancy?

Ideas do not influence man deeply when they are only taught as ideas and thoughts. Usually, when presented in such a way, they change other ideas; new thoughts take the place of old thoughts; new words take the place of old words. But all that has happened is a change in concepts and words. Why should it be different? It is exceedingly difficult for a man to be moved by ideas, and to grasp a truth. In order to do that, he needs to overcome deep-seated resistances of inertia, fear of being wrong, or of straying away from the herd. Just to become acquainted with other ideas is not enough, even though these ideas in themselves are right and potent. But ideas do have an effect on man if the idea is lived by the one who teaches it; if it is personified by the teacher, if the idea appears in the flesh. If a man expresses the idea of humility and is humble, then those who listen to him will understand what humility is. They will not only understand, but they will believe that he is talking about a reality, and not just voicing words. The same holds true for all ideas which a man, a philosopher, or a religious teacher may try to convey.

Those who announce ideas—and not necessarily new ones—and at the same time live them we may call *prophets*. The Old Testament prophets did precisely that: they announced the idea that man had to find an answer to his existence, and that this answer was the development of his reason, of his love; and they taught that humility and justice were inseparably connected with love and reason. They lived what they preached. They did not seek power, but avoided it. Not even the power of being a prophet. They were not impressed by might, and they spoke the truth even if this led them to imprisonment, ostracism or death. They were not men who set themselves apart and waited to see what would happen. They responded to their fellowman, because they felt responsible. What happened to others happened to them. Humanity was not outside, but within them. Precisely because they saw the truth they felt the responsibility to tell it; they did not threaten, but they showed the *alternatives* with which man was confronted. It is not that a prophet wishes to be a prophet; in fact, only the false ones have the ambition to become prophets. His becoming a prophet is simple enough, because the alternatives which he sees are simple enough. The prophet Amos expressed this idea very succinctly: 'The lion has roared, who will not be afraid. God has spoken, who will not be a prophet.' The phrase 'God has spoken' here means simply that the choice has become unmistakably clear. There can be no more doubt. There can be no more evasion. Hence the man who feels responsible has no choice but to become a prophet, whether he has been herding sheep, tending his vineyards, or developing and teaching ideas. It is the function of the prophet to show reality, to show alternatives and to protest; it is his function to call loudly, to awake man from his customary half slumber. It is the historical situation which makes prophets—not the wish of some men to be prophets.

Many nations have had their prophets. The Buddha lived his teachings; Christ appeared in the flesh; Socrates died according to his ideas; Spinoza lived them. And they all made a deep imprint on the human race precisely because their idea was manifested in the flesh in each one of them.

Prophets appear only at intervals in the history of humanity. They die and leave their message. The message is accepted by millions, it becomes dear to them. This is precisely the reason why the idea becomes exploitable for others who can make use of the attachment of the people to these ideas, for their own purposes—those of ruling and controlling. Let us call the men who make use of the idea the prophets have announced the *priests*. The prophets live their ideas. The priests administer them to the people who are attached to the idea. The idea has lost its vitality. It has become a formula. The priests declare that it is very important how the idea is formulated; naturally the formulation becomes always important after the experience is dead; how else could one control people by controlling their thoughts, unless there is the 'correct' formulation? The priests use the idea to organize men, to control them through controlling the proper expression of the idea, and when they have anaesthetized man enough they declare that man is not capable of being awake and of directing his own life, and that they, the priests, act out of duty, or even compassion, when they fulfil the function of directing men who, if left to themselves, are afraid of freedom. It is true not all priests have acted that way, but most of them have, especially those who wielded power.

There are priests not only in religion. There are priests in philosophy and priests in politics. Every philosophical school has its priests. Often they are very learned; it is their business to administer the idea of the original thinker, to impart it, to interpret it, to make it into a museum object and thus to guard it. Then there are the *political* priests; we have seen enough of them in the last one hundred and fifty years. They have administered the idea of freedom, to protect the economic interests of their social class. In the twentieth century the priests have taken over the administration of the ideas of social-ism. While this idea aimed at the liberation and independence of man, the priests declared in one way or another that man was not capable of being free, or at least that he would not be for a long time. Until then they were obliged to take over, and to decide how the idea was to be formulated, and who was a faithful believer and who was not. The priests usually confuse the people because they claim that they are the successor of the prophet, and that they live what they preach. Yet, while a child could see that they live precisely the opposite of what they teach, the great mass of the people are brain-washed effectively, and eventually they come to believe that if the priests live in splendour they do so as a sacrifice, because they have to represent the great idea; or if they kill ruthlessly they only do so out of revolutionary faith.

No historical situation could be more conducive to the emergence of prophets than ours. The existence of the entire human race is threatened by the madness of preparing nuclear war. Stone-age mentality and blindness have led to the point where the human race seems to be moving rapidly toward the tragic end of its history at the very moment when it is near to its greatest achievement. At this point humanity needs prophets, even though it is doubtful whether their voice will prevail against that of the priests.

Among the few in whom the idea has become manifest in the flesh, and whom the historical situation of mankind has transformed from teachers into prophets, is Bertrand Russell. He happens to be a great thinker but that is not really essential to his being a prophet. He, together with Einstein and Schweitzer, represents the answer of Western humanity to the threat to its existence, because all three of them have spoken up, have warned, and have pointed out the alternatives. Schweitzer lives the idea of Christianity by working in Lambaréné. Einstein lived the idea of reason and humanism by refusing to join the hysterical voices of nationalism of the German intelligentsia in 1914 and many times after that. Bertrand Russell for many decades expressed his ideas on rationality and humanism in his books; but in recent years he has gone out to the market place to show all men that when the laws of the country contradict the laws of humanity a true man must choose the laws of humanity.

Bertrand Russell has recognized that the idea, even if embodied in one person, gains social significance only if it is embodied in a group. When Abraham argued with God about Sodom's fate, and challenged God's justice, he asked that Sodom be spared if there were only ten just men, but not less. If there were less than ten, that is to say, if there were not even the smallest group in which the idea of justice had become embodied, even Abraham could not expect the city to be saved. Bertrand Russell tries to prove that there are the ten who can save the city. That is why he has organized people, has marched with them, and has sat down with them and been carried off with them in police vans. While his voice is a voice in the wilderness it is, nevertheless, not an isolated voice. It is the leader of a chorus; whether it is the chorus of a Greek tragedy or that of Beethoven's ninth symphony only the history of the next few years will reveal.

II

Among the ideas which Bertrand Russell embodies in his life, perhaps the first one to be mentioned is man's right and duty to disobedience.

By disobedience I do not refer to the disobedience of the 'rebel without cause' who disobeys because he has no commitment to life except the one to say 'no'. This kind of rebellious disobedience is as blind and impotent as its opposite, the conformist obedience which is *incapable* of saying 'no'. I am speaking of the man who can say 'no' because he can affirm, who can disobey precisely because he can obey his conscience and the principles which he has chosen; I am speaking of the revolutionary, not of the rebel.

In most social systems obedience is the supreme virtue—disobedience the supreme sin. In fact, in our culture most people, when they feel 'guilty' actually are feeling afraid because they have been disobedient. They are not really troubled by a moral issue, as they think they are, but by the fact of having disobeyed a command. This is not surprising; after all, Christian teaching has interpreted Adam's disobedience as a deed which corrupted him and his seed so fundamentally that only the special act of God's grace could save man from this corruption. This idea was, of course, in accord with the social function of the Church which supported the power of the rulers by teaching the sinfulness of disobedience. Only those men who took the biblical teachings of humility, brotherliness and justice seriously rebelled against secular authority, with the result that the Church, more often than not, branded them as rebels and sinners against God. Protestantism, in its main stream, did not alter this. On the contrary, while the Catholic Church kept alive the awareness of the difference between secular and spiritual authority, Protestantism allied itself with secular power. Luther was only giving the first and drastic expression to this trend when he wrote about the revolutionary German peasants of the sixteenth century, 'Therefore let us everyone who can, smite, slay and stab, secretly or openly, remembering that nothing can be more poisonous, hurtful or devilish than a rebel'.

In spite of the vanishing of religious terror, authoritarian political systems continued to make obedience the human cornerstone of their existence. The great revolutions in the seventeenth and eighteenth centuries fought against royal authority, but soon man reverted to making a virtue of obedience to the king's successors, whatever name they took. Where is authority today? In the totalitarian countries it is overt authority of the state, supported by the strengthening of respect for authority in the family and in the school. The Western democracies, on the other hand, feel proud at having overcome nineteenth century authoritarianism. But have they—or has only the character of the authority changed?

This century is the century of the hierarchically organized bureaucracies in government, business, and labour unions. These bureaucracies administer things *and* men as one; they follow certain principles, especially the economic principle of the balance sheet, quantification, maximal efficiency, and profit, and they function essentially as an electronic computer would that has been programmed with these principles. The individual becomes a number, transforms himself into a thing. But just because there is no overt authority, because he is not 'forced' to obey, the individual is under the illusion that he acts voluntarily, that he follows only his own will and decision, or that he follows only 'rational' authority. Who can disobey the 'reasonable', who can disobey the computer-bureaucracy, who can disobey when he is not even aware of obeying? In the family and in education the same thing happens. The corruption of the theories of progressive education have led to a method where the child is not told what to do, not given orders, nor punished for failure to execute them. The child just 'expresses himself'. But he is filled from the first day of his life onward with an unholy respect for conformity, with the fear of being 'different', with the fright of being away from the rest of the herd. The 'organization man' thus reared in the family and in the school, and having his education completed in the big organization has opinions, but no convictions; he amuses himself, but is unhappy; he is even willing to sacrifice his life and that of his children in voluntary obedience to impersonal and anonymous powers. He accepts the calculation of deaths which has become so fashionable in the discussions on thermonuclear war: half the population of a country dead—'quite acceptable'; two thirds dead—'maybe not'.

The question of disobedience is today of vital importance. While according to the Bible human history began with an act of disobedience—Adam and Eve—while according to Greek myth civilization began with Prometheus' act of disobedience, it is not unlikely that human history will be terminated by an act of obedience, by the obedience to authorities who themselves are obedient to archaic fetishes of 'State sovereignty', 'national honour', 'military victory', and who will give the orders to push the fatal buttons to those who are obedient to them and to their fetishes.

Disobedience, then, in the sense in which we use it here, is an act of the affirmation of reason and will. It is not primarily an attitude directed *against* something, but *for* something: for man's capacity to see, to say what he sees, and to refuse to say what he does not see. To do so he does not need to be aggressive or rebellious; he needs to have his eyes open, to be fully awake, and willing to take the responsibility to open the eyes of those who are in danger of perishing because they are half asleep.

Karl Marx once wrote that Prometheus, who said that he 'would rather be chained to his rock than to be the obedient servant of the gods', is the patron saint of all philosophers. Bertrand Russell, a philosopher himself, is renewing this Promethean function in his own life.

Marx's statement points very clearly to the problem of the connection between philosophy and disobedience. Most philosophers were not disobedient to the authorities of their time. Socrates obeyed by dying, Spinoza declined the position of a professor, rather than to find himself in conflict with authority, Kant was a loyal citizen, Hegel exchanged his youthful revolutionary sympathies for the glorification of the State in his later years. Yet, in spite of this, Prometheus was their patron saint. It is true, they remained in their lecture halls and their studies and did not go to the market place, and there were many reasons for this which I shall not discuss now.

72

But as philosophers they were disobedient to the authority of traditional thoughts and concepts, to the clichés which were believed and taught. They were bringing light to darkness, they were waking up those who were half asleep, they 'dared to know'.

The philosopher is disobedient to clichés and to public opinion because he is obedient to reason and to mankind. It is precisely because reason is universal and transcends all national borders, that the philosopher who follows reason is a citizen of the world; man is his object—not this or that person, this or that nation. The world is his country, not the place where he was born.

Nobody has expressed the revolutionary nature of thought more brilliantly than Bertrand Russell himself: 'Men', he wrote in *Principles of Social Reconstruction* (1916), 'fear thought more than they fear anything else on earth—more than ruin, more even than death. Thought is subversive and revolutionary, destructive and terrible; thought is merciless to privilege, established institutions, and comfortable habits; thought is anarchic and lawless, indifferent to authority, careless of the well-tried wisdom of the ages. Thought looks into the pit of hell and is not afraid. It sees man, a feeble speck, surrounded by unfathomable depths of silence; yet bears itself proudly, as unmoved as if it were lord of the universe. Thought is great and swift and free, the light of the world, and the chief glory of man.'

'But if thought is to become the possession of many, not the privilege of the few, we must have done with fear. It is fear that holds men back—fear lest their cherished beliefs should prove delusions, fear lest the institutions by which they live should prove harmful, fear lest they themselves should prove less worthy of respect than they have supposed themselves to be. "Should the working man think freely about property? Then what will become of us, the rich? Should young men and young women think freely about sex? Then what will become of morality? Should soldiers think freely about war? Then what will become of military discipline? Away with thought! Back into the shades of prejudice, lest property, morals, and war should be endangered! Better men should be stupid, slothful, and oppressive than that their thoughts should be free. For if their thoughts were free they might not think as we do. And at all costs this disaster must be averted." So the opponents of thought argue in the unconscious depths of their souls. And so they act in their churches, their schools, and their universities.'

Bertrand Russell's capacity to disobey is rooted, not in some abstract principle, but in the most real experience there is—in his love of life. This love of life shines through his writings as well as through his person. It is a rare quality today, and especially rare in the very countries where men live in the midst of plenty. Many confuse thrill with joy, excitement with interest, consuming with being. The necrophilous slogan 'Long live death', while consciously used only by the fascists, fills the hearts of many people living in the lands of plenty, although they are not aware of it themselves. It seems that in this fact lies one of the reasons which explain why the majority of people are resigned to accept nuclear war and the ensuing destruction of civilization and take so few steps to prevent this castastrophe. Bertrand Russell, on the contrary, fights against the threatening slaughter—not because he is a pacifist, not because some abstract principle is involved—but precisely because he is a man who loves life. For the very same reason he has no use for those voices which love to harp on the evilness of man, in fact thus saying more about themselves and their own gloomy moods than about men. Not that Bertrand Russell is a sentimental romantic. He is a hard-headed, critical, caustic realist; he is aware of the depth of evil and stupidity to be found in the heart of man; but he does not confuse this fact with an alleged innate corruption which serves to rationalize the outlook of those who are too gloomy to believe in man's gift to create a world in which he can feel himself to be at home. 'Except for those rare spirits', wrote Russell in *Mysticism and Logic: A Free Man's Worship* (1903), 'that are born without sin, there is a cavern of darkness to be traversed before that temple can be entered. The gate of the cavern is despair, and its floor is paved with the gravestones of abandoned hopes. There Self must die; there the eagerness, the greed of untamed desire must be slain, for only so can the soul be freed from the empire of Fate. But out of the cavern the Gate of Renunciation leads again to the daylight of wisdom, by whose radiance a new insight, a new joy, a new tenderness, shine forth to gladden the pilgrim's heart.' And later, in *Philosophical Essays* (1910), he wrote: 'But for those who feel that life on this planet would be a life in prison if it were not for the windows onto a greater world beyond; for those to whom a belief in man's omnipotence seems arrogant, who desire rather the Stoic freedom that comes of mastery over the passions than the Napoleonic domination that sees the kingdoms of this world at its feet—in a word, to men who do not find Man an adequate object of their worship, the pragmatist's world will seem narrow and petty, robbing life of all that gives it value, and making Man himself smaller by depriving the universe which he contemplates of all its splendour.' His views on the alleged evilness of man, Russell expressed brilliantly in the *Unpopular Essays* (1950): 'Children, after being limbs of Satan in traditional theology and mystically illuminated angels in the minds of educational reformers, have reverted to being little devils—not theological demons inspired by the Evil One, but scientific Freudian abominations inspired by the Unconscious. They are, it must be said, far more wicked than they were in the diatribes of the monks; they display, in modern textbooks, an ingenuity and persistance in sinful imaginings to which in the past there was nothing comparable except St Anthony. Is all this the objective truth at last? Or is it merely an adult imaginative compensation for being no longer allowed to wallop the little pests? Let the Freudians answer, each for the others.' One more quotation from Russell's writings which shows how deeply this humanist thinker has experienced this joy of living. 'The lover,' he wrote in *The Scientific Outlook* (1931), 'the poet, and the mystic find a fuller satisfaction than the seeker after power can ever know, since they can retain the object of their love, whereas the seeker after power must be perpetually engaged in some fresh manipulation if he is not to suffer from a sense of emptiness. When I come to die I shall not feel I have lived in vain. I have seen the earth turn red at evening, the dew sparkling in the morning, and the snow shining under a frosty sun; I have smelt rain after drought, and have heard the stormy Atlantic beat upon the granite shores of Cornwall. Science may bestow these and other joys among more people than could otherwise enjoy them. If so, its power will be wisely used. But when it takes out of life the moments to which life owes its values, science will not deserve admiration, however cleverly and however elaborately it may lead men along the road to despair.'

Bertrand Russell is a scholar, a man who believes in reason. But how different he is from the many men whose profession is the same: scholarship. With these the thing that counts is the intellectual grasp of the world. They feel certain that their intellect exhausts reality, and that there is nothing of significance which cannot be grasped by it. They are sceptical towards everything which cannot be caught in an intellectual formula, but they are naïvely un-sceptical towards their own scientific approach. They are more interested in the results of their thoughts than in the process of enlightenment which occurs in the inquiring person. Russell spoke of this kind of intellectual procedure when discussing pragmatism in his *Philosophical Essays* (1910): 'Pragmatism', he wrote, 'appeals to the temper of mind which finds on the surface of this planet the whole of its imaginative material; which feels confident of progress, and unaware of non-human limitations to human power; which loves battle, with all the attendant risks, because it has no real doubt that it will achieve victory; which desires religion, as it desires railways and electric light, as a comfort and a help in the affairs of this world, not as providing non-human objects to satisfy the hunger for perfection and for something to be worshipped without reserve.'

'But for those who feel that life on this planet would be a life in prison if it were not for the windows onto a greater world beyond; for those to whom a belief in man's omnipotence seems arrogant, who desire rather the Stoic freedom that comes of mastery over the passions than the Napoleonic domination that sees the kingdoms of this world at its feet—in a word, to men who do not find man an adequate object of their worship, the pragamatist's world will seem narrow and petty, robbing life of all that gives it value, and making Man himself smaller by depriving the universe which he contemplates of all its splendour.'

For Russell, in contrast to the pragmatist, rational thought is not the quest for certainty, but an adventure, an act of self-liberation and of courage, which changes the thinker by making him more awake and more alive.

Bertrand Russell is a man of faith. Not of faith in the theological sense, but of faith in the power of reason, faith in man's capacity to create his own paradise through his own efforts. 'As geological time is reckoned,' so he wrote in 'Man's Peril from the Hydrogen Bomb' (1954), 'Man has so far existed only for a very short period— 1,000,000 years at the most. What he has achieved, especially during the last 6,000 years, is something utterly new in the history of the Cosmos, so far at least as we are acquainted with it. For countless ages the sun rose and set, the moon waxed and waned, the stars shone in the night, but it was only with the coming of Man that these things were understood. In the great world of astronomy and in the little world of the atom, Man has unveiled secrets which might have been thought undiscoverable. In art and literature and religion, some men have shown a sublimity of feeling which makes the species worth preserving. Is all this to end in trivial horror because so few are able to think of man rather than of this or that group of men? Is our race so destitute of wisdom, so incapable of impartial love, so blind even to the simplest dictates of self-preservation, that the last proof of its silly cleverness is to be the extermination of all life on our planet? —for it will be not only men who will perish, but also the animals and plants, whom no one can accuse of communism or anti-communism.

'I cannot believe that this is to be the end. I would have men forget their quarrels for a moment and reflect that, if they will allow themselves to survive, there is every reason to expect the triumphs of the future to exceed immeasurably the triumphs of the past. There lies before us, if we choose, continual progress in happiness, knowledge, and wisdom. Shall we, instead, choose death, because we cannot forget our quarrels? I appeal, as a human being to human beings: remember your humanity, and forget the rest. If you can do so, the way lies open to a new Paradise; if you cannot, nothing lies before you but universal death.'

This faith is rooted in a quality without which neither his philosophy nor his fight against war could be understood: his love for life. To many people this may not mean much; they believe that everybody loves life. Does he not cling to it when it is threatened, does he not have a great deal of fun in life and plenty of thrilling excitement?

In the first place the fact is that people do not cling to life when it is threatened; how else could one explain their passivity before the threat of nuclear slaughter? Furthermore, people confuse excitement with joy, thrill with love of life. They are 'without joy in the midst of plenty'. The fact is that all the virtues for which capitalism is praised—individual initiative, the readiness to take risks, independence—have long disappeared from industrial society and are to be found mainly in Wild West movies and among gangsters. In bureaucratized, centralized industrialism, regardless of political ideology, there is an increasing number of people who are 'fed up' with life and willing to die in order to get over their boredom. They are the ones who say 'better dead than red'—but deep down their motto is 'better dead than alive'. The extreme form of such an orientation was to be found among those fascists whose motto was: 'Long live death.' Nobody has recognized this more clearly than did Unamuno when he spoke for the last time in his life in the University of Salamanca, where he was Rector at the time of the beginning of the Spanish Civil War; the occasion was a speech by General Millán Astray, whose favourite motto was 'Viva la Muerte!' (Long live death!) and one of his followers shouted it from the back of the hall. When the general had finished his speech Unamuno rose and said: '. . . Just now I heard a necrophilous and senseless cry: "Long live death!" And I, who have spent my life shaping paradoxes which have aroused the uncomprehending anger of others, I must tell you, as an expert authority, that this outlandish paradox is repellent to me. General Millán Astray is a cripple. Let it be said without any slighting undertone. He is a war invalid. So was Cervantes. Unfortunately there are too many cripples in Spain just now. And soon there will be even more of them if God does not come to our aid. It pains me to think that General Millán Astray should dictate the pattern of mass psychology. A cripple who lacks the spiritual greatness of a Cervantes is wont to seek ominous relief in causing mutilation around him.' At this Millán Astray was unable to restrain himself any longer. '*Abajo le inteligencia!*' (Down with intelligence), he shouted. 'Long live death!' There was a clamour of support for this remark from the Falangists. But Unamuno went on: 'This is the temple of the intellect. And I am its high priest. It is you who profane its sacred precincts. You will win, because you have more than enough brute force. But you will not convince. For to convince you need to persuade. And in order to persuade you would need what you lack: Reason and Right in the struggle. I consider it futile to exhort you to think of Spain. I have done.'[1]

However, the attraction to death which Unamuno called necrophily is not a product of Fascist thought alone. It is a phenomenon deeply rooted in a culture which is increasingly dominated by the bureaucratic organizations of the big corporations, governments and armies and by the central role of man-made things, gadgets and machines. This bureaucratic industrialism tends to transform human beings into things. It tends to replace nature by technical devices, the organic by the inorganic. One of the earliest expressions of this love for destruction, for machines and of the contempt for woman (woman is a manifestation of life for man just as man is a manifestation of life for woman), is to be found in the futuristic Manifesto (1909) by Marinetti, one of the intellectual fore-runners of Italian Fascism.

He wrote: '. . . 4. We declare that the world's splendour has been enriched by a new beauty; the beauty of speed. A racing motor-car, its frame adorned with great pipes, like snakes with explosive breath . . . a roaring motor-car, which looks as though running on a shrapnel is more beautiful than the VICTORY OF SAMOTHRACE.

5. We shall sing of the man at the steering wheel, whose ideal stem transfixes the Earth, rushing over the circuit of her orbit.

. . . 8. Why should we look behind us, when we have to break in the mysterious portals of the Impossible? Time and Space died yesterday. Already we live in the absolute, since we have already created speed, eternal and ever-present.

9. We wish to glorify War—the only health giver of the world—militarism, patriotism, the destructive arm of the Anarchist, the beautiful Ideas that kill, the contempt for woman.

10. We wish to destroy the museums, the libraries, to fight against moralism, feminism and all opportunistic and utilitarian meannesses.'

There is indeed no greater distinction among human beings than

[1] Quoted from H. Thomas, *The Spanish Civil War*, 1961, p. 35–45. Thomas quotes Unamuno's speech from L. Portillo's translation of this speech, published in *Horizon* and reprinted in Connolly, *The Golden Horizon*, 397–409. Unamuno remained under house arrest until his death a few months later.

that between those who love life and those who love death. This love of death is a typically human acquisition. Man is the only animal that can be bored, he is the only animal that can love death. The impotent man (I am not referring to sexual impotence) while he cannot create life, can destroy it and thus transcend it. The love of death in the midst of living is the ultimate perversion. There are some who are the true necrophiles—and they salute war and promote it, even though they are mostly not aware of their motivation and rationalize their desires as serving life, honour or freedom. They are probably the minority; but there are many who have never made the choice between life and death, and who have escaped in busy-ness in order to hide this. They do not salute destruction—but they also do not salute life. They lack the joy of life which would be necessary to oppose war vigorously.

Goethe once said that the most profound distinction between various historical periods is that between belief and disbelief, and added that all epochs in which belief dominates are brilliant, uplifting, and fruitful, while those in which disbelief dominates vanish because nobody cares to devote himself to the unfruitful. It seems to me that the 'belief' Goethe spoke of is deeply rooted in the love of life. Cultures which create the conditions for loving life also are cultures of belief; those which cannot create this love also cannot create belief.

Bertrand Russell is a man of belief. In reading his books and in watching his activities for peace his love of life seems to me the mainspring of his whole person. He warns the world of impending doom precisely as the prophets did, because he loves life and all its forms and manifestations. He, again like the prophets, is not a determinist who claims that the historical future is already determined; he is an 'alternativist' who sees that what is determined are certain limited and ascertainable alternatives. Our alternative is that between the end of the nuclear arms race—or destruction. Whether the voice of this prophet will win over the voices of doom and weariness depends on the degree of vitality the world and especially the younger generation has preserved. If we are to perish we cannot claim not to have been warned.

7

LINUS PAULING

Would Civilization Survive a Nuclear War?

In his book *Has Man a Future?*, Bertrand Russell said, 'What exact degree of damage would be done by a nuclear war with present weapons is uncertain, and we must all hope that it will remain so. It is just possible that, after a nuclear war between NATO and the powers of the Warsaw Pact, some neutral nations might retain a degree of social cohesion which would enable them to keep civilization alive.'

The intensity of our efforts to prevent the catastrophe of a great nuclear war may be to some extent determined by our estimates of the probability of destruction of a major part of the world, perhaps of civilization itself, in such a war, were it to take place. In this essay I shall attempt to estimate the size of the world's stockpile of nuclear weapons and the effects of a possible nuclear war in which these weapons were used.

A Small Nuclear War

In 1958, in my book *No More War!*, I discussed the probable effects of a hypothetical nuclear attack on the United States with 2,500 megatons of bombs (50 per cent fission and 50 percent fusion), and an attack on the Soviet Union with 5,000 megatons of bombs. It is estimated that, because of the larger size of the Soviet Union than of the United States, about twice as much nuclear explosive would be needed to cause the same damage in the USSR as in the US.

An estimate of the damage that would be done to the United States by a nuclear attack of 2,500 megatons is to be found in the volumes *The Nature of Radioactive Fallout and its Effects on Man*, Hearings before the Special Subcommittee on Radiation of the Joint Committee on Atomic Energy of the Congress of the United States, May 27, 28, 29, and June 3, 1957. The 250 nuclear weapons were of three sizes: 5-megaton, 10-megaton, and 20-megaton. There were 144 areas of attack: fifty-three of the areas were basically population and industrial centres, fifty-nine were basically military installations, and fifty-two were intermediate in character. The attack was assumed to take place during two hours of one day.

The analysis of the effects of this hypothetical attack was made by Dr W. W. Kellogg of the Rand Corporation and Mr Charles Shafer of the United States Weather Bureau (on assignment to the Federal Civil Defense Administration). Their estimate, corrected for the increase in population since 1957, is that sixty days after the day on which the attack with 2,500 megatons took place 98,000,000 of the 190,000,000 American people would be dead and 28,000,000 would be seriously injured but still alive, and there would be about 70,000,000 relatively uninjured survivors, who, however, would be suffering some radiation effects. It was estimated that about half of the deaths and injuries would be the result of blast and fire and the other half the result of high-energy radiation, including that from local fallout.

Similar estimates have been made by other scientists. Especially valuable is the extensive study of the distribution and effects of fallout in large nuclear-weapon campaigns that was carried out by Hugh Everett, III, and George E. Pugh, of the Weapons Systems Evaluation Division, Institute for Defense Analyses, Washington, D.C. Their report is published in the volume *Biological and Environmental Effects of Nuclear War*, Hearings before the Special Subcommittee on Radiation of the Joint Committee on Atomic Energy of the Congress of the United States, June 22–26, 1959. Their estimate is that sixty days after a 2,500-megaton attack, with the intensity of the attack in various regions proportional to the population density, 103,000,000 of the 190,000,000 American people would be dead, 23,000,000 injured, and 64,000,000 relatively uninjured.

There is, I think, a considerable possibility that the United States could survive such an attack and that the Soviet Union could survive a corresponding attack with 5,000 megatons. I have, however, reached the conclusion that it is not justified to hope that a nuclear war would be such a small one, if it were to be initiated. On the basis of the information available to us about the size of the stockpiles of nuclear weapons possessed by the United States and the Soviet Union, I conclude instead that the nuclear war, if it were to occur in the near future, would be about ten times as great as this small hypothetical one.

The Size of the Stockpiles of Nuclear Weapons
Neither the United States nor the Soviet Union has announced the size of its stockpile of nuclear weapons. On the basis of the bits of information that have been released, I have reached the conclusion that at the middle of the year 1963, the stockpile of nuclear weapons in the possession of the United States totaled 240,000 megatons.

Taking into consideration the fact that the Soviet Union was about three years later in starting and may be assumed to have worked about as intensively in its military activity, I guess that the Soviet stockpile amounted to about 80,000 megatons.

In recent years the United States has been purchasing uranium at the rate of about 30,000 tons per year. Some of this uranium is used to make the fissionable substances uranium-235 and plutonium-239. In April 1957 James Van Zandt, who was at that time a Congressman and a member of the US Joint Congressional Committee on Atomic Energy, stated that the United States then had enough fissionable material for 35,000 atomic bombs and that the Soviet Union had an estimated stockpile of 10,000 bombs. In January 1959 I received a letter from Lester Pearson, of Canada, in which he wrote that he had information that he considered to be reliable that for the preceding two years the United States had been manufacturing plutonium at the rate of 200,000 pounds per year. Although no official statement has been made about this matter, it seems likely that ten pounds of plutonium is enough to constitute the explosive material of a small atomic bomb or the first-stage material of an H-bomb or superbomb (fission-fusion-fission bomb). The manufacture of plutonium at the rate of 200,000 pounds per year would accordingly permit the addition of 20,000 atomic bombs to the US stockpile each year.

Dr Ralph E. Lapp, an able American physicist who has played an outstanding part in educating the American people about the nature of the nuclear age, has estimated on the basis of the amount of uranium feed material flowing into the plutonium plants and uranium-235 plants, the amount of electric power the plants use, the capital investments in the plants, and the annual sums spent for operation of the plants that in 1960 the American stockpile of fissionable material amounted to 700,000 pounds, enough for 70,000 atomic bombs.

A 20-megaton bomb has as its explosive materials ten pounds of plutonium for the first stage, about 200 pounds of lithium deuteride for the second-stage nuclear fusion reaction, and 1,000 pounds of ordinary uranium metal for the third stage (fission). The supply of lithium deuteride is great enough so that each of the 20,000 atomic bombs that may be added to the stockpile each year could be converted into an H-bomb. Moreover, the third stage of 1,000 pounds of ordinary uranium metal could be added to each of the 20,000 bombs with use of only one third of the uranium stockpiled each year. The supply of fissionable and fusionable materials is accordingly such that 20,000 superbombs with explosive energy 20 megatons apiece could be added to the US stockpile each year, a total increase of 400,000 megatons per year.

We know, however, from the statements of military and governmental authorities in the United States that many of the nuclear weapons in the American stockpile are smaller ones. Some missiles, such as Polaris and Minuteman, carry at the present time a nuclear warhead of only one or two megatons explosive energy (the new warheads will be larger). Moreover, it has been the announced policy of the US Department of Defense and Atomic Energy Commission to develop small nuclear weapons, possibly to be used in a limited war, as well as the great nuclear weapons, and many of the nuclear tests carried out by the United States have been in the range from 0·001 to 0·1 megaton. The bombs exploded over Hiroshima and Nagasaki in 1945 were small nuclear weapons; each had explosive energy 0·02 megaton, 1000 times smaller than the 20-megaton bomb exploded by the United States on March 1, 1954.

In January 1960 President John F. Kennedy mentioned 30,000 megatons as the size of the world's stockpile of nuclear weapons. Nearly one year later, in December 1960, the scientists of the Pugwash Conference in their discussions made use of the estimate 60,000 megatons, without discussing the basis of the estimate. I used the estimate 120,000 megatons in January 1962 and 240,000 megatons in January 1963, and my present estimate is somewhat over 320,000 megatons.[1]

These estimates do not contradict one another; instead, they are mutually consistent.

The explosive power of the stockpiled weapons in the world has been increasing exponentially over the last eighteen years. The rate of exponential increase corresponds to doubling every year.

During the Second World War conventional bombs, with chemical explosives such as TNT, were used at the rate of about one megaton per year. It is reasonable for us to take one megaton as the amount of military explosive in the world's stockpile in 1945. By 1946, with plutonium and uranium-235 being produced in the United States at the rate of a few pounds per day, about fifty old-fashioned atomic bombs of the Hiroshima-Nagasaki type (0·02 megaton apiece) had been made, increasing the world's stockpile of explosives to two megatons. The rate of production of fissionable material doubled during the next year, and the stockpile became four megatons. The development of H-bombs and three-stage superbombs later led to a great increase in the explosive power of the individual bombs, permitting the exponential increase in the size of the world's stockpile to continue.

[1] Late 1963.

After eighteen years of annual doubling of the stockpile, it would have reached 2^{18} megatons, that is, 262,144 megatons.

Increase by the factor two each year accordingly explains the change from President Kennedy's 30,000 megatons in January 1960 to 60,000 megatons a year later, 120,000 megatons two years later, and 240,000 megatons three years later.

It seems unlikely that the exponential increase will continue, even though it is possible. The stockpiles of nuclear weapons have long ago become irrationally great.

My present estimate that the United States has 240,000 megatons of nuclear weapons can be made credible by consideration of the following facts. On the 12th of November 1961 us Secretary of Defense Robert S. McNamara stated that the United States Strategic Air Command includes 630 B-52s, 55 B-58s, and 1,000 B-47s, a total of 1,685 great bombers. It is known that these bombers carry about fifty megatons of bombs apiece—two 25-megaton bombs on each bomber. Accordingly these 1,685 intercontinental bombers carry a load of bombs totalling 84,000 megatons. I do not believe that any person would contend that the bombs for these bombers do not exist. Secretary McNamara has also stated that we have over 10,000 other vehicles (bombers, fighter-bombers, Polaris missiles and other missiles) capable of carrying nuclear weapons in the megaton range.

In the days following October 22, 1962, during the Cuba crisis, 750 great SAC bombers were deployed at airfields about the United States on 15-minute alert. Events might have developed in such a way that these 750 bombers would have set off for the Soviet Union, with the probability that most of them would have reached their goal. Even if 20 per cent of them were prevented from delivering their weapons, the attack on the Soviet Union by this fraction of the SAC bombers alone would have amounted to 30,000 megatons.

If the Cuba crisis had not been resolved, but had led to nuclear war, the initial attack on the Soviet Union by the 750 SAC bombers that were on 15-minute alert would have been supplemented within a few hours by an even greater attack carried out by the remaining SAC bombers and the other vehicles able to deliver nuclear weapons. Our knowledge about the number of SAC bombers and about their payload indicates clearly that in a nuclear war between the United States and the Soviet Union the bombs exploded over the Soviet Union might well amount to far over 50,000 megatons.

It would, I think, be optimism of an entirely unjustified sort to assume that the attack on the United States by the Soviet Union would be less than 25,000 megatons, which would achieve the same amount of damage.

The Nature of a Great Nuclear War

Everett and Pugh made studies of hypothetical nuclear attacks on the United States and the Soviet Union with weapons totalling between 100 megatons and 50,000 megatons. From their careful studies we may conclude that an attack carried out in the near future on the United States with 10,000 megatons or more of nuclear weapons would kill nearly everybody and would destroy the nation essentially completely. A similar result would be achieved with an attack on the Soviet Union with 20,000 megatons or more of nuclear weapons. It is interesting that, according to their estimates, the same fraction of the people of the United States, 88 per cent, would be dead sixty days after a nuclear attack with 10,000 megatons whether the weapons were exploded in various areas in amounts proportional to the population density or were exploded with uniform distribution over the entire country. For attacks smaller than 10,000 megatons a greater yield of deaths is achieved by distributing the weapons proportionately to the population density, and for attacks greater than 10,000 megatons a greater yield is achieved by distributing the bombs uniformly over the country. The explanation of the paradox in the last statement is that for large nuclear attacks some of the weapons would be wasted over completely destroyed areas if they were distributed proportionately to population density.

A 10,000 megaton attack on the United States, of either type, would, according to Everett and Pugh, achieve the result that sixty days after the day on which the war was fought about 170,000,000 of the 190,000,000 American people would be dead, 15,000,000 seriously injured, and 5,000,000 alive and uninjured, except for the effect of some exposure to high-energy radiation.

As to the final result, we may quote from Everett and Pugh: 'Finally, it must be pointed out that the total casualties at sixty days may not be indicative of the ultimate casualties. Such delayed effects as the disorganization of society, disruption of communications, extinction of livestock, genetic damage, and the slow development of radiation poisoning from the ingestion of radioactive materials may significantly increase the ultimate toll.'

An attack on the United States with 10,000 megatons would lead to the death of essentially all of the American people and to the destruction of the nation. An attack on the Soviet Union with 20,000 megatons would achieve the same result there. The present stockpiles and the present means of delivery are such that it is not unlikely that the attacks on these countries, in case that there were to be a great nuclear war, would be much larger than 10,000 and 20,000 megatons, respectively. I think that a great nuclear war would destroy these two nations. Moreover, it is probable that some fraction of the nuclear weapons would be used in attacks on European nations and other nations in which there are weapons bases, and that most of the people in these countries would also be killed.

The Degree of Overkill

Using 20,000 megatons as the amount necessary to destroy the Soviet Union completely and my estimate 240,000 megatons for the present US stockpile, I may say that we have a 12-fold degree of overkill capability; similarly, with 10,000 megatons needed to destroy the United States completely and a stockpile of 80,000 megatons, the Soviet Union has an eight-fold overkill capability.

There is another way of discussing the factor by which the powers of destruction have been needlessly amplified. In the course of the First World War about 20,000,000 people were killed, and in the course of the Second World War about 40,000,000. We might follow a logarithmic curve in extrapolating in a 'rational' way to the Third World War, and conclude that the war might be expected to come to an end (with one side victorious) when 80,000,000 people had been killed.

In their analysis, Everett and Pugh assumed that the nuclear weapons would not necessarily be delivered very accurately—they assumed that one half of them would explode within 100 miles of their targets, and one half would explode at a greater distance from the targets. Missiles have now been developed that permit nuclear weapons to be delivered with probable errors of only a few miles, and we may turn our attention to a small war waged with missiles with high accuracy.

As a basis for the estimate of the megatonnage required in such a war I select the testimony of Eugene J. Quindlen, Deputy Assistant Director for Federal, State and Local Plans of the US Office of Civil and Defense Mobilization, before the Special Subcommittee on Radiation of the Joint Congressional Committee on Atomic Energy. This testimony was given on June 26, 1959, and is to be found beginning on page 843 of the volume *Biological and Environmental Effects of Nuclear War*. Mr Quindlen discussed the estimated effects of an attack on seventy-one cities of the United States with 110 bombs, ranging from one megaton to ten megatons in size (with two ten-megaton bombs exploded over each of the largest cities).

Correcting the populations to 1963, the reported estimate is that such a hypothetical attack, involving a total of only 567 megatons, would find 52,000,000 Americans dead at the end of sixty days and 21,000,000 seriously injured. An attack with twice as much mega-tonnage on the cities of the Soviet Union would kill and injure about the same fraction of the Soviet people: that is, about 66,000,000 of the Soviet people would be killed and 26,000,000 seriously injured. Accordingly a nuclear war in which the United States used about 1,100 megatons and the Soviet Union about 550 megatons of bombs would be a greater war than the 'rational' Third World War corre-sponding to geometric extrapolation from the First and Second, as a war that, if nuclear weapons had not been developed, would have caused enough destruction and enough death to force the nations to bring it to an end.

On this basis the United States has an overkill capability greater than 200, and the Soviet Union has an overkill capability greater than 140.

During the Second World War about 3,000,000 tons of high explosive were used in strategic bombing of Germany and Japan. The total amount of explosives used was about twice as great—the war could be called a six-megaton war. The significance of the presently stockpiled total of about 320,000 megatons of nuclear explosives may be brought out by the following statement: if there were a six-megaton war (equivalent to the Second World War in the power of the explosives used) tomorrow, and another such war the following day, and so on, day after day, for 146 years, the present stockpile would then be exhausted—but, in fact, this stockpile might be used in a single day, the day of the Third World War.

The Need for Disarmament by International Agreement

As we consider the facts about the capabilities of destruction that are possessed by the Soviet Union and the United States (with, of course, some contribution by Great Britain and a small one by France), we are forced to the conclusion that we are doomed to die if the world continues along the path of insanity. Unless some steps are taken immediately in the direction of disarmament, beginning with the international agreement to stop the testing of all nuclear bombs, the United States and the Soviet Union and probably many other countries in the Northern Hemisphere will be destroyed. It is possible that the civilization developed by man during the past few thousands of years will come to its irrational end.

I believe that we can prevent this great catastrophe, that we can meet the challenge of the crisis. The time has come when it is essential that an international agreement be made to stop the testing of nuclear weapons, to be followed by other agreements leading to general and complete disarmament. We must abandon the mistaken policy of transferring nuclear weapons to NATO, where they may come under the control of the West Germans. Immediate steps should be taken to set up demilitarized zones in the areas of greatest tension, beginning with Central Europe. We are now forced to eliminate from the world the immoral institution of war, and to replace war by international law, based upon the principles of justice and morality. I believe that we are going to grasp this opportunity, which will eliminate the suffering caused by war but will also permit the world community to be freed from hunger, disease, illiteracy, and fear, and will permit us to achieve economic, political, and social justice and to develop a culture worthy of man.

III

PHILOSOPHER AND WRITER

8

ALDOUS HUXLEY

The Relevance of Style

There are three kinds of censorship—political, economic and stylistic. Political censorship is a prohibition to communicate unorthodox ideas, and it is enforced (in the name, needless to say, of Truth, Justice and Morality) by policemen. Economic censorship is a reluctance to communicate unpopular ideas evoked in the minds of writers, editors, publishers, producers of plays and films, by the exorbitantly high and rising costs of communication. Stylistic censorship is the inability to communicate anything adequately, and is due to the communicator's misuse of his native language.

About economic censorship there is nothing much that any single individual can do. That no serious periodical can now be printed and circulated without the assistance of an 'angel', that the publishers of books cannot break even on a sale of less than six or seven thousand copies, that to put on a play now calls for a massive investment of capital—these are facts which the philosopher can only deplore, not hope to change. But in regard to political and stylistic censorship the case is different. If he has had the luck to be born into a democratic society, he is free to argue the case for yet greater freedom. And even under a totalitarian dictatorship he retains a measure of stylistic freedom, and can say whatever he is permitted to say with precision and clarity.

By precept and in luminous practice, Bertrand Russell has fought unwearyingly against political and stylistic censorship. 'I should make it my object', he says in his 'Essay on Education in Early Childhood', 'to teach thinking, not orthodoxy, or even heterodoxy. And I should absolutely never sacrifice intellect to the fancied interest of morals.' And here is what he has to say about one of those orthodoxies, which the censors impose and which any honest philosopher must refuse to teach—the twentieth-century orthodoxy of Communism. 'In relation to any political doctrine there are two questions to be asked: (1) Are its theoretical tenets true? (2) Is its practical policy likely to increase human happiness? For my part, I think the theoretical tenets of Communism are false, and I think its practical maxims are such as to produce an immeasurable increase of human misery.'

These clear, plain sentences are doubly liberating. They state the case for humane and realistic thinking against political censor-ship, and at the same time they *are* the denial of stylistic censor-ship.

Rationality and the common decencies have many enemies, and among those enemies must be counted, alas, all those would-be friends whose studied ineptitude imposes a stylistic censorship on the communication of their often excellent ideas. For those who care for the art of literature, and even for those who merely desire to be instructed, there are few experiences more depressing than the perusal of a learned journal. Natural scientists, social scientists, psychologists and even philosophers—how rarely do we find in their ranks a competent writer! Most of them censor their own produc-tions by a style so abominable that they can hardly be read. Their grammar is bad, their syntax even worse than their grammar. To a wretchedly poor vocabulary they add, along with the indispensable technical terms of which every specialist feels the need, a heavy infusion of jargon and entirely superfluous neologisms. Jargon and neologisms obscure the sense of what is being said; but for the learned men who indulge in them, this does not matter. What matters, so far as they are concerned, is that jargon and neologisms constitute a private, esoteric language that sets them apart from the common herd of those who merely speak English. Better still, jargon and neologisms may foster, in the bewildered reader's mind, the illusion that some thought of exceptional profundity and importance is being expressed.

Eighty years ago my grandfather was lamenting the fact that students of literature were being made to spend less time on the great eighteenth century masters of style than on earlier authors whose sole merit was the merely historical one of having written in Middle English. More familiar with Hoccleve than with Swift or Hume or Berkeley, these students of Middle English were capable of writing only middling English. Today the middling English of last century's learned writing has become the abysmal English of the text books and the specialists' journals. The decline cannot be attributed to an excess of medieval scholarship. The neologists and the jargon-mongers have not been bemused by too much learning in an irrelevant field; they are merely following a bad convention, merely imitating and hideously improving upon earlier neologists and jargon-mongers. Other models exist, of course; but the wish to seem profounder than they really are, the desire to be looked upon as the possessors of esoteric knowledge not available to the rest of us and expressible only in a private language known to a few initiates, overrides any desire for literary excellence or even plain comprehensibility. They continue to model themselves, not on Swift or Hume or that great continuator and enricher of the eighteenth-century tradition of clear and precise communication, Bertrand Russell, but on Professor X's monumental Introduction to Social Sociology, on Dr Y's latest paper in contribution to the Journal of Something-or-Other.

After an enforced diet of Introduction to Clinical Economics, Dr Y's latest Contribution to the Journal of Animal Metaphysics, after an enforced diet of Textbook sociology and psychological abstracts, what a blessed relief it is to read what Bertrand Russell has to say about politics, or psychology, or the conduct of life, or Nobel Prize Acceptance Speech! No jargon, not a single neologism. Nothing but plain English. There is no hiding behind obscurities, no pretending that the subject is understandable only by specialists and can be talked about only in a private language. Everything is perfectly clear and above-board. Of German scholars Bentley used to say that they dived deeper and came up muddier than any others. Bertrand Russell dives deep, but comes up every time as clean as a whistle. Here, for example, is a passage from his Nobel Prize Acceptance Speech:

'If men were actuated by self-interest, which they are not except in the case of a few saints—the whole human race would co-operate. There would be no more wars, no more armies, no more navies, no more atom bombs. There would be no armies of propagandists employed in poisoning the minds of Nation A against Nation B, and reciprocally of Nation B against Nation A. There would not be armies of officials at frontiers to prevent the entry of foreign books and foreign ideas, however excellent in themselves. . . . All this would happen very quickly if men desired their own happiness as ardently as they desire the misery of their neighbours. But, you will tell me, what is the use of these Utopian dreams? Moralists will see to it that we do not become wholly selfish, and until we do, the millennium will be impossible.

'I do not wish to end upon a note of cynicism. I do not deny that there are better things than selfishness, and that some people achieve these things. I maintain, however, on the one hand that there are few occasions upon which large bodies of men, such as politics is concerned with, can rise above selfishness, while, on the other hand, there are a great many circumstances in which populations will fall below selfishness, if selfishness is interpreted as enlightened self-interest. And among the occasions on which people fall below self-interest are most of the occasions on which they are convinced that they are acting from idealistic motives. Much that passes for idealism is disguised hatred and disguised love of power.'

It would be easy, fatally easy, to express these ideas in words and whole phrases borrowed from Freud and Pavlov, from Skinner, Sorokin, the Cyberneticists, and worked up, with a few neologisms, into a notable passage of learned jargon, a darkling hodge-podge, repellent and almost incomprehensible. But in this case the man who made the analysis and had the ideas was never tempted to become their stylistic censor. The philosopher is also a writer, the humanistic psychologist and social scientist knows English. How fortunate for us!

9

HERBERT READ

A Philosophical Debt

The most honest tribute one can make to a philosopher is to acknowledge as exactly as possible one's own permanent debt to him. But it is easier to acknowledge a debt than to come to a final settlement. In my own case the phase of absorption was relatively short but very intense. It began with *The Problems of Philosophy*, the little volume which was published in 1910, which I bought at the age of 19 at a time when I was devouring Nietzsche and other mental excitements indiscriminately. Its severely logical approach to a limited number of philosophical problems had a disciplinary effect and sent me to Hume and Kant for a historical grounding. I was too busy with other studies in the years immediately preceding the outbreak of the 1914 war, and with more extravert activities during the war, to have much opportunity to develop my natural liking for philosophy, but I bought and read *Principles of Social Reconstruction* as soon as it appeared in 1916, and towards the end or immediately after the war I acquired and read in quick succession, and in this order, *Mysticism and Logic*, *Roads to Freedom* and *Our Knowledge of the External World*. Then in May and June, 1920, I attended a course of eight lectures given by Russell held in Dr Williams' Library, London—it was the first and only direct tuition in the subject I ever received, and the experience still remains vivid. These lectures were afterwards published as *The Analysis of Mind* (1921), and were followed six years later by the companion volume on *The Analysis of Matter*. There, I regret to say, either my devotion or my understanding expired.

But I had gained an immense amount of insight from these seven volumes. I use the word 'insight' because it was a word used by Russell with a particular meaning that appealed to me then and has remained effective in my thought. It was, I now suppose, an acceptable substitute for the word 'intuition', which I was told was a dirty word in philosophical circles. At the same time as I was reading Russell I was also reading Bergson, and for some time these two philosophers were to play a game of see-saw in my mind. If in the end Bergson triumphed, if only temporarily, it was not for lack of heeding the warning of Russell. But when Russell observed that intuition 'seems on the whole to diminish as civilization increases', I was inclined to answer 'all the worse for civilization'. I might agree that 'direct acquaintance' with things is given fully in sensation, and does not require any special faculty for its apprehension. But I was already seeking for a definition of the kind of 'direct acquaintance' embodied in the work of art, and 'intellect' did not seem to describe it. Curiously enough it was Russell's account of mathematics, a subject outside my comprehension, which seemed to offer the right kind of analogy, and I underlined with enthusiasm the following passage in 'The Study of Mathematics' (an essay in *Mysticism and Logic*):

'Against that kind of scepticism which abandons the pursuit of ideals because the road is arduous and the goal not certainly attainable, mathematics, within its own sphere, is a complete answer. Too often it is said that there is no absolute truth, but only opinion and private judgment; that each of us is conditioned, in his view of the world, by his own peculiarities, his own taste and bias; that there is no external kingdom of truth to which, by patience and discipline, we may at last obtain admittance, but only truth for me, for you, for every separate person. By this habit of mind one of the chief ends of human effort is denied, and the supreme virtue of candour, of fearless acknowledgement of what is, disappears from our moral vision. Of such scepticism mathematics is a perpetual reproof; for its edifice of truths stands unshakable and inexpugnable to all the weapons of doubting cynicism.'

Not that as a young man I was in any danger of succumbing to this kind of scepticism. I had drunk from the heady fountains of Nietzsche and was seeking for confirmation of his doctrine of the Superman! What Russell offered was not scepticism, but what he called 'scientific method', and though the phrase was a little drastic, as defined by Russell it offered me the necessary loophole into aesthetics. In his essay on 'Scientific Method in Philosophy', which I read in 1920, 'insight' is given further significance as a 'first suggestion' of 'the most important truth'. 'Instinct, intuition, or insight is what first leads to the beliefs which subsequently reason confirms or confutes; but the confirmation, where it is possible, consists, in the last analysis, of agreement with other beliefs no less instinctive. Reason is a harmonizing, controlling force rather than a creative one. Even in the most purely logical realms, it is insight that first arrives at what is new.'

There was the concept I needed, and this was the sense I gave to reason in my first book of literary criticism (1946), which I called *Reason and Romanticism* with this definition in mind. It might just

as well have been called *Reason and Insight*, for insight is another
name for the creative faculty in the philosophy of romanticism.

Some marginalia I wrote into my copy of *Our Knowledge of the
External World* are perhaps of more interest as reflecting on the
limitations of my own philosophy at that time than as a valid
criticism of Russell's philosophy, but I will quote them because they
do illustrate the kind of stimulus that Russell gave to a younger
generation forty years ago:

Russell: 'If philosophy is to become scientific . . . it is necessary
first and foremost that philosophers should acquire the disinterested
intellectual curiosity which characterizes the genuine man of science.'
My comment: This is the fallacy of the 'scientific' school. Once
philosophy loses its humanistic relativity it becomes abstract and
unreal: limited, like mathematics. Knowledge for knowledge's sake
is as futile a doctrine as art for art's sake.

At the conclusion of the essay on 'Scientific Method in Philosophy'
I observed:

'Scientific method can do no more than discover "truth", i.e. true
facts. But truth has value only when related to human life.

'Conclusion: The scientific method is superior to the "logical"
and intuitive methods; but its results possess value only when
related to human life: unrelated they become a mere abstract fantasy.

Philosophy is a prior synthetic activity of the mind. Ethics follows
and is selective. The two activities should be regarded as inseparable
and fallible in isolation.'

But I found more to approve than to criticize throughout the volume,
and I marked with especial emphasis a sentence towards the end
which reads: 'These two processes, of doubting the familiar and
imagining the unfamiliar, are correlative, and form the chief part
of the mental training required for a philosopher'—a precept which
I hope I have followed in all my intellectual activities.

The Analysis of Mind was first published in 1921, and I was rash
enough to give it a long review in *The New Age* (September 1, 1921).
I concentrated on whatever relevance the book might have for the
psychology of the imagination, and welcomed what seemed to me to
be a rational explanation of the process (a process 'reducible to
ordinary physical causation in nervous tissue'). But I then pointed
to 'a further development of Mr Russell's analysis that quite
decisively alters the complexion of the case—I mean the problem of
truth and falsehood', and I proceeded to invoke Russell's support
for a belief in the inadequacy of any formal approach to a solution
of the problem. Verifying propositions by relating their constituent

images to the objectives meant does not, I wrote, quoting Russell, 'throw any light upon our preference for true beliefs rather than false ones. This preference is only explicable by taking account of the causal efficacy of beliefs, and of the greater appropriateness of the responses resulting from true beliefs. But appropriateness depends upon purpose, and purpose thus becomes a vital part of theory of knowledge.' And, I then added, of theory of aesthetic. 'Art, in so far as it is expression, is a material process. Within the limits of this process much beauty, of "gem-like flame", may exist. But the beauty that is non-material—that is spiritual and thereby so definitely higher—derives its existence and nature from the existence and nature of a purpose.' I was openly arguing against the theories of Roger Fry and Clive Bell, and was anxious to retain for art 'a quality of moral action, as well as of significant form'. 'Beauty is dynamic as well as static: and this is the be-all and end-all of all confused theories about "pure" art, about art for its own sake, art "striving to be independent of the mere intelligence".'

All this had very little to do with the main purpose of *The Analysis of Mind*, which was rather to show that a wrong philosophy of matter had caused many of the difficulties in the philosophy of mind, and that 'consciousness is a complex and far from universal characteristic of mental phenomena'. This led me straight to Freud and Jung, and if the consequent switch meant that I to a large extent abandoned philosophy for psychology, this is to be attributed largely to *The Analysis of Mind*.

By way of compensation I had already been drawn in another direction taken by Russell's own interests. *Principles of Social Reconstruction* was published in 1916, five years before *The Analysis of Mind*; and *Roads to Freedom* in 1918. I read both books immediately after their publication, while serving in the Army. I should explain that I was already calling myself an anarchist, and I read these two volumes for whatever support they might lend to my own political philosophy. I found a great deal, especially in *Roads to Freedom*, where Anarchism is indeed considered as one of the three possible 'roads', the others being socialism and syndicalism. As a matter of fact, I was equally interested in syndicalism, having been drawn by Orage into the Guild Socialist movement. Syndicalism, or Guild Socialism, I argued, was the practical application of anarchist principles to an industrial community. Russell gave a good deal of support to these ideals, always reverting, however, to the psychological realities. 'The supreme principle, both in politics and in private life,' he asserted, '*should be to promote all that is creative, and so diminish the impulses and desires that centre round possession.*'

'Production without possession, action without self-assertion, development without domination' was the epigraph (from Lao-Tzu) that he put on the title-page of *Roads to Freedom*. But what do these ideals amount to when translated into practical politics? In his Introduction to *Roads to Freedom* Russell considered and rejected Anarchism, Marxism, Socialism and Syndicalism and decided in favour of Guild Socialism (which he distinguished from Syndicalism): 'the best practicable system', and he even conceded, on the last page of his book, that his conception of Guild Socialism leant 'more, perhaps, towards Anarchism than the official Guildsman would wholly approve'. 'It is in the matters that politicians usually ignore—science and art, human relations, and the joy of life—that Anarchism is strongest. . . . The world that we must seek is a world in which the creative spirit is alive, in which life is an adventure full of joy and hope, based rather upon the impulses to construct rather than upon the desire to retain what we possess or to seize what is possessed by others.' This, and much more, followed by the confident assertion that 'such a world is possible: it waits only for men to wish to create it', aroused my youthful enthusiasm; but then came the post-war years, the great disillusion with politicians and trade unionists, the gradual abandonment of hope and the growth of cynicism and despair. *Roads to Freedom* makes sad reading today. It is not that the roads led to nowhere: none of them was ever trodden; and I think Russell himself turned away from any faith in political action, concentrating on the slow piecemeal process of education, the principles of which he practised as well as preached. Someone once expressed the view that the best form of government is tyranny tempered with assassination; Russell would probably substitute democracy modified by direct action. But I hope that he still believes that pure Anarchism is the ultimate ideal. *123069*

I cannot make any cold assessment of Bertrand Russell's position as a philosopher—partly because I am not competent in this field and partly because I do not think that he is a philosopher of any assessable academic status. He has been essentially a teacher: a teacher in the sense that Socrates was a teacher, and he has had a great influence on the minds of at least three generations—his own, mine, and the generation that has just reached maturity. This influence, I believe, has been wholly for the good, not in any specifically ethical sense, but in the sense of the good life. He has vitalized thought at innumerable points and has always represented for me and I am sure for many others the embodiment of these Socratic virtues—self-control, fairness, courage, liberality and truth—which are the characteristics of a mind free from anxiety and fear.

10

C. D. BROAD

(I) *Some Personal Impressions of Russell as a Philosopher*

The Editor has asked me to preface my contribution with a brief account of what I believe myself to owe, in philosophic matters, to Lord Russell personally and to his writings. I am very glad to have this opportunity to express, however inadequately, my sense of obligation and my feeling of gratitude to Russell for all that he has done for me.

I came up to Trinity College, Cambridge, as a freshman from Dulwich, in October 1906, and spent my first two academic years working for Part I of the Natural Sciences Tripos. During that period my interest in philosophy and my certainty that I should never be a first-rate natural scientist were steadily growing, and I decided to switch over to Moral Science (as philosophy is called in Cambridge), and to spend the next two years working for Part II of the Moral Sciences Tripos.

That decision was not due to any personal influence of Russell's, for he was away from Cambridge during my time as an undergraduate (1906 to 1909). He had gained a Fellowship at Trinity under the then 'Title (α)' in the election of 1895. The Fellowship expired in 1901 after the normal period of six years. It imposed no obligation either of research or of residence; and Russell had already left Cambridge in 1894 and was engaged in various external activities during his tenure of it, as was very usual at that time. But I had, while still at Dulwich, heard of Russell and become interested in one of his books. It happened that my mathematical master, the late Mr F. W. Russell (no relative of Lord Russell's, but a former member of Trinity College) had bought and read Vol. I of *The Principles of Mathematics*, which was published in 1903. Knowing that I was interested in philosophy, he gave me his copy in 1905, and I then tried to read it. Much of it was, of course, wholly beyond me at the time; but I was excited by the parts which I thought I could understand, and, when I came up to Trinity, I found that it was being eagerly discussed by many intelligent undergraduates, and by some brilliant younger Fellows, such as G. H. Hardy.

The prevalent type of philosophy in the universities of Great

Britain and the USA, was a form of Absolute Idealism. Its most important representatives in England were Bradley and Bosanquet, and in the USA Royce. Bradley's *Appearance and Reality*, first published in 1892, was still, and remained for some years later, the centre around which most philosophical discussion turned. Cambridge, indeed, had always been rather aloof from the current orthodoxy of Oxford and the Scottish universities. Sidgwick had been a severe critic of T. H. Green and of Absolute Idealism in general. Ward, though a mentalist and an admirer of Kant, was a pluralist and a theist, and much more akin to Leibniz than to Hegel. McTaggart, far the most brilliant of the Cambridge philosophers of that period, did indeed count himself as a Hegelian; but his interpretation of Hegel was peculiar to himself, and made orthodox Absolute Idealists blush all over. Nevertheless, Bradley and Bosanquet were names to conjure with even in Cambridge. Russell's first philosophical book, *The Foundations of Geometry* (1897) is dedicated with gratitude to McTaggart. The Preface acknowledges the author's chief debt in Logic to Bradley, and an only slightly lesser debt to Bosanquet; and the theory of Space developed and defended in the book is essentially Kantian.

I had been given Bradley's *Appearance and Reality* as a Christmas present by my parents in 1905, and had read it with the fascination and excitement which it is so well fitted to produce in any intelligent young man interested in philosophy. I had also struggled with Kant's *Critique of Pure Reason*, and had been immensely impressed by the little that I understood and the much which I could not understand. So I arrived in Cambridge in October 1906 in the philosophical condition of an enthusiastic but woolly Idealist.

By that time the influence of G. E. Moore and, through him, of Russell, had become predominant among the younger men who were interested in philosophy. Moore, two years junior academically to Russell, had been attracted to philosophy by the latter. He had been elected to a Fellowship at Trinity in 1898, had published *Principia Ethica* in 1903, and had left Cambridge in the following year. He had converted Russell from the Idealism of the *Foundations of Geometry* period to the rather naïve Realism and Pluralism of *Principles of Mathematics*, Vol. I. That was not destined to be a permanent resting-place for either of them; but, owing to the immense influence which these two great men exercised, both through their intellect and their personality, on their contemporaries and their juniors, it was the latest word in philosophical up-to-dateness in the circles into which I now entered.

The reactions of clever young men, following able and inspiring leaders, in an exciting attack on the orthodoxy of their immediate predecessors, are inevitably accompanied by a pleasant glow of intellectual contempt and *quasi*-moral indignation. We felt this strongly about such old fogies as Bradley and Bosanquet, to whom we must have appeared insufferably uppish and superficial; and we were no doubt often highly deficient in understanding and appreciation of what they had taught and of their reasons for it. When one has become an old fogy oneself, and is exposed to similar treatment by one's clever and scornful and terribly earnest juniors, it is amusing and wholesome to recognize in them oneself and one's friends of fifty to sixty years ago. It is not given to any of us to see 'ourselves as others see us', but it is possible and often salutary to see ourselves as we saw others. And most entertaining of all is to watch the swift inevitable decline, by which those who have been in the van of philosophical progress gradually become the last word but two, and end with what Oscar Wilde called 'a great future behind them'.

Allowing for all this, it still seems to me that the criticisms of Moore and of Russell in the early years of this century did explode for good and all most of the dialectical *arguments* against the reality of Matter, Space, Time, Causality, Relations, etc., which are deployed in Book I of *Appearance and Reality* and were very widely accepted by extremely able philosophers. It may well be that there was something true and important in what the Absolute Idealists were arguing for, and it is not impossible that better arguments might be devised in support of it. (Bradley, who said that 'Metaphysics is the finding of bad reasons for what we believe upon instinct, but to find these reasons is no less an instinct', might justifiably feel that his withers were not much wrung.) But it *was* a great intellectual relief to have these rubbishy fallacious arguments finally dismissed.

In 1910 a special lectureship in Logic and Philosophy was created for Russell in Trinity College, and he returned in the October of that year to the College as Lecturer and member of the High Table, and with the right to rooms in College, though without a Fellowship. I had taken Part II of the Moral Sciences Tripos in May 1910, and had begun working on a dissertation to be submitted in the Fellowship competition of September 1911. Russell took up his Lectureship in October 1910. It was then that I first met him, and it was immediately after that that I saw most of him and was most influenced by him.

Principia Mathematica Vol. I came out in that year, and Russell was actively engaged, in collaboration with Whitehead, who had recently left Cambridge for London, on Vols. II and III, which appeared respectively in 1912 and 1913. Russell lectured on topics from these books, and I attended his lectures and derived great help and stimulus from them. Another Trinity man, contemporary with me, was the mathematician E. H. Neville, soon to become a Fellow of the College and later Professor of Mathematics at Reading. He attended these lectures of Russell's, and we used to go together to Russell's rooms in College to read and discuss with him the proofs of certain forthcoming chapters in *Principia Mathematica*.

I had been from boyhood a student of natural science, interested primarily in physics and to a lesser degree in chemistry and crystallography. I have not the kind of brain needed for distinction in pure mathematics and pure logic. But I take a deep interest in those subjects, and am not (as many otherwise intelligent persons appear to be) frightened out of my wits by them. In particular I have always been fascinated by the mathematical aspects of natural science, and therefore by philosophical questions concerning Space, Time, Motion, and Causation. Now Russell had treated such topics very fully, and in a most exciting and illuminating way, in *The Principles of Mathematics*. Part V of that book is concerned with Infinity and Continuity, Part VI with Space, and Part VII with Matter and Motion. In the last of these Russell treats of the Laws of Motion and the notion of Causality in dynamics, and he defends the unpopular Newtonian doctrine of Absolute Space and Time. Here he was dealing with just those topics which most interested me. It seemed, and it still seems, to me that he had illuminated a region, in the obscurities of which philosophers had strayed since the time of Zeno, and which the Absolute Idealists had exploited in the interests of their own philosophy.

At the time when I first met Russell he was not, I think, greatly interested in such questions. I should suppose that his main philosophical concern at that period was with the logical difficulties which had emerged in connexion with the notion of Classes, and with attempts to obviate these by some form or other of the Theory of Types. It was inspiring to see for oneself a great thinker grappling with a definite and extremely difficult problem; and Russell conveyed to me some of the excitement that he felt, though the question was peripheral to my interests and I was not competent to contribute anything to its solution.

Undoubtedly the most concrete debt which I owe to attending Russell's lectures at that period is familiarity with the notation and methods of *Principia Mathematica*, and a certain facility in handling them. Of course one was somewhat inclined at the time to over-estimate the importance for philosophy of putting questions and arguments into symbolic form. That was inevitable with young men newly furnished with a fascinating gadget and anxious to 'show off' with it, as one might with a new sports-model. But I have repeatedly found this technique extremely useful in analysing and formulating philosophical problems, and in freeing one from the hopeless ambiguity and muddle of ordinary language when used for anything but the everyday practical purposes in subservience to which it has evolved. One has learned not to expect symbolic logic to supply solutions to the problems which it enables one to formulate clearly, or to furnish a decision between the alternatives which it helps one to distinguish and envisage. And one has come to realize that it is dangerous to assume blindly that the system of *Principia Mathematica* covers all the categories and principles of rational thinking and discourse. (It takes no account, e.g. of 'modality' and of 'modal propositions'; and it is doubtful whether it provides a satisfactory formulation for 'nomic propositions', such as the alleged laws of nature appear *prima facie* to be, viz., something intermediate between mere statements of *de facto* uniformity and statements of logical or metaphysical necessity or impossibility.) But such a system may be (and in fact is) of inestimable value over a very wide range, though it does not cover everything and may become an instrument of distortion in the hands of those who fail to realize that fact.

Although, as I have said, Russell's main interest in 1910–11 was elsewhere than in the philosophy of physics, he was always ready to discuss such topics. I consulted him as to a suitable subject for my Fellowship dissertation, and, if I am not mistaken, he advised me to write on the philosophy of mechanics. He certainly brought to my attention several works in German in that field, which he had studied when writing the relevant parts of *The Principles of Mathematics*, and I read them carefully and critically and discussed them with him. As I worked at the dissertation, however, I found myself more and more involved in epistemological questions about the nature and validity of our ostensible perceptions of a world of material things interacting in accordance with general laws. The thesis was submitted in September 1911 and was successful. During the next two years I re-wrote it, and it was published in 1914 under the title 'Perception, Physics, and Reality'. I believe, but I am not quite certain and cannot now ascertain, that Russell was one of the examiners who reported on the thesis and advised that a Fellowship should be awarded to me. If so, he contributed substantially to causing what I should regard as the most important single event in my life.

Anyone who may have time and inclination to flutter the pages of a book which has for long been a museum piece will see that in the end only one chapter out of five, and that the last, is devoted to the Laws of Mechanics. In the Preface I acknowledge my obligations to the relevant parts of *The Principles of Mathematics*, as regards the discussion of Causality in Chapter II and as regards the Laws of Mechanics in Chapter V, and in general to Russell's lectures and conversation. Though I was indeed very greatly indebted to him, I was by no means an unquestioning disciple. I did not consider his arguments for Absolute Space and Time, and against those who had maintained a Relational Theory, to be valid. Of course, Russell himself very soon came to abandon the Absolute Theory, though I am not aware that he ever took the trouble to refute publicly the arguments which he had published in favour of it.

I had already left Cambridge to take up a minor academic post in the university of St Andrews at the time when I was elected to my Fellowship, and I did not return into residence. But I used to spend six weeks or so in Trinity during each Long Vacation until the outbreak of the First World War in August 1914. During those periods I saw much of Russell and immensely enjoyed his conversation. His little book *The Problems of Philosophy*, which he used to refer to as his 'shilling shocker', had come out in the *Home University Series* in 1912[1]. It is an extremely exciting book, and much of it was highly relevant to the work on which I was then engaged of re-writing my Fellowship dissertation to be published as a book. The many talks that I had with Russell at that time on topics arising from *The Problems of Philosophy* were extremely helpful to me.

The years immediately preceding the First World War were marked by very embittered political controversies in England, e.g. the struggles over Lloyd George's budget, its rejection by the House of Lords, and the subsequent restriction of the powers of the Upper House; the violence of the militant advocates of women's suffrage; continual unrest in industry; and controversies, leading very nearly to civil war, over the question of home-rule for Ireland. And, as a background to these domestic issues, was continually mounting tension between Continental nations, and the growth of German naval power which seemed to threaten England's safety. I was at that time, and for some years after the end of the war, as far left of centre in politics as I have ever been, and far more so than I should now, with fuller knowledge of the facts and the actual outcome of events, think it reasonable to be. Russell was, of course, passionately involved in all this; and I largely sympathized with his views and was to some extent carried along by his enthusiasm and eloquence. I could never excite myself, as he did, over the question

[1] Oxford University Press.

of women's suffrage. I had, indeed, no serious objection to it, since it seemed to me antecedently unlikely that the average woman could be appreciably less competent than the average man to exercise the right of voting. And the 'arguments' put forward by opponents of women's suffrage were obviously, like most 'arguments' for or against any course in politics, just hot air, in argumentative form, expressive or evocative of strong emotions. I should suppose that the granting of the suffrage to women has had the merit of removing a grievance strongly felt by many of them, and that it has had no appreciable effect, for good or for ill, on the subsequent course of English politics. The 'reasons' alleged by politicians for doing it, when it was done, were as absurd as those which had been alleged against it while it was still being refused.

I can well remember the Long Vacation of 1914, towards the end of which the First World War broke out. Maynard Keynes had by then got the proofs of his *Treatise on Probability*, and had lent them to Russell for his critical comments. Russell and I used to go over these proofs together in the latter's rooms in Neville's Court and to discuss them. We were doing this up to that fatal and accursed Fourth of August, when war was declared. Keynes was reft away to London (if I am not mistaken, on the back of his brother-in-law's, A. V. Hill's, motor-bicycle) to help with the nation's war-finances, and 'the lights of European civilization went out'.

Most fortunately for myself I was away from Cambridge during the whole of the four years of war and for some years later. The atmosphere in the College must have been highly strained and unpleasant, and I should hate to have been forced to take sides. There exists one and only one complete and thoroughly fair and reliable account of the relations of Trinity College with Russell during that period. That is the pamphlet written during the Second World War by G. H. Hardy, and privately printed for him by the Cambridge University Press in 1942, entitled *Bertrand Russell and Trinity: A college controversy of the last war*. Hardy had access to all the relevant College archives, and, although the controversy was one in which he had been personally involved and about which he still felt strongly, his pamphlet is a model of accuracy, completeness, and judicial fairness. It is also written, like everything of Hardy's, in a most admirable style. Unfortunately, it has always been a collector's piece. Any reader who is interested in learning the truth about this most involved affair is strongly advised to beg or borrow a copy. (I will not add 'or steal', since my own copy was stolen by an apparently respectable person, to whom I lent it with the strictest injunctions to treat it as a rare copy of a unique work and to return it to me within a short time.)

So far as I can remember, I saw nothing of Russell and was only in very occasional touch with him by letter during the First World War and for many years afterwards. But I owe very much to the philosophical works which he published from 1914 to 1927 (both included), viz., *Our Knowledge of the External World* (1914), *Analysis of Mind* (1921), and *Analysis of Matter* (1927). My debt to the first two of these will be obvious to any reader of my books *Scientific Thought* (1923) and *The Mind and its Place in Nature* (1925), and it is duly acknowledged in both of them. While I was professor of philosophy at Bristol University (1920–23) I made a careful study of *The Analysis of Mind* and gave a course of lectures on it. It seems to me to be one of the most exciting books on philosophy that Russell ever wrote; and I think that the theory of 'Neutral Monism', which is put forward in it, is (whether it be ultimately tenable or not) about the most important contribution which has been made to speculative philosophy in my life-time.

The Analysis of Mind is a rather curious amalgam of Neutral Monism and Behaviourism, and the latter ingredient in it seems to me to be of minor interest. In *The Analysis of Matter* Russell took up, what appears to me to be obviously one of the most important and interesting tasks of philosophy, and one for which he was peculiarly well qualified, viz., the philosophical analysis of contemporary mathematical physics—in this case the then recent Special and General Theories of Relativity. This book developed out of the Tarner Lectures, which Russell gave in 1925 at the invitation of Trinity College, the trustees of the Tarner Bequest.

After that I did not see Russell again, to the best of my belief, until the October Term of 1944. On the motion of his old friend, Professor H. A. Hollond, Fellow of Trinity, the College Council had unanimously decided, toward the end of 1943, to offer Russell a Fellowship under Title B. Russell accepted this and was formally elected on January 4th, 1944, and admitted on October 10th of that year. He was invited by the College to give lectures during the academic years 1944–5, 1945–6, and 1946–7. He accepted, and his lectures attracted huge audiences. During part of that period Russell was living in London and travelling to Cambridge, and during part of it he was living in Cambridge, at one time in his own house and at another in rooms in College. For a while in 1946, when I was away for some eight months in Sweden, he occupied my rooms; which may thus fairly be described to future visitors, not only as Sir Isaac Newton's, but also as Bertrand Russell's rooms. (I am glad to record that, however destructive he may have been as a thinker, he appeared on my return to have been a model tenant.) It was an immense pleasure to us all at Trinity to have Russell among us once again,

per varios casus, per tot discrimina rerum,

full of vigour, making many new friends among the younger Fellows, and adding enormously by his good company and his brilliant conversation to the pleasure of dining in Hall and frequenting the Parlour afterwards. When the tenure of his Title B Fellowship was about to end in 1948 the Council prolonged it until Michaelmas 1949. And when Russell vacated the prolonged Fellowship on September 30th of that year, he entered the haven which all good Fellows of Trinity hope to reach, viz., a Fellowship under Title E, in virtue of which he is now a Fellow of the College for the rest of his life.

In latter years Russell has unfortunately not been able to be much with us in Trinity. On May 18th, 1962, his nintieth birthday, the Fellows of the College assembled in the Combination Room after dinner to drink his health. We should have been delighted if he had been able to be present; but he had had to decline our very cordial invitation because he was, very naturally, involved as the central figure in the more formal and more widely representative celebrations of the event which were taking place in London. So we had to be content to drink his health *in absentia*. There was a record attendance of Fellows and their guests in the Combination Room, and it was only just possible to seat the whole company. I was invited by the College Council to make the speech proposing Russell's health. I felt it to be a great honour to be entrusted with that duty, and it was extremely pleasant to me personally to have this opportunity of expressing, in presence of my friends and colleagues, my gratitude to Russell for all his kindness to me as a young man, for the stimulation of his wit and humour, and for the immense debt which I owe, in respect of my philosophical work, to his conversation and his writings.

It is on that note that I would wish to end.

(II) *Some Remarks on Sense-Perception*

I shall try to elucidate some of the main concepts which seem to me to be involved in the philosophical analysis of sense-perception, and to define the meanings which I should at present be inclined to attach to certain technical terms which have frequently been employed in discussing that topic.

(1) *Ostensible Perception,*

I shall use this as a general phrase to cover such experiences as ostensibly seeing or hearing or touching, etc., external bodies or physical events or processes, and also to cover such experiences as ostensibly feeling states of, or processes in, one's own body. The phrase is intended to include normal waking sense-perceptions, waking hallucinations (whether delusive, or—if such there be— veridical), and dreams.

Whenever a person is having such an experience he would, if he were to describe it to himself or to another, say: 'I am seeing so-and-so', 'I am hearing so-and-so', etc. The phrase 'so-and-so' would be a name or a description of an actual or possible *body* or *part of a body*, or of an actual or possible *physical event, process, or state of affairs*. E.g. 'a cow', 'the top of a penny', 'a flash of lightning', 'a booming noise', 'an itching in my toe', and so on.

Now we ordinarily use words like 'seeing', 'hearing', 'touching', etc., in such a way that, e.g. a statement of the form 'I am *seeing* so-and-so' would not be true unless the following two conditions were fulfilled, viz. (i) that the experience is in the main *veridical*, and (ii) that is is *normally evoked*.

By calling such an experience 'veridical' I mean that, at the time when it was happening (or at such an earlier time as would be required by light, sound, etc., to have reached the percipient's body from the place which he ostensibly saw or heard 'so-and-so' as occupying), there did exist, at the place which 'so-and-so' was ostensibly perceived as occupying, something answering fairly closely to the description 'so-and-so'. By calling such an experience 'normally evoked' I mean that it was evoked by the stimulation of the appropriate sense-organ (e.g. *eyes*, in the case of seeing) in the normal way by an appropriate physical process (e.g. *light-waves*, in the case of seeing), coming, directly or indirectly, from the thing, event, process, or state of affairs ostensibly perceived.

These two conditions are different, though they are no doubt as a rule closely bound up with each other. A telepathic or clairvoyant experience might take the form of an ostensible seeing, hearing, etc., and it might be veridical; but it would not be normally evoked. Conversely, an experience of an optical illusion would be normally evoked, but it would not be veridical. In neither case, if one were fully informed of the facts, would one accept a statement of the form: 'I am *seeing* so-and-so', made by the experient. In the former case one would say: 'He is not really *seeing*; though what he is ostensibly seeing as occupying a certain place does answer, to a degree not reasonably ascribable to mere chance-coincidence, to the particular thing or event or state of affairs which is in fact occupying that place at that time.' In the latter case one would say: 'No doubt he is really *seeing something*, but it is not what he takes himself to be seeing.' Similar remarks would apply *mutatis mutandis* to ostensible hearing, ostensible touching, and so on.

If and only if an ostensible perception is *normally evoked*, I shall call it 'non-hallucinatory'. Otherwise I shall call it 'hallucinatory'. So far as these definitions go, an ostensible perception of either of these two kinds may be either *veridical* or *delusive*. Veridicality is a matter of degree. An hallucinatory ostensible perception may be, and usually is, *completely non-veridical*. A non-hallucinatory ostensible perception generally has *some* degree of veridicality. A *completely non-veridical* ostensible perception may be called 'delusive'. An example would be an ordinary dream. An ostensible perception which is non-hallucinatory, but is predominantly though not completely non-veridical, may be called 'illusive'. An example would be the experience of 'seeing a mirage'.

There is a close phenomenological resemblance between all such experiences, whether hallucinatory or non-hallucinatory, veridical or non-veridical. And they all differ utterly from such experiences as *thinking of* a body or of a physical event or process or state of affairs in absence, *remembering* such an object, *calling up an image* of such an object, and so on. I use the name 'ostensible perceptions' to mark off the class of experiences having these phenomenological features common and peculiar to them. I will now consider these features in more detail.

(2) 'Ostensible Peceptum'

In every ostensible perception the experient takes himself to be perceiving a certain body or part of a body, a certain physical event or process, or a certain physical state of affairs. Let us lump these alternatives together under the phrase 'physical entity'. The sentence '*O* is the *ostensible perceptum* of the ostensible perception *P*' is to be understood as follows: The word or phrase '*O*' correctly names or describes the object (actual or possible) which the person who is having the ostensible perception *P* then takes himself to be perceiving by it. According as the ostensible perception is an ostensible seeing, an ostensible hearing, and so on, we can call its ostensible perceptum an 'ostensible *visum*', an 'ostensible *auditum*', and so on.

An ostensible perception is *delusive*, if there is, at the relevant time, *no* physical entity at the relevant place, answering even remotely to the description of its ostensible perceptum. It is *more or less veridical* in so far as there is, at the relevant time and place, a physical entity answering more or less accurately to that description. If an ostensible perception is (*a*) non-hallucinatory, and (*b*) predominantly veridical, we can speak of the physical entity which fulfils the above conditions as its '*actual* perceptum'.

(3) '*Sensibly Appearing*'

In having an ostensible perception the experient does not merely take himself to be 'in presence of' an object of a certain kind (e.g. a penny, a flash of lightning, the sound of Big Ben striking, and so on). The object also 'sensibly appears' or 'sensibly presents itself' to him as characterized in certain ways, e.g. it *looks* brown and flat and round, it *feels* cold and smooth and round, it *sounds* booming and rhythmic, and so on.

Very often the experient simply takes for granted that the object which he is ostensibly perceiving *is* as it then looks or feels or sounds to him to be. On some occasions, however, he is doubtful whether it is or is not as it sensibly appears to him to be, or he may be practically certain that it is *not* so. In ordinary life we tend to use phrases like '*looks* so-and-so', '*feels* so-and-so', etc., only or mainly on occasions of the *latter* kind. I intend to ignore that restriction, and to use such phrases *without* any implication or suggestion either that the ostensibly perceived object is *not*, or that it *is*, as it looks or feels or sounds to the person who is ostensibly perceiving it. I shall use the phrases 'sensibly appearing so-and-so', or 'sensibly presenting itself as so-and-so', to cover 'looking so-and-so', 'feeling so-and-so', etc., where these latter phrases are to be understood in the way in which I have said above that I intend to use them.

Now we must carefully distinguish the following two things: (i) A *sensory experience*, in and through which an ostensible perceptum sensibly presents itself to the experient as so-and-so. (ii) A *judgment* to the effect that such and such an ostensible perceptum is sensibly presenting itself as so-and-so to a certain experient. Such a judgment might be either autobiographical or heterobiographical, i.e. either made by the experient himself or made by some other person concerning him. If it be heterobiographical, it is obvious that it differs from the sensory experience. So we may confine our attention to autobiographical judgments of this kind. Such an autobiographical judgment might be concerned either with a *past* sensory experience had by the same person, or it might be concerned with a *simultaneous* sensory experience of his. It is obvious that a *retro-*

spective judgment must differ from the *past* sensory experience with which it is concerned. So we need consider only the case of a person who is (i) having a sensory experience in which an ostensible perceptum sensibly presents itself to him as so-and-so; and who is (ii) simultaneously making a judgment to the effect that such and such an ostensible perceptum is sensibly presenting itself to him as so-and-so.

Even in this case, it is certain that the distinction must still be drawn. *No* judgment of any kind can be made except by a being who has appropriate general ideas; and the capacity to have such ideas and to make judgments seems to be inextricably bound up with the ability to use some kind of language. But one can hardly doubt that an animal or a young child has sensible experiences in which an ostensible perceptum presents itself to him as what *we* (who have language and general ideas) would call 'red' or 'squeaky' or 'sour'. Moreover, when an ostensible perceptum sensibly presents itself as so-and-so to a being who is capable of making judgments, he does not in fact usually make a judgment to the effect that it is doing this.

Granted that the distinction must be drawn, I propose to call such a sensory experience a '*sensation*', and such a judgment a '*judgment of sensible appearance*'. It is certain that a sensation (or a *quasi*-sensation) is an essential factor in every ostensible perception; and it is equally certain that a judgment of sensible appearance is *not*. (I have added the alternative '*quasi*-sensation' to cover the case of *hallucinatory* ostensible perceptions. Here the experient is certainly having colour-experiences, sound-experiences, etc., extremely like those which are normally evoked by the stimulation of his eyes by light-waves, of his ears by sound-waves, and so on; and these experiences certainly play an essential part in his hallucinatory ostensible perception. But it might be thought misleading to call these 'sensations', since they are not evoked by the normal stimulation of a sense-organ. In the sequel I shall sometimes use the word 'sensation' to cover what would more accurately be called '*quasi*-sensations'.)

Any judgment is, as such, capable of being true or false. But it is difficult or impossible to formulate and to apply tests for judgments of sensible appearance. So such judgments are often described (rightly or wrongly) as 'incorrigible'.

(4) *Analysis of Ostensible Perception*

(i) Whenever a person is having an ostensible perception he is *ipso facto* having a certain sensation or *quasi*-sensation.

Let us take as an example the case of a person who is ostensibly seeing a cricket-ball. An essential factor in any such experience would be a sensation or *quasi*-sensation in which he is sensibly presented with a 'round-looking', 'brown-looking', 'convex-looking' expanse. (I use the phrases which I have put in inverted commas, in order to make it clear that 'round', 'brown', 'convex', etc., are to be understood in the sense in which they are intelligible and familiar to all speakers of English who can see and are not colour-blind, and would be unintelligible to anyone blind from birth.)

(ii) Although a sensation or *quasi*-sensation is an essential factor in any ostensible perception, there is always another and no less essential factor. In order to show this we will revert to our example of an experience which could be correctly described as 'ostensibly seeing a cricket-ball'.

By a 'cricket-ball' is meant something which is spherical and solid; which has coolness or warmness, smoothness and hardness, beside the brownness which is all that it presents to sight. It is something which has parts that are not at the moment presenting themselves sensibly to the person who is said to be seeing it; though they might do so to him at other times, and might do so to other percipients, differently situated, at the same time. It is something which has *causal* properties, such as mass, impenetrability, and elasticity; which cannot, from the nature of the case, be *sensibly* presented, like colour, temperature, textural-quality, etc., though they are ascribed, no doubt, *on the evidence of* certain regular conjunctions and sequences among sensations. By 'ostensibly seeing a cricket-ball' we mean (*a*) having a visual sensation or *quasi*-sensation of the special kind described above, *and* (*b*) being led by it (without any explicit process of inference, and without even any experience of associative transition) to take oneself to be facing an object answering more or less to the above description of a 'cricket-ball'.

This second factor has been called by Professor H. H. Price '*perceptual acceptance*'. It certainly cannot be identified with *judging*, in the sense in which that involves formulating and accepting or rejecting a proposition. The higher animals, other than man, almost certainly have experiences which may fairly be called 'ostensible perceptions'; but they are almost certainly incapable of making judgments, in the sense described above. Perceptual acceptance resembles judgment, in that it can be significantly described as 'true' or 'false', 'correct' or 'mistaken'. And there are well known and readily applicable tests for its correctness or incorrectness. Again, an experient who *is* capable of making judgments, could, if he should set himself to it, usually make a judgment corresponding more or

113

less accurately to what he is perceptually accepting on any given occasion.

We might put the case as follows. In order for an ostensible perception to occur there must already exist in the experient certain dispositions, which have been generated and organized in him through his having experienced repeatedly in the past certain conjunctions and certain immediate sequences of sensations. When he now receives the stimulus which produces a certain sensation in him, certain of these dispositions are simultaneously activated; and the experience which he has is the joint product of the sensory stimulus and the activated disposition. In an experient capable of making judgments, and in a frame of mind to do so at the time, the contribution made by the activated disposition might develop into an *explicit perceptual judgment*, such as: 'That which I am now seeing is a brown, cool, smooth, hard, massive, elastic, spherical body.' Even in an experient who is *capable* of making judgments, the contribution made by the activated disposition does not usually develop so far. Generally it issues only in a *readiness* to accept such judgments and to reject others incompatible with them, *if* suggested; in the acceptance of certain immediate developments of the present situation as *normal and unsurprising*, and the meeting of certain others with *surprise or dismay*; in the automatic adjustment of the relevant sense-organs and other parts of the body in ways which *would* be appropriate, *if* one had made such and such perceptual judgments; and so on. In an experient who is *incapable* of making explicit judgments, it is plain that the contribution added by the activated disposition to the sensational core can take *only* one or other of the latter forms.

Before leaving this topic I would like to add the following two remarks: (*a*) I should think it unlikely that visual, auditory, or tactual sensations, of appreciable intensity, often occur, in adult human beings in an attentive waking state, *without* activating some of the dispositions in question. I should therefore suspect that such sensations would seldom, if ever, occur in such persons, except as the sensory core of some *ostensible perception*, however vague and inchoate. (*b*) I should think it likely that the disposition to form such dispositions as lead to perceptual acceptance and ultimately to perceptual judgment, is innate in human beings and other animals. (We might call it an 'aptitude', borrowing that useful word from Professor Ducasse.) No doubt the *particular* dispositions, which are formed in an individual possessed of such an aptitude, depend on the particular kinds of frequently recurring conjunctions and sequences of sensations which he has experienced. But there is a *general* character, common and peculiar to all such dispositions—a common and peculiar *theme*, on which they are all so many different variations. This expresses itself in the *categories* which are *explicit* in all perceptual judgments and implicit in all states of perceptual acceptance; e.g. that of *persistent thing and variable states*; that of a *single spatial system*, in which all things are located, and a *single temporal system*, in which all their states are dated; that of *causal interaction* between things, determining changes in their states; and so on.

In illustration of this second point, I would say this. I can imagine sentient beings, who shared with us the general capacity to form associations, and who had experienced the same kinds of repeated conjunctions and sequences of sensations as we have done; but who never attained to perceptual acceptance (and therefore never had ostensible perceptions), simply because they lacked our innate aptitude to form the peculiar kind of dispositions required. Conversely, of course, a creature might have the innate aptitude and yet never form the dispositions; simply because his sensations lacked that kind and degree of regular concomitance and sequence which is needed in order to set the aptitude at work and provide it with suitable materials.

(5) *Alternative Analyses of Sensation or quasi-Sensation*

At least three different kinds of analysis of sensation or *quasi-*sensation have been suggested, viz. the *Act-Object Analysis*, the *Internal Accusative Analysis*, and the *Neutral Monist Analysis*. I shall now say something about each in turn.

(A) *Act-Object Analysis.* Consider those visual and tactual sensations which occur as essential factors in experiences of ostensibly seeing or ostensibly touching a body of *definite outline*, to which one is *selectively attending*. In such cases, at any rate, the following account of the sensation seems *prima facie* plausible, viz. that to have such a sensation consists in being *immediately aware* of a certain particular *as having certain characteristics*. Or, to put it in another way, it consists in a certain particular *directly presenting itself* to one *as having certain characteristics*. Examples of such characteristics are *red* (in the sense in which a thing 'looks red'), *cold* (in the sense in which a thing 'feels cold'), and so on. We will call them '*sensible qualities*'.

The above is what I call the 'Act-Object' analysis of sensations. Such technical terms as 'sensible', 'sense-datum', and 'sensum' are bound up with and presuppose this type of analysis. I will now develop this further.

(i) On the assumption that the act-object analysis applies to at least some sensations, we can give the following definitions: (*a*), *Sensing*' is the mental act of being immediately aware of a certain particular as having a certain sensible quality or qualities. (*b*) A '*sensibile*' is any particular which is capable of being sensed. (*c*) A sensibile is a '*sense-datum*' for a certain person when and only when he is sensing it.

These definitions are intended to leave open all the following questions: (*a*) Whether or not a sensibile can be *sensed as having* a quality which it *does not have in any form whatever* (e.g. as red, though it has in fact no colour. (*b*) Whether or not a sensibile can be sensed as having a quality in *a different determinate form* from that in which it in fact has that determinable quality (e.g. as elliptical, though it is in fact circular). (*c*) Whether or not one and the same sensibile can *combine* sensible qualities which it can manifest only through *different kinds of sensation* (e.g. whether it could be both sensibly red and sensibly hot). (*d*) Whether or not one and the same sensibile could be sensed *on various separated occasions* by the same person, either through sensations of the same kind (e.g. all visual) or of different kinds (e.g. visual on some occasions, and tactual on others). (*e*) Whether or not one and the same sensibile could be sensed by *different* persons, either through sensations of the same kind or of different kinds. (*f*) Whether or not there could be sensibilia which are sometimes not sensed by anyone, or sensibilia which are never sensed by anyone. (*g*) Whether the sensibile which a person senses when he ostensibly sees or touches a certain part of a certain body is *always*, or *sometimes but not always*, or *never* identical with that part of the surface of that body.

It is plain that certain answers to some of these questions would have a logical bearing on the answers to certain others of them. Suppose, e.g. that it be admitted that a sensibile can be *sensed as having* a quality in a certain determinate form, though *in fact* it has that quality in a different determinate form. Then some of the arguments for *denying* that the sensibile which a person visually senses when he ostensibly sees a certain part of the surface of a certain body, *is ever identical with* that part of the surface of that body, will collapse.

(ii) It has very commonly been assumed that any quality which a sensibile is sensed as having *must* in fact belong to it, and that the sensibile must *have* that quality in *the very same determinate form* in which it is sensed as having it. I shall call this the '*Assumption of Sensal Inerrancy*'. On any view, as I have already said, to sense a sensibile as having a certain quality is utterly different from judging

116

that it has that quality. But, on the Assumption of Sensal Inerrancy, that difference is even more radical than the difference, already indicated, between perceptual acceptance and perceptual judgment. For, on that assumption, there can be no question of possible error in the case of *sensing*; whilst there is always the possibility of error in *perceptual acceptance*.

(iii) It seems to me that the Assumption of Sensal Inerrancy may be, and in fact has been, regarded in two fundamentally different ways.

(*a*) It might be held that 'to *have* the sensible quality *q*' and 'to be *sensed by someone as having* the quality *q*' have *different meanings*, and that the meaning of the second is *no part of* that of the first. On that view, the Assumption of Sensal Inerrancy is a *synthetic* proposition. It might be accepted either because it seemed self-evident on reflexion, though not analytic; or because there was thought to be adequate empirical evidence for it; or just as a convenient working hypothesis, against which there is no conclusive evidence.

(*b*) On the other hand, it might be held that, in the case of a *sensible* quality, the only meaning that can be attached to '*having* the quality' is *being sensed by someone as having it*. We might parody Berkeley by summing up the view which leads to this conclusion in the phrase: 'To be sensibly qualified = To be sensed as qualified.' I will call this '*The re-formulated Berkeley Principle*'.

I suppose that some philosophers may have started from the other end. They may have found the Assumption of Sensal Inerrancy self-evidently necessary. They may then have argued that, in order to be necessary, it must be analytic. And they may then have been led to the re-formulated Berkeley Principle as ensuring its analyticity.

(iv) The re-formulated Berkeley Principle would carry with it more than the analytic truth of the Assumption of Sensal Inerrancy. It would entail that it is self-contradictory to suppose either (α) that a sensibile has *any* sensible qualities except when it is a sense-datum to someone, or (β) that, when a sensibile is a sense-datum to someone, it has any sensible qualities *beside* those which it is then sensed as having.

It is important to notice, however, that the re-formulated Berkeley Principle would *not logically exclude* any of the following possibilities: (*a*) That there might be sensibilia which are *sometimes* not sense-data to anyone, or sensibilia which are *never* sense-data to anyone. (*b*) That one and the same sensibile might be sensed *on various occasions* by the same person, either through sensations of the same kind on each occasion or through sensations of different kinds on various occasions. (*c*) That one and the same sensibile might be sensed by *different* persons, either through sensations of the same kind or of different kinds.

But, although none of these 'possibilities' would be inconsistent with the re-formulated Berkeley Principle, it might fairly be asked whether any of them are 'real' possibilities. It will be noted that all of them presuppose the notion of *one and the same* sensibile, considered in various contexts. Now that is not really intelligible unless there be some generally accepted and applicable criterion of identity or diversity for sensibilia. It may be doubted whether any satisfactory criterion has ever been formulated.

(B) *Internal Accusative Analysis.* The last paragraph forms a natural transition from the Act-Object analysis of sensation to what Professor Price has called the 'Internal Accusative' analysis of it.

According to this, a sensation or *quasi*-sensation is a unitary experience, not analysable into act of sensing and object sensed. To have a sensation of tiredness or of sickness, e.g. seems *prima facie* just to be feeling in a certain *way* ('tiredly' or 'sickly'), and not to be sensing a certain *object* as having a certain quality ('tiredness' or 'sickliness'). The Act-Object analysis seems most unplausible here, whilst the Internal Accusative analysis seems most unplausible in the case of such sensations as we considered under (A) above.

I suppose that the best that supporters of the Internal Accusative analysis could say of such a sensation as that which a person has in looking at a cricket-ball in a good light and in a fully attentive state, would be somewhat as follows. He might say that such a sensation has two different but inseparable aspects. In respect of one of them, which might be called its 'subjective' aspect, it counts as *so-and-so's sensation*, an event or phrase in a certain person's mental history. In respect of the other, which might be called its 'objective' aspect, it counts as a *sensation-of such-and-such*, e.g. of a brown-looking, convex-looking expanse. On this view, the fundamental mistake of the Act-Object analysis is to suppose that 'of' here has the same kind of meaning as 'of' in such phrases as 'perception of x', 'memory of x', 'thought of x', etc. In the latter phrases the word 'of' denotes the relation of a cognitive act or process to a cognized object. But in the phrase 'sensation-of such-and-such' it does not. It would be safer to talk of the 'content' or the 'objective aspect' of a sensation, and not of its 'object'.

For anyone who holds this kind of view the word 'sensibile', as I have defined it above, becomes otiose and possibly misleading. The word 'sense-datum' might still be retained, for a sensation considered in its *objective* aspect. Speaking in terms of 'sensibilia', if one cared to retain the word, one would have to say that any sensibile is necessarily a sense-datum of one particular sense to one particular person on one particular occasion. On this view it could safely be *denied* that the sense-datum involved in ostensibly seeing or touching a body is *ever* a part of the surface of the body ostensibly seen or touched.

(C) *Neutral Monist Analysis*. There is a third analysis of sensation, which has been put forward by Lord Russell in some of his writings. It differs from both the Act-Object and the Internal Accusative analysis, but has certain affiliations with each of them. According to it, the primary notion is that of *sensibile*, and a sensibile is a particular which has one or more sensible qualities. In so far as it stands in a certain kind of relation to a complex of inter-related sensibilia of a certain kind, it counts as a 'part' (in a highly technical sense of that word) of a 'body' or of a 'physical event or process' (also to be understood in a highly technical sense). In so far as it stands in a certain quite different kind of relation to a complex of inter-related sensibilia and images of a certain different kind, it counts as a 'sense-datum' to a certain person. It is *logically possible* for a sensibile to be either (*a*) at one and the same time *both* a 'part' of a 'body' or of a 'physical event or process' *and* a sense-datum to a person, or (*b*) to have *either* status *without the other*, or (*c*) to have *neither* status. And it is logically possible for one and the same sensibile to be at one time in one, and at another time in another, of these situations.

(6) *The so-called 'Sensum Theory'*

I have so far had no occasion to use the word 'sensum'. I think that what is often referred to as the 'Sensum Theory' *commonly* (though by no means invariably) presupposes all the following propositions: (i) That ostensible perception must be analysed in terms of (*a*) a sensation, and (*b*) a state of perceptual acceptance based upon it. (ii) That the act-object analysis applies, at any rate to those sensations which are involved in ostensibly seeing or touching a body of fairly definite outline, to which the percipient is selectively attending. (iii) That any sensibile must have any sensible quality which it is sensed as having, and must have it in the determinate form in which it is sensed as having it. (iv) That, nevertheless, 'to have the sensible quality *q*' and 'to be sensed as having *q*' do *not* have the same meaning, and that the meaning of the latter is no part of the meaning of the former. (v) That there is, therefore, nothing *logically inconsistent* in supposing that the very same sensibile, which is at one time sensed as having a certain quality, should at other times be unsensed and yet have precisely the same quality. Nor is there

119

anything *logically inconsistent* in supposing that there may be sensi-bilia which *never are* sensed and which yet have sensible qualities.

Subject to all the above assumptions, we might define a '*sensum*' as follows. It is a particular, capable of being sensed, which has certain sensible qualities. If it should be sensed, it will sensibly present itself as having some or all of the sensible qualities which it has. It will not be sensed as having any qualities other than these, or as having these in any but the determinate forms in which it actually has them. But its *having* any sensible quality is *logically* independent of its *being sensed as having it*.

It should be noted that it is only *logical* independence that is relevant here. A person who accepted the existence of sensa, as defined above, might hold that it is *causally* impossible or highly improbable that a sensum should exist except as a sense-datum to one particular person on one particular occasion. Or he might hold that the supposition of unsensed sensa, though not ruled out by definition, is otiose or that it has no clear positive meaning. But he would have to adduce specific facts, and to produce specific argu-ments, in support of such opinions.

I think that *most* people who have held the Sensum Theory have accepted, explicitly or tacitly, one or more of the following propo-sitions, in addition to those which I have given above as essential to it: (i) That one and the same sensibile cannot combine sensible qualities which are normally manifested through the stimulation of *different kinds of sense-organ*, e.g. sensible whiteness and sensible coldness. (ii) That one and the same sensibile cannot be a sense-datum to *more than one person*, and cannot be a sense-datum to a person on *several separated occasions*. (iii) That the sensibile which a person senses when he ostensibly sees or touches a body (even in the most normal cases of sane waking sense-perception) is *never* identical with the part of the surface of the body which he is then seeing or feeling; and, indeed, is never identical with any part of the surface of *any* body, but is a particular existent of a quite peculiar kind.

Perhaps many philosophers would regard some or all of these propositions as an essential part of the content of any doctrine which they would recognize as a form of the Sensum Theory. (I note, e.g. that I included the third of them in my *definition* of the 'Sensum Theory' on pp. 181–2 of a book which I wrote many years ago, entitled *The Mind and its Place in Nature*.) However that may be, it is important to see clearly that these propositions are *not* logically entailed by the five assumptions, stated above as characteristic of the Sensum Theory, together with the definition of 'sensum' pro-posed above.

In this essay I have been concerned mainly with matters of linguistic usage, partly that of ordinary language and partly that of the technical terminology employed by certain philosophers. I am sure that this is a valuable and even a necessary *preliminary* to philosophical discussion on the topic of sense-perception. But it seems to me absurd to suppose that it could be anything *more* than an essential preliminary. The philosophical problems of sense-perception arise because of the co-existence of a number of relevant and closely inter-related *non-linguistic facts*, which are *prima facie* difficult to fit together into any one coherent system. Important instances of such facts are the following: Those of normal veridical sense-preception; those of incipient, moderate, and extreme illusory perception; those of hallucinatory *quasi*-perception, whether occurring in sleep or in the waking state, and whether delusive or (on rare occasions) veridical; those which physicists have established as to the finite velocity of light and of sound; those which physiologists have established as to the parts played by the brain, the sensory nerves, and the sense-organs in sense-perception; and so on. The business of the philosopher of sense-perception is to suggest and to defend a coherent and synoptic view of *all* such facts.

Many of these facts (e.g. the physical and the physiological ones) remained completely unsuspected until millions of years after the language that we use in daily life had fully developed. To imagine that a careful study of the usages, the implications, the suggestions, and the *nuances*, of the ordinary speech of contemporary Englishmen could be a substitute for, or a valuable contribution towards, the solution of the philosophical problems of sense-perception, seems to me one of the strangest delusions which has ever flourished in academic circles.

11

MAX BORN

Reflections of a Physicist

This is a poor attempt of an octogenarian to pay tribute to the genius of young Bertrand Russell. His name has been known to me since I came to Göttingen as a student of mathematics and physics in 1903. In those days the mathematical scene in Göttingen was dominated by three great men whose interest extended far beyond the limits of their special subjects: Felix Klein had given in his 'Erlanger Programme' a kind of constitution to the whole realm of mathematics by systematizing it according to the ideas of group theory. Deeply interested in all sciences which used mathematical methods he was active in extending these subjects by stimulating the foundation of new chairs and new laboratories. Hermann Minkowski, though mainly working in analysis and theory of numbers, had become interested in the difficulties of electrodynamics of moving bodies which led him to his celebrated work on relativity. David Hilbert, after having published his fundamental book on the axioms of geometry, turned to the much greater and deeper problem of the logical foundations of mathematics as a whole. I attended a lecture of his on the 'Logical Principles of Mathematics' and another given by one of his circle, the young lecturer Zermelo, on Mengenlehre (theory of sets). In these courses Cantor's proof of the non-enumerability of the set of real numbers made a deep impression on my mind, but the Russell paradox (set of sets which do not contain themselves as elements) perhaps an even deeper one. It made the whole structure of mathematics and logics to appear doubtful and insecure.

Thus, together with Cantor and Hilbert, Russell appeared to me, right from the beginning, as a master of critical thinking and scientific doubt. I owe to these men that sceptical attitude in science which is the source of new ideas.

However I have never studied Russell's great masterpiece, the *Principia Mathematica*, published jointly with A. N. Whitehead (in 1910, 1912, 1913), because I soon abandoned definitely pure mathematics and turned to mathematical physics. In the small library which I kept after my retirement from my Edinburgh chair there are only a few books by Russell, all of a later period, among them *Mysticism and Logic* (1918) and *Our Knowledge of the External*

World (1926)—not to mention several recent publications, such as *Nightmares* (1954) and *Has Man a Future?* (1961). I cannot reconstruct my reactions as a student on Russell's philosophy in general, nor on his ideas about the foundation of empirical science. I only remember that he helped me to extricate myself from the spell of some transcendental or idealistic philosophers who had impressed me strongly for a while. One of these was Edmund Husserl whose 'phenomenology' claimed to reveal through pure reason the 'essence' ('das Wesen') of things. There is still a large community of his followers, mainly in America. Another philosopher who influenced my thinking in my student days was Leonhard Nelson, the head of a considerable group of gifted people, who called themselves the School of Fries, a disciple of Kant. I think that this training in Kantian criticism was quite wholesome for a young mind. But I soon discovered that Kant's claim of the *a priori* character of geometrical axioms was in contradiction with the actual progress of geometry, and that great mathematicians like Gauss and Riemann had not accepted it but preferred an empirical standpoint. Later I read Russell's analysis of Kant's treatment of the antinomies of space and time which disclosed its weakness.

Since those times I have never attached myself to any of the philosophical schools, ancient or modern, but preferred to take from them what seemed to me sound, always prepared to give it up for something better. It was a consolation to read in Russell's short, delightful autobiography, published in volume V of 'The Library of Living Philosophers' (edited by P. A. Schilpp) that he began by being a follower of Kant and Hegel, but abandoned them under the influence of G. E. Moore. It is refreshing to read that he came to think of all that Hegel says about mathematics as 'muddle-headed nonsense'.

My emancipation from Kant and his successors was mainly due to studying Einstein's papers and later to discussions with him. He was at that time strongly influenced by Ernst Mach and made me read Mach's critical investigations on the foundations of mechanics and physics in general. But he was always sceptical towards Mach's positivistic epistemology. One can read about all this in another volume of the Schilpp series ('The Library of Living Philosophers', vol. VII). What I learned from Einstein was mainly this: that empirical research may produce results which are not compatible with philosophical ideas derived from previous experience, and that no conviction based on intuition (Anschauung) or tradition should be regarded as final. This is not a philosophy but an attitude of mind, and I think it is not at variance with Russell's way of philosophizing which aims at analysing the meaning and logical structure of science as it actually is, and not at establishing fundamental principles *a priori*.

I have re-read the sections of the Russell Schilpp volume (vol. V, quoted above) dealing with science, especially the article by E. Nagel (No. 10) and Russell's reaction to it (p. 700). The discussion concerns mainly the place which perception has in the physical universe. I feel hardly competent to give an opinion about this question. Russell's causal theory of perception seems to me an answer acceptable to a physicist from the standpoint of his own science. But whether a psychologist would agree I do not know.

After having lived through two great revolutions in physics, relativity and quantum theory, I have come to the conclusion that the problem of the reality of the external world and of its relation to our perceptions ought to be considered by the scientist in a manner which looks superficially like a compromise between naïve realism and a more abstract philosophy, but actually is a new approach. It has its roots in the difficulties encountered by interpreting the micro-phenomena of atomic physics and was, I think, first indicated by Niels Bohr. It is well known that the behaviour of atoms, electrons, protons, neutrons and other particles can be clearly and unambiguously described by mathematical formulae. But when one tries to translate these into ordinary language one is led to strange consequences: spaces of more than three, even of infinitely many dimensions; two contradicting ways of describing one and the same event, in terms of particles or of waves; lack of individuality of particles connected with strange statistical behaviour, etc. To reconcile all this with our accustomed ways of thinking we should not try to modify or give up the naïve realism but restrict it to the ordinary dimensions for which the human body and mind have been biologically adapted, i.e. to macroscopic dimensions. For otherwise we could not describe our experiments. All our instruments consist of ordinary bodies and cannot be discussed but by ordinary language with the help of concepts of Euclidean geometry. It is of course left to the philosopher to analyse this macroscopic domain. But the physicist has enlarged it enormously by using magnifying apparatus: telescopes, microscopes, amplifiers, multipliers, etc. These produce data which, though consisting primarily of ordinary sense perceptions, cannot be conceived as meaningful structures with the help of the experience collected and the language learned in childhood.

One has to apply abstract thinking. This is the domain of Russell's theory of empirical knowledge. For the physical world revealed here is a construction of the mind, armed with mathematics, from raw material obtained by the senses, armed by the magnifying tools of science.

I wish to add two considerations which support this reasoning. The first argument refers to the fact that the decomposition of the perception of the world into chaotic 'sense data' is a result of a late state of scientific analysis. We learn to know things and their properties, and some of us learn later on that they are composed of sense data. No conscious effort is necessary to do this composition by thinking. It has happened to us in childhood unconsciously and automatically.

The second argument is derived from results of physiological research in the transmission of perturbations along the nerve fibres from the sense organs to the brain and from the brain to the muscles and the organs. These signals consist in regular pulses without any specific quality, and the special nature of the message carried, whether optical, acoustical, thermic or other, depends only on the spot where the nerve starts in a surface organ and where it ends in the brain.

The quality of any sense impression is therefore fully determined by the anatomical structure of the nerve system and the brain, and the shape of things perceived must therefore be the result of an unconscious analysis of the chaotic welter of signals. The brain sorts out invariant qualities and makes them conscious as shapes or motions, colours or noises, hotness or coldness, etc. It seems to me impossible to assume that this incredibly involved and fast process of interpretation of the nerve signals could be the result of any 'construction', a word which implies the application of willed and conscious effort.

But if one accepts this fact Russell's theory of the objective world remains still valid if it is applied to the domain which transcends ordinary, biological experience and which has to do with quantities and structures unknown to 'animal man', but explored by civilized society's collective effort, called science.

Here strange results are obtained: In large, celestial dimensions space appears curved. The idea of simultaneity of events, so obvious to the ordinary mind, becomes meaningless and has to be replaced by a relative concept, which merges space and time to a higher unit. In small, atomic dimensions still greater deviations from the 'normal' have to be accepted, and even the revolutionary result that there is a limit to causal, or better deterministic description, which gets replaced by a new type of statistical laws. The only restriction in this field to the imagination of the scientist is the condition that in the limiting case of ordinary dimensions for which 'animal man' is adapted the new concepts and laws must go over into those of ordinary experience (called 'classical' by the physicists).

I am aware that by suggesting this modification of Russell's theory of physical knowledge I am transgressing into the realm of philosophy where I am an amateur. But the facts and ideas on which I base my reasoning are new and have only emerged during the course of my scientific life. This seems to me a justification to deviate from the teaching of the master who taught me the art of thinking. Another motive is this: By claiming the right to apply naïve realism to every-day experience including the craft of experimenting we physicists get the freedom to concentrate on the problems of atomic and cosmic physics in which we are interested, unhampered by doubts about the use of ordinary language for our manipulations.

Russell's investigations on other problems of science are narrowly related to the theory just discussed, but I have not studied them carefully enough to speak about them.

Nor can I express an opinion on his numerous books and articles dealing with other subjects of great diversity, as metaphysics, psychology, ethics, religion, sociology, politics, economy, history, education a.o. apart from a deep admiration for a mind which encompasses the whole of human activity. But I wish to say a word about Russell's *History of Western Philosophy*. It is not only a source of information but also an intellectual delight for a philoso-phizing scientist. When I occasionally discussed it with German philosophers I found that some of them dislike it because they see in it more a reflexion of Russell's mind than an objective presentation of the historical personalities and their ideas. But Russell's mind is so extraordinary that we should be grateful to see history through his eyes. I dare say that the picture given by him might not be photo-graphically accurate but true in a deeper sense.

I never had the luck to meet Bertrand Russell in person. I did not attend meetings of philosophers, nor did he attend conferences of physicists. When I was professor at Edinburgh University I once invited him to give a lecture to the students of my department of 'Natural Philosophy'. But he was unable to come.

A closer connection between us developed later when I had returned to Germany after the war, through our common passionate concern in the problem of survival of the human race in our nuclear age.

My father who had participated in the French-German war of 1870–71 as medical officer in a Prussian regiment and who had seen the darkest side of warfare in the field ambulances and hospitals had told me about his experiences. They made a deep impression on my young mind and counteracted the nationalistic and militar-istic influence of patriotic school teachers. I disliked war but was not a pacifist because in the society to which we belonged (in Breslau,

Silesia) the peace movement was regarded as a matter of cranks and lunatics. Thus I did my military service, without pleasure yet without resentment, and when I was dismissed because of a strong asthmatic disposition I took it as good luck. Ten years later, when the great war of 1914 broke out, I became much more rebellious. The causes of the fighting seemed to me incredibly stupid. I hated the propaganda swindle, and when during the first weeks a considerable number of my young students and friends were killed on the battle fields of Flanders I felt an abhorrence of the slaughter. This was shared by Einstein and other friends in Berlin, but the idea that one could go over from mental to actual resistance hardly occurred to us. The concept of the Conscientious Objectors was not known to us at that time. All I could do was just to save a number of young gifted students from the trenches by getting them appointed assistants in the military office where I had been given a scientific job as an expert on 'sound ranging'. In some cases I succeeded, as for instance in that of Alfred Landé who later became a leading figure in atomic theory during the period of transition between classical and modern physics. In other cases I failed dismally; I remember vividly the feeling of desperate grief when a charming mathematical student, the most gifted for decades in Göttingen, named Herkner, was killed a day before the telegram of the transfer to Berlin, much delayed by red tape, reached his regiment. About the middle of the war I took part in meetings arranged by a group of Berlin intellectuals, amongst them Einstein, the historian Delbrück, the aged economist Brentano, to meet some high officials of the German Foreign Office in order to persuade them that the planned declaration of 'unrestricted U-boat warfare' (the sinking of neutral ships) was disastrous, as it would be bound to bring the United States into the war and thus lead to final defeat. This is what actually happened. Being a scientific officer I was not allowed to take part in any political activities. That I disregarded this was the whole risk I took.

It was years after the end of the war when I learned what Bertrand Russell had done: His opposition to the war had cost him his academic position, led to imprisonment and forced him to emigrate to USA. He had firmly stood to his convictions and refused to take part in the general outbreak of insanity which swept the world at that time. And ever since he stuck to his principles and acted without fear.

Only after we had come to Great Britain as refugees from Nazi persecution did we learn that Russell was not alone in his objection to war. We came in close contact with Quakers and learned that many of these had suffered imprisonment in the First World War for upholding their religious Peace Testimony. While my wife became a member of the Society of Friends I felt much attracted by their ethical convictions, particularly those concerned with war. Yet I found myself in an inner conflict. The Second World War was altogether different in kind from the first one. Hitler and his Nazis represented a concentration and accumulation of Evil such as had never existed before. Even a convinced pacifist could not help wishing victory for the Allies. However I was spared to participate in war work and especially in developing the atomic bomb.

I do not know much of what Bertrand Russell thought and did during those dark years.

But when the war ended with the dropping of the atomic bombs on Japanese cities Russell was one of the first to grasp the meaning of this event and began to write and speak against nuclear weapons.

One of his most important actions was the foundation of the Pugwash movement. I am glad that I was among those who were asked to sign the manifesto initiated by Russell and Einstein. I took part in the third Pugwash Conference at Kitzbühel, Tyrol, in 1958. It showed me that discussions between scientists from East and West on the most difficult and delicate political questions can be conducted on a high level of reason and ethics which politicians seldom attain, just as Russell and Einstein had intended. The meeting ended in Vienna with a declaration signed almost unanimously by all participants. As this document had been discussed and accepted already at Kitzbühel my wife and I did not go to the closing ceremony at Vienna.

We do regret this now, as we missed meeting Bertrand Russell who came especially to Vienna, well knowing that the political effect of a political declaration depends as much on the solemnity of the ceremony with which it is made public as on its content and importance.

Since those days I have been in correspondence with Russell and have followed his activities with the greatest interest and sympathy. Our common ground is the conviction that only a complete change of attitude towards war, expressed in the abandonment of traditional politics, can save the human race from extinction. Russell calls for civil disobedience in order to induce his government to renounce nuclear armament. Again he suffered imprisonment for his conviction. I think he is completely right in proclaiming that there is no safety in the possession of atomic weapons and that unilateral nuclear disarmament by Great Britain would give a moral lead to the world which might stop the race to destruction.

I wish him success with all my heart.

12

HANS REICHENBACH

An Early Appreciation

Translator's note: The following article appeared in the *Vossische Zeitung* on December 2, 1928, under the heading 'Great Thinkers of our Time'. Russell was then fifty-six years old. Reichenbach's portrait of Bertrand Russell attests not only to the author's superb understanding of the great philosopher, but also to Bertrand Russell's consistency of character. I am happy to contribute the translation of the article to this volume dedicated to Bertrand Russell in his tenth decade.

MARIA REICHENBACH

Contrary to the layman's belief that the essence of philosophy is embodied in the great philosophical systems of the past and that only a new system builder has to appear in order to construct the ultimate philosophical system of our time, a development has taken place through which philosophical thinking has found a new direction: a new philosophical method and a new approach to philosophy have emerged with the help of science. The result has been a rejection of system building and of sweeping syntheses of philosophical dogmas. Instead, philosophy has been transformed into detailed analyses of specific problems. This procedure alone can legitimately be called the philosophical method and promises to become the philosophy of the future.

Although phenomenology took a similarly negative view of system building, it was unable to cope with the fundamental epistemological problems because of its rejection of scientific methods. Such problems can be solved only in close conjunction with discoveries in the natural sciences. Indeed, the philosophers who are likely to offer resolutions of these problems are well versed in the exact sciences. The new philosophy has its roots imbedded so firmly in the mathematical sciences that the uninitiated does not even recognize its philosophical character and takes it for a part of mathematics or mathematical physics. And yet, the problems which are attacked by means of the modern method of mathematical logic pertain to the most profound and perennial epistemological questions even though they had frequently to be rephrased under the influence of modern analysis. Bertrand Russell is one of the foremost representatives of this scientific philosophy and its most outstanding leader.

Russell's work which began during the nineties of the last century is closely connected with set theory, a part of mathematics founded by Georg Cantor, Dedekind, and Frege, that has so little similarity with the discipline of mathematics as taught in our schools that the non-mathematician would not even recognize it as belonging in mathematics. The logical problem of infinity became the central issue of set theory, with reference to the infinitely great as well as the infinitely small. Actually, this difference plays the least important role within the problem of infinity. Set theory deals with infinite numbers and these occur already in connection with finite segments. An infinite number of points lie on any arbitrarily small line segment. It is preferable to speak of 'set' or 'class' instead of 'cardinality' and to define infinite cardinals as numbers of infinite classes. The laws governing infinite classes had to be expressly formulated since they deviate from those governing finite classes. In particular, the Aristotelian law that the whole is greater than its parts is invalid for infinite classes.

Starting from such considerations Russell investigated the question what is meant by 'number'. This seems to be a strange question because everybody believes that he has learned in school what constitutes a number. But what one learns in school is only the manipulation of numbers—yet such a skill has very little to do with a precise definition of 'number'. Russell gave the apparently puzzling answer that numbers are nothing but classes. If we stipulate three things, say, an inkwell, a house, and a taxi, they form a class. It is a special class which we shall call a triad. By means of this name we have said something about this class, namely, that it has a relation to the number 3. What constitutes the 'triadness' of this class? Russell answers: the 'triadness' is not a separate entity, nothing existing in addition to the class; rather, it is the statement that this class is related to other classes, i.e. to other triads. The class which we specified has the same number as the class given by the men Brown, Jones, and Robinson, or as the class of words 'one, two, three'. Having the number 3 is a common property of all triads, i.e. of all classes which have three members. Or as Russell formulates it by means of the concept of class, the number 3 is the class of all triads, a class whose elements are classes.

The significance of this theory consists in the fact that those independent logical entities which played such strange roles in the old philosophical systems are eliminated. The meaning of logical symbols is exhausted by statements about physical things. The mysteries with which naïve philosophical thinking had invested the notion of number are mercilessly rejected and only as much meaning is retained as is necessary for an application of these symbols to scientific and practical problems. Russell's theory exemplifies the realistic orientation characteristic of the new philosophy of science.

This new conception of number, as Russell himself later emphasized, had been developed by the German mathematician Frege before Russell had been aware of it. However, Russell utilized the new definition as a premise for developing far-reaching philosophical consequences. He derived from it a logical analysis of mathematics which contends that mathematics is nothing but logic, i.e. a special and very complicated concatenation of fundamental logical concepts. In the epoch-making work *Principia Mathematica*, published in co-operation with the mathematician Whitehead, Russell pursued his major thesis and transformed the logical calculus extensively. These logical investigations are carried through by means of a new formal notation which became an indispensable tool.

Even more important perhaps is Russell's theory of the logical paradoxes. He showed that traditional logic leads to contradictions compared to which the paradoxes of the ancient Greeks, for instance those of Zeno, must be considered simple. In order to eliminate these paradoxes Russell constructed his type theory, a theory of logical levels based on the thesis that in addition to true and false propositions there exists a third category, meaningless propositions.

It took some time before Russell's ideas became known in Germany; at first they were shared only by a small circle of mathematicians and logicians. More recently, Russell helped to spread them through more popular writings, and the wide distribution of his numerous books, most of which have been translated into German, shows how many adherents his logic has found in Germany.

Russell did not restrict himself to problems of mathematical logic but proceeded to epistemological questions some of which he treated in his important book *Our Knowledge of the External World*. His ontological parsimony which we encountered in his treatment of the concept of number as well as his realistic attitude led him to the ideas of positivism. His analysis of the concept of existence is similar to that of Mach whose influence can be felt quite clearly in Russell's postwar works. The basic constituents of our knowledge are not things; things are logical constructs that can be further analysed into their elements. The basic elements of knowledge are perceptions, the immediate data of our experience. These data, as Russell subsequently showed in his books *Analysis of Mind* and *Analysis of Matter*, constitute the 'neutral stuff' of all things. He goes beyond Mach by applying his mathematical logic very skilfully to this problem; he interprets physical things as classes of elements by analogy with his interpretation of numbers as classes of classes.

131

This kind of treatment is an essentially modern trait of Russell's philosophy which is perhaps more important than the basic positivistic thesis. More and more people are becoming convinced that epistemological problems can be solved only with the help of mathematical logic. The precision of his formulations is accompanied by profound insight that will be for ever denied to the adherents of traditional logic who cling to ordinary grammar. Russell's objection to the subject-predicate conception of propositions, his theory of relations, and of contextual definitions are fundamental for an analysis of the problem of existence. It is to be expected that the next decades will find solutions to this age-old philosophical problem which compare with the solutions of the classical philosophical systems as modern quantum theory compares with the atomism of antiquity. The student of philosophy will have to widen his philosophical training considerably in order to be able to grasp the meaning and significance of the questions asked.

Russell is now fifty-five years old; his enormous productivity of the last decade indicates that he is constantly generating new ideas. These last years have disclosed him not only as a great logician and epistemologist, but also as a social philosopher. Russell is one of those rare geniuses who are not satisfied by working in a limited scientific domain, but who delve with the same philosophical earnestness into questions of life and personal action. Russell is the descendent of an old aristocratic family whose history can be traced back to the time of Henry VIII and which has produced many a famous leader of the Whig Party and many a statesman, such as Russell's grandfather, the Earl of Kingston-Russell. Despite his lineage Russell did not hesitate to break with tradition and, during World War I, to protest vigorously against war itself. He staunchly proclaimed pacifism, was thrown into prison as a conscientious objector, and deprived of his teaching position at Trinity College, Cambridge. Undeterred by such adversity, he published his social philosophy in several books such as *Principles of Social Reconstruction* and *Prospects of Industrial Civilization,* soon to appear in German translations. His views are close to British Syndicalism. He has also travelled to Russia and China and has described his experiences in several books.

These writings show Russell as an accomplished master of language; his pithy and concise style, his dry humour, his simple sentences are as delightful aesthetically as they are convincing. One need only look into his book on China where he gives an account of Chinese history in less than 30 pages; one feels as if one had actually seen something of China after reading this description. Or one may read in his *Introduction to Mathematical Philosophy* (written during the First World War), chapter 16, on the definite article 'the' where he writes: 'I would give the doctrine of this word if I were "dead from the waist down" and not merely in prison.' In this work he analyses the existence of pseudo-objects and says: 'A robust sense of reality is very necessary in framing a correct analysis of propositions about unicorns, golden mountains, round squares and other such pseudo-objects.' He is remarkable among philosophers for his literary flair, and one is tempted to compare him with his great compatriot Hume whom he resembles in the style of his writing and in his sober and realistic approach to problems. Indeed, Russell just like Hume has awakened many from their 'dogmatic slumbers'.

However surprising Russell's combination of mathematical logic and pacifist-anticapitalist ethics may appear, it becomes understandable if one looks for its psychological roots. He who is ready to overthrow the oldest traditions in logic and to uncover the illusory nature of ancient ideals will also look with more freedom at the ideals of bourgeois ethics and not be afraid to give up values which those who are tradition-bound are unable to renounce. Russell has demonstrated with indomitable courage the strength of his character and the seriousness of his convictions. An uncompromising man, a fighter for freedom, Russell belongs with the philosophers of action as well as with philosophers of theory. Perhaps the way Russell lives his philosophy is his greatest contribution to our time so deeply torn between thoughts and deeds.

13

MARIA REICHENBACH

Rudolf Carnap : The Cross Currents[1]

Our century has witnessed a successful revolt against the traditional metaphysical approach to philosophy. The success of this revolt was to a great extent contingent upon the fact that science had made tremendous advances. A new philosophical approach was needed which would encompass the new scientific discoveries and the new scientific thinking. The traditional philosophical systems served mainly the aim of trying to justify preconceived views of the world while neglecting at the same time to take new scientific developments into account. Joergensen expressed the characteristics of the new philosophical movement as follows: '. . . it is an expression of a need for clarification of the foundations and meaning of knowledge . . .; it attempts to make philosophy scientifically tenable through critical analysis of details rather than to make it universal by vague generalizations and dogmatic construction of systems.'[2]

As frequently happens in history whenever the need for the solutions of new problems arises, small groups of men become the nucleus of a new movement. The new philosophical movement may most comprehensively be called by the name of Analytic Philosophy. The centres of the activity of the new analytic movement were located in Great Britain (Cambridge), Austria (Vienna), and Germany (Berlin). Three men instrumental in their respective centres in fostering the movement and in influencing the present-day generation of philosophers, were Bertrand Russell, Rudolf Carnap, and the late Hans Reichenbach. They were scientists as well as philosophers, and this combination enabled them to make many contributions to the philosophy of science, in particular, to the foundations of mathematics and physics.

Although all three of them have played decisive roles in creating the new Analytic Philosophy, Bertrand Russell is considered the father of the movement and his creative importance is acknowledged by Reichenbach as well as Carnap. In 1928 Reichenbach appraised Bertrand Russell's work and personality in an article entitled 'Great Thinkers of our Time: Bertrand Russell' (see p. 129). Carnap traces

[1] Professor Carnap, who had agreed to write an essay in appreciation of Bertrand Russell, became seriously ill. Despite his illness he insisted on discussing his contribution with Maria Reichenbach, so that she could express his feelings in her own words, but words faithful to his purpose.

[2] Joergen Joergensen, *The Development of Logical Empiricism, International Encyclopedia of Unified Science*, Vol. II, No. 9, 1951.

the influence of Bertrand Russell on his own development in the volume, *The Philosophy of Rudolf Carnap*.[1] This book starts with Carnap's intellectual autobiography entitled 'The Development of my Thinking' in which he discusses philosophers who influenced him and helped him to crystallize his conception of philosophy. No one had a greater impact upon him than Bertrand Russell. The sources for the following passages dealing with Carnap's relationship to Russell are Carnap's autobiography, Carnap's unpublished notes and his statements made during conversations with the author. They attest to Russell's influence on Carnap and at the same time pay homage to the great philosopher Bertrand Russell.

Although Carnap did not meet Russell until 1934, he had been acquainted with Russell's works for a long time. Carnap relates:

'Around 1919 I studied the great work *Principia Mathematica* by Whitehead and Russell. . . . I was strongly impressed by the development of the theory of relations in this work. . . . I began to apply symbolic notation, now more frequently in the *Principia* form . . ., in my own thinking about philosophical problems or in the formulation of axiom systems. When I considered a concept or a proposition occurring in a scientific or philosophical discussion, I thought that I understood it clearly only if I felt that I could express it, if I wanted to, in symbolic language. I performed the actual symbolization, of course, only in special cases where it seemed necessary or useful.

'. . . in my philosophical thinking in general I learned most from Bertrand Russell. In the winter of 1921 I read his book *Our Knowledge of the External World, as a Field for Scientific Method in Philosophy*. Some passages made an especially vivid impression on me because they formulated clearly and explicitly a view of the aim and method of philosophy which I had implicitly held for some time.'[2]

'My philosophical insights are usually gained not in sudden moments of inspiration but rather through a slow process of growth and development. It is only on rare occasions that I can point to specific moments when a book or a talk made a strong, lasting impression on me. This happened one day in the winter of 1921 while I was in bed with influenza reading Russell's book which had just arrived.'[3]

'In the Preface he speaks about "the logical-analytic method of philosophy". . . . And on the very last pages of the book he gives a summarizing characterization of this philosophical method in the following words:

[1] This book will be cited hereafter as Ph.C. Quotations from this book are by permission of the Library of Living Philosophers, from the volume entitled *The Philosophy of Rudolf Carnap*, Paul A. Schilpp, ed., 1963.
[2] Ph.C., p.13.   [3] Unpublished notes.

"The study of logic becomes the central study in philosophy: it gives the method of research in philosophy, just as mathematics gives the method in physics. . . .

"All this supposed knowledge in the traditional systems must be swept away, and a new beginning must be made. . . . To the large and still growing body of men engaged in the pursuit of science, . . . the new method, successful already in such time-honoured problems as number, infinity, continuity, space and time, should make an appeal which the older methods have wholly failed to make. . . . The one and only condition, I believe, which is necessary in order to secure for philosophy in the near future an achievement surpassing all that has hitherto been accomplished by philosophers, is the creation of a school of men with scientific training and philosophical interests, unhampered by the traditions of the past, and not misled by the literary methods of those who copy the ancients in all except their merits." [1]

This quotation from Russell contains the fundamental tenets of Analytic Philosophy and constitutes the common basis for the many philosophers who accepted Russell's guidance. To be 'unhampered by the traditions of the past' became the guiding spirit of the scientifically oriented philosophers, and this attitude generated a desire for co-operation which gave the new movement strength and vitality. One must not think of the new philsophical movement as a school with rigid creeds and dogmas. Although united in their general aims and outlook, individual adherents of Analytic Philosophy often did and do profess different positions concerning specific problems. Lively discussions among the analytic philosophers have characterized the movement.

Carnap expresses the impact of Russell's passages quoted above in the following words:

'I felt as if this appeal had been directed to me personally. To work in this spirit would be my task from now on! And indeed henceforth the application of the new logical instrument for the purposes of analysing scientific concepts and of clarifying philosophical problems has been the essential aim of my philosophical activity.'[2]

Carnap continues:

I now began an intensive study of Russell's books on the theory of knowledge and the methodology of science. I owe very much to his work, not only with respect to philosophical method, but also with

[1] Ph.C., p. 13. [2] *Ibid.*

regard to the solutions of specific problems.'[1] 'For example, his construction of material things from experienced "perspectives" provided an important stimulus for the task which I had set myself in *Der logische Aufbau der Welt*.'[2]

'I also continued to occupy myself with symbolic logic. Since the *Principia Mathematica* was not easily accessible I began to work on a textbook of symbolic logic. There was no copy of the *Principia* in the University Library at Freiburg. The price of a new copy was out of reach because of the inflation in Germany. Since my efforts to find a secondhand copy in England were unsuccessful, I asked Russell whether he could help me to find one. Instead, he sent me a long list containing the most important definitions of *Principia*, handwritten by himself, on 35 pages, which I still cherish as a priceless possession. In 1924 I wrote the first version of the later book *Abriss der Logistik* (1929). It was based on the *Principia*.

'. . . Inspired by Russell's description of the aim and the method of future philosophy, I made numerous attempts at analysing concepts of ordinary language relating to things in our environment and their observable properties and relations, and at constructing definitions of these concepts with the help of symbolic logic. . . . For the description of the structure of any complex, the new logic of relations as in *Principia Mathematica* seemed to me just the required tool.'[3]

To meet Bertrand Russell in person is an extraordinary experience. Let us see how Carnap felt when he met Russell in 1934 in England:

'I welcomed the opportunity to become personally acquainted with British philosophers. Above all I enjoyed meeting Bertrand Russell for the first time. I visited him in his residence some distance south of London. We talked on various problems of philosophy and also on the world situation. Among other topics he asked me whether anybody had made use of his logic and arithmetic of relations. I told him that his concept of relation number (relational structure) played an important role in our philosophy. I mentioned also my axiom system of space-time topology using only relational logic and no real numbers. He expressed the conviction that it should be possible to go much further in representing the essential content of Einstein's general theory of relativity in the same framework without using differential equations or co-ordinate systems. I was deeply impressed by his personality, the wide horizon of his ideas, from technicalities of logic to the destiny of mankind, his undogmatic attitude in both

[1] Ph.C., p. 13.   [2] Unpublished notes.   [3] Ph.C., p. 16.

theoretical and practical questions, and the high perspective from which he looked at the world and at the actions of men.'[1]

The destiny of mankind was indeed at stake. About this time history had taken a sharp turn. Most European countries became occupied by Hitler's armies, and the Nazi oppression created a most unfavourable climate for the free exchange of ideas. Besides, many of the philosophers active within the analytic movement were socialists and in danger of being politically persecuted. Not all of them could escape death. Many emigrated to the United States where the atmosphere was more conducive to unhampered philosophic discussions. In America the philosophical refugees continued their research within the framework of Analytic Philosophy. As time went by, these men became the leaders of the most influential movement in contemporary American philosophy.

Carnap who lived in Prague from 1931 to 1935 offers us a picture of the situation that prevailed in Europe:

'With the beginning of the Hitler régime in Germany in 1933, the political atmosphere, even in Austria and Czechoslovakia, became more and more intolerable. The great majority of the people in Czechoslovakia, like Benes's government, had a clearly democratic point of view. But the Nazi ideology spread more and more among the German-speaking population of the Sudeten region and therewith among the students of our university and even among some of the professors. Furthermore, there was the danger of an intervention by Hitler. Therefore, I initiated efforts to come to America, at least for a time. In December of 1935 I left Prague and came to the United States.'[2]

In 1936 Carnap accepted a permanent position at the University of Chicago where he later met Russell again. Carnap writes:

'In the winter of 1939 Russell was at the University of Chicago and gave a seminar on questions of meaning and truth, which became the basis of his book *Inquiry into Meaning and Truth.* . . . I attended this seminar. Russell had the felicitous ability to create an atmosphere in which every participant did his best to contribute to the common task.'[3]

Co-operation in a common task, intellectual intercourse, and the dissemination of fruitful ideas fare best during times of peace. Hatred

[1] Ph.C., p. 33.   [2] *Ibid.*, p. 34.   [3] *Ibid.*, p. 35.

breeds irrationality and destroys understanding. Marching armies create anxieties and generate aggressions thus preventing a meeting of minds. At such times anti-intellectualism grows and rational thinking is suspended.

The preservation of peace becomes an important issue for all men who have dedicated their lives to constructive thinking and thoughtful actions. Carnap and Russell are deeply concerned about the question of peace. Both of them are convinced that peace can be preserved only if rational men will get together and seek constructive answers to the many pressing problems of our time. Both of them are also convinced that war would bring annihilation to mankind.

Bertrand Russell is very actively engaged in the fight for preserving the peace, for disarmament, and for avoiding nuclear disaster. May his spirit prevail and may he reach his goal so that rational thinking, the highest form of thinking achieved by human beings, can continue for the best of mankind.

14

WERNER BLOCH

Russell's concept of 'Philosophy'

Whoever occupies himself with philosophy otherwise than in his own quiet room and strictly for himself, whoever talks and writes about it, whoever discusses philosophical questions with acquaintances or pupils, will sooner or later find himself facing the question of what philosophy really is, what it is that he's doing. And this question is not at all easy to answer. If you ask any reasonably well-educated man what astronomy, physics, chemistry or biology is, he will have no very great difficulty in giving you a reasonable reply. Perhaps he would even be able to tell you fairly readily what psychology or sociology is. At least, he will always be able to indicate the sphere to which any particular science refers: astronomy has to do with the stars; physics has to do with what happens to and in bodies and in space; chemistry deals with changes in the body itself, and so on. His answers may not always be precisely accurate, particularly as there are sciences—physical chemistry for example— which relate to more than one sphere. Even so, this raises no particular difficulty. Every educated person knows that Ohm's law has to do with physics, the disintegration of water by an electric current with physical chemistry, the investigation of sun spots with astronomy. All these sciences have a long history, and in this or that case it is even possible to mention the name of the man with whom it all started. Now philosophy has the longest history of all to look back on. It represents nothing less than the original basis from which all other sciences took their rise. In his *History of Western Philosophy* Russell tells us that philosophy began with Thales, and that originally no distinction was made between philosophy and science. Thus in those days a certain form of reflective thought could be called philosophical thought. Philosophy could therefore be better characterized by its attitude to its subjects rather than by the particular sphere of the subjects themselves. Now in the course of time the character of philosophy changed, so that nowadays we are entitled to ask what we mean historically by philosophy, and what we now reckon as belonging to the sphere of philosophy.

So let us put this question to Bertrand Russell, who is beyond all question a philosopher, and one who is thought by many people who are interested in philosophy (including the author of this article) to be the greatest amongst living philosophers. And in putting the question to him we shall do our best to answer it on the basis of his works, and if possible in his own words.

As far as I know, Russell has never made this question the subject of any of his books, but at the same time he has often been compelled to discuss it more or less deliberately in his books. Now Russell, unlike many other philosophers, is prepared to admit that during the course of many years devoted to scholarly and scientific study, his opinions and his convictions have changed. Now the difficulty in discovering what Russell means by philosophy is not caused so much by the fact that in the course of time his view has gradually changed, but by the fact that whilst his view on philosophy has remained fundamentally the same he has given so many different answers. Some of his critics feel that they have discovered contradictions in these various attitudes. However, I would rather say that the various statements which seem to contradict each other in their expression actually all go back to a common fundamental opinion. Let me compare philosophy with white light, which, when it is broken up by a prism, disintegrates into the colours of the rainbow. According to the connection in which Russell is talking about philosophy so he is describing one or other of the various colours. At the same time it is only the spectrum as a whole which allows us to recognize all the many possibilities in their relation to each other. The white light is the starting point and the object of the consideration, but between the two lies the analysis: the examination of the various tasks of philosophy. In connection with chromatology, or the science of colours, there is a well-known error made by Goethe with regard to Newton's theory. Goethe thought that the breaking up of light into the colours of the spectrum was an impermissible trick, but since then we have realized what we owe to Newton's analytical process. I hope to be able to show that the colourful variety of Russell's individual utterances focus ultimately in the brilliant clarity of white light.

1. RUSSELL'S DEFINITION OF PHILOSOPHY
IN THE BROADER SENSE

If anyone sets out to write a history of philosophy one may reasonably assume that he has given some thought beforehand to the question of what it is whose history he proposes to write, and the obvious thing might appear to look to Russell's *History of Western Philosophy* for a definition of what he means by philosophy; and, in fact, in the very first pages of his book we find a very happy formulation for everything that he proposes to include in his inquiries: 'Philosophy is a word which has been used in many ways, some wider, some narrower. I propose to use it in a very wide sense, which I will now try to explain.'

'Philosophy, as I shall understand the word, is something inter-mediate between theology and science. Like theology it consists of speculations on matters as to which definite knowledge has, so far, been unascertainable; but like science it appeals to human reason rather than to authority, whether that of tradition or revelation. All definite knowledge—so I should contend—belongs to science; all dogma as to what surpasses definite knowledge belongs to theology. But between theology and science there is a no-man's-land exposed to attack from both sides. This no-man's-land is philosophy.'[1]

For my own part I am not quite sure that the word theology adequately describes the sphere Russell proposes to mark off from philosophy. He probably means those affirmations about the world as a whole which derive from poetic fantasy or from a supposedly supernatural standpoint, and which have consolidated into firm teachings which claim to be truth and wisdom beyond the criticism of reason. If in this way the no-man's-land is bordered on the one hand by science and on the other by dogmatism then philosophy is not fundamentally defined either by a sphere or a method, but at least it includes everything that is traditionally described as philo-sophy. When Russell now goes on to say: 'Philosophy begins with Thales. . . . Philosophy and science—which were not originally separate—were therefore born together at the beginning of the sixth century',[2] he excludes the pre-philosophical mythical conceptions of the world from the sphere of philosophy. Right from the beginning philosophy is characterized by the scientific attitude. And this definition of philosophy is then excellently supplemented by another one: 'The definition of "philosophy" will vary according to the philosophy we adopt. All that we can say to begin with is that there are certain problems, which certain people find interesting, and which do not, at least at present, belong to any of the special sciences. These problems are all such as to raise doubts concerning what commonly passes for knowledge; and if the doubts are answered, it can only be by means of a special study, to which we give the name "philo-sophy".'[3] It is from this conception of philosophy that Russell derives a form of presentation for his history of Western philosophy that makes it so particularly attractive to me. Russell does not content himself with presenting the teachings of the philosophers;

[1] *History of Western Philosophy*, p. 10.   [2] *Ibid.*, p. 21.
[3] *An Outline of Philosophy*, p. 1.

he joins issue with them as though he were their contemporary; that is to say, not with the superiority of a man taking advantage of the fact that he is living centuries after them, but by putting forward arguments that they should not have overlooked had they been as critical towards themselves as they were anxious to prove that they were right.

Thus philosophy occupies a strange intermediate position. It is not a science and yet it operates with the scientific method. In consequence you can dispute with philosophers, which you can't with theologians, and don't need to with men of science. In extreme cases the former are prepared to profess the *credo quia absurdum*; the second are prepared to acknowledge as science only what is and can be acknowledged by all the experts. Bolzano defined science as that which can be set out in a text-book. Three different text-books on physics or astronomy may differ in style and in manner of presentation, but fundamentally the contents of the one will agree with the contents of the other two. All text-books on physics will contain the same law on the bending and refraction of light, and all text-books on astronomy will contain the same observations concerning the rings of Saturn and the structure of the Milky Way system. If, on the other hand, you take up two contemporary books dealing with the same philosophical theme, you will find little agreement and much dispute.

If Russell is right when he says that philosophy is a no-man's-land between theology and science, that is to say, between affirmations concerning God and the world and the right way of life on the one hand, and objective science on the other, then in consequence the philosopher stands between the saint and the scientist, between the priest and the scholar. But perhaps we shall be able to secure a deeper insight into the nature of philosophy if we now ask a different question, namely:

2. HOW DOES ONE BECOME A PHILOSOPHER AND WHAT IS A PHILOSOPHER

The relationship between philosophy and the philosopher is something like that between the hen and the egg. Which came first? Similarly one can ask: is a philosopher a man who teaches philosophy, or is philosophy what a philosopher teaches? I asked myself this question when I read the following observations on Spinoza and Leibniz in Russell's *History of Western Philosophy*: 'Spinoza (1643–77) is the noblest and most lovable of the great philosophers. Intellectually some others have surpassed him, but ethically he is supreme.'[1] And on Leibniz: 'Leibniz (1646–1716) was one of the supreme intellects of all time, but as a human being he was not admirable . . . he was wholly destitute of those higher philosophic virtues that are so notable in Spinoza.'[2] What Russell is obviously trying to say here is that the more intelligent scholar was the inferior philosopher!

If you hold these two viewpoints together in mind—on the one hand that the sphere of philosophy is only very vaguely determined, and on the other that the estimate of a man as a philosopher depends on qualities which are independent of the state of his knowledge— then it is difficult to imagine that anyone would decide early on to become a philosopher in the way that people do decide early on to become, say, a carpenter, a civil servant or a lawyer. It would appear therefore that being a philosopher is not a trade or profession. If you ask a university professor what he is, he will not hesitate to tell you that he is a physicist, an archaeologist, an Arabist, a professor of jurisprudence, of medicine, or whatever he is. But who is likely to say of himself: 'I am a philosopher'? A professor of, or lecturer in, chemistry will be referred to by everyone without more ado as an analytical chemist, quite irrespective of whether he has already done anything worth while and generally recognized in his field or not. On the other hand, the description 'philosopher' is not awarded like a diploma as the result of an examination. It can also not be awarded *honoris causa* as other titles can. Nevertheless it very frequently happens that men are called philosophers although their real sphere of activities is quite different. For example, the 'Library of Living Philosophers' edited by Professor Schilpp contains a volume entitled *The Philosophy of Bertrand Russell*. Right! But then there is another and no less important volume which is devoted to the work of Albert Einstein, though if you ask any knowledgeable man who Einstein was, he will answer without hesitation that he was a great physicist.

Very well, if one can hardly decide to become a philosopher, and if one does nevertheless become one it is almost involuntary, so how does one get into the business at all? There are one or two cases in the history of philosophy which record that this or that person was persuaded by some particular mental or spiritual experience to devote himself to philosophy. This was more or less true, for example, of Descartes and Pascal. On the other hand, it is hardly likely that they would have had these experiences at all if they had not already possessed the general mental qualities that we find in other philosophers. Very few outstanding philosophers have set

[1] *History of Western Philosophy*, p. 592. [2] *Ibid.*, p. 604.

down the history of their intellectual development in such detail as Augustin and Descartes have; and the most detailed description I know of the way a man became a philosopher we owe to Bertrand Russell himself. The story strikes me as fairly typical of almost all European philosophers. It is to be found in two of Russell's writings: *My Mental Development*[1] and *My Philosophical Development*. In an appendix to this latter book Alan Wood conducts an inquiry into the development of Russell's philosophy, and finds that it is marked throughout by 'a consistency of purpose and direction, and a consistency of method'.[2] These words reinforced me in my intention of seeking passages in Russell's works to show what ideas he always held on the mission of philosophy and of philosophers, and of defining these ideas as clearly as possible. Purpose, direction and method are, according to Alan Wood, the three constants in the wide sphere of Russell's thought which draw his ideas together into a philosophic unity; and whoever reads Russell's writings to any extent will be compelled to agree with Alan Wood, though he may well have reservations about the word 'purpose'. 'Utility does not belong to philosophy. If the study of philosophy has any value at all for others than students of philosophy, it must be only indirectly, through its effects upon the lives of those who study it.'[3] Thus Russell. And Alan Wood himself leaves no doubt about what he regards as Russell's purpose: '"I wanted certainty", Russell wrote in retrospect, "in the kind of way in which people want religious faith." ('Reflections on my Eightieth Birthday' in *Portraits from Memory*.) I believe the underlying purpose behind all Russell's work was an almost religious passion for some truth that was more than human, independent of the minds of men, and even of the existence of man. It is well to be brought face to face, at the start, with one of the problems of conflicting quotations which faces any student of Russell. For we can also quote him as calling on us, in the context of a popular essay, "to recognize that the non-human world is unworthy of worship".'[4]

'He sought impersonal objective truth successively in religion, mathematics and science. *Not* in philosophy (for one thing, he never made up his mind exactly what he meant by philosophy). In his heart he usually thought of philosophy as an inferior pursuit compared with mathematics and science.' 'The key to understanding

[1] Paul Arthur Schilpp, *The Philosophy of Bertrand Russell*, pp. 3–20. Tudor Publishing Co., 1944. 3. Edit. 1951.
[2] Bertrand Russell, *My Philosophical Development*, p. 260.
[3] Bertrand Russell, *The Problems of Philosophy*, p. 153.
[4] *My Philosophical Development*, p. 260.

Russell's philosophy is that it was essentially a by-product.' 'In a sense, therefore, it could be said that Russell's career was a threefold failure: (a) he not only had to abandon religion, but objective ethical knowledge as well; (b) he was not fully satisfied with the system of *Principia Mathematica*, and Wittgenstein convinced him—or almost convinced him—that in any case mathematical knowledge was only tautological ("Reflections on my Eightieth Birthday" in *Portraits from Memory*); (c) his defence of scientific knowledge in "Human Knowledge" was not in accordance with the kind of standards he had earlier hoped to live up to (*Introduction to Mathematical Philosophy*, page 71).'[1]

In his autobiographical passages Russell reproduces some notes he made as an eighteen-year-old, and they give us some insight into his motives. Almost like Descartes girding himself in his belief before venturing on the great undertaking of doubt, Russell describes the basis from which he begins and the direction in which he is going: 'I may say to begin with that I do believe in God, and that I shall call myself a theist if I have to give my creed a name. Now finding reasons for believing in God I shall only take account of scientific arguments. This is a vow I have made, which costs me much to keep and to reject all sentiment.'[2] 'My rule of life which I guide my conduct by, and a departure from which I consider a sin, is to act in the manner which I believe to be most likely to produce the greatest happiness considering both the intensity of the happiness and the number of people made happy.'[3] 'My original interest in philosophy had two sources. On the one hand I was anxious to discover whether philosophy would provide any defence for anything that could be called religious belief, however vague; on the other hand, I wished to persuade myself that something could be known in pure mathematics if not elsewhere.'[4] 'In all things I have made a vow to follow reason, not the instincts inherited partly from my ancestors and gained gradually by selection and partly due to my education.'[5] But even Russell's preoccupation with mathematics—as scientific as it may have been in method—was conducted less in order to attain mathematical insight than in order to find at least somewhere that certainty for which he so much longed, and from which he might hope to find security in other spheres too. 'Most of my time was taken up by mathematics, and mathematics largely dominated my attempts at philosophical thinking, but the emotional drive which caused my thinking was mainly doubt as to the fundamental dogmas of religion.'[6] And what did he actually attain with all his efforts?

[1] *My Philosophical Development*, pp. 262–4. [2] *Ibid.*, pp. 28–9.
[3] *Ibid.*, p. 32. [4] *Ibid.*, p. 11. [5] *Ibid.*, p. 33. [6] *Ibid.*, p. 28.

'I used never for a moment to doubt that truth was a good thing to get hold of. But now I have the very greatest doubt and uncertainty. ... The search for truth has shattered most of my old beliefs and has made me commit what are probably sins where otherwise I should have kept clear of them. I do not think it has in any way made me happier.'[1] But in his book *The Conquest of Happiness* he writes in retrospect: 'In adolescence I hated life and was continually on the verge of suicide, from which, however, I was restrained by the desire to know more mathematics. Now, on the contrary, I enjoy life. ... This is due partly ... to having successfully dismissed certain objects of desire—such as the acquisition of indubitable knowledge about something or other—as essentially unattainable.'[2] In fact ultimately he progressed beyond this state of happiness by renunciation so that he was able to write: 'In more purely intellectual ways, on the contrary, I have found as much satisfaction in philosophy as one could reasonably have expected. Many matters which, when I was young, baffled me by the vagueness of all that had been said about them, are now amenable to an exact technique, which makes possible the kind of progress that is customary in science.'[3]

I feel that most of what is said about or by Russell here could be said with some caution about many other philosophers. Almost all of them have striven for something noble that filled them with enthusiasm. Some of them have called it 'the good, the beautiful and the true'. For most of them religion, mathematics and science played an important role in their lives. Not one of them, when we review the course of philosophy, has ever reached his objective, but only very few of them have been granted to see the limits of the attainable as clearly as Russell has. For most philosophers their philosophy is wish fulfilment irrespective of ultimate honesty. Generally speaking they started off with certain accepted opinions which were dear to them, opinions which were generally held in the educated circles in which they moved. But they wanted to do more than believe them; they wanted to be sure that they were true. They started off with the hope that they would find it possible to prove what others merely believed; and most of them were not above a little subterfuge when they discovered that their proofs were not really taking them where they wanted to go. Descartes is an excellent example of this kind of philosophy. He urgently wanted certainty, absolute certainty that his views were correct. He started off on the difficult but hopeful path of doubting everything it was possible to doubt, and believing

1 *My Philosophical Development*, pp. 33–4.
2 Bertrand Russell, *The Conquest of Happiness*, p. 13.
3 *The Philosophy of Bertrand Russell*, p. 20.

only what was indubitable. But when he sets out to exclude the possibility of an evil spirit intent on constantly deceiving him he is content to accept a proof of the existence of God which can hardly strike us as appearing so convincing to him as he pretends.

Amazement at the things that are and the way they are, the desire to give one's own prejudices and standards a basis in reason, or on the other hand doubt of one's own opinions, and doubt in particular of the world around, are probably the strongest of the impulses which persuade a man to engage in such thoughts as are later described as philosophy.

But if it were intellectual attainments alone which stamp the man who spends his life in no-man's-land as a philosopher, what are we to say when Russell tells us that he considers Spinoza the greatest philosopher whilst granting Leibnitz intellectual superiority?

Russell even goes so far in one place as to classify philosophers not according to the nature of their teachings, but according to the motives which led them to come to their conclusions: 'Thus we shall have philosophies of feeling, inspired by the love of happiness; theoretical philosophies, inspired by the love of knowledge; and practical philosophies, inspired by the love of action.'[1]

Obviously therefore there are a number of related but nevertheless different definitions of the word philosophy, and thus different viewpoints for judging whether a man can be called a philosopher or not.

The Germans have the expression *Weltanschauung*. As there is no corresponding expression in English it is usually translated 'philosophy', or left as it is as an untranslatable foreign term. In 1913 I had reason to deal with this German expression in some detail in a study I was writing on pragmatism because William James had refused to allow pragmatism to be described as a *Weltanschauung*, specifically using this German expression. He wanted pragmatism to be regarded as a philosophy. Thus he was aware that the German expressions *Philosophie* and *Weltanschauung* are different in meaning, although they are often both translated into English as 'philosophy'. What is, in fact, the difference? Simply that philosophy is fundamentally a teaching which, once it is established, exists apart from its creator. A book can contain a philosophy and communicate its knowledge. A *Weltanschauung* on the other hand is a psychological complex comparable to character. At the time I defined it as follows: '*Weltanschauung* is the adequately philosophically buttressed, self consistent intellectual basis of practical behaviour.'[2] It differs from character, which is of course also a permanent basis of

---

[1] *History of Western Philosophy*, p. 819.   [2] Werner Bloch, *Der Pragmatismus von James and Schiller*, p. 14. (J. A. Barth, Leipzig 1913).

human behaviour, in that it originates from mental reflection, in that a man can give account from it for his actions, since it embodies his standards of value. In discussing the *Weltanschauung* of Spinoza or Leibniz one will often use words that are also used in any presentation of their philosophical teachings, but it is not a question of their philosophy. There are some people of whom it can be said that their particular *Weltanschauung* is derived from their philosophy. This was the case with Spinoza. There are other people—and unfortunately they are by no means rare—whose *Weltanschauung* is but little influenced by their philosophy. This was the case with Leibniz. And this is probably the reason why when comparing the two Russell regards Spinoza as a better philosopher than Leibniz, whilst at the same time regarding the latter as the keener thinker.

For himself, and probably for all other present-day philosophers, Russell admits that philosophy has very little influence on *Weltanschauung*: 'I am accused of inconsistency, perhaps justly, because, although I hold ultimate ethical valuations to be subjective, I nevertheless allow myself emphatic opinions on ethical questions. If there is an inconsistency, it is one I cannot get rid of without insincerity; moreover, an inconsistent system may well contain less falsehood than a consistent one.'[1] This passage would hardly be understandable with a thinker like Russell who persistently strives in all his works for consistency, were it not for the difference, so readily expressible in German, between philosophy and *Weltanschauung*. Russell explains this apparent contradiction by saying that ethical valuations are subjective. But this probably means that affirmations such as 'Honesty is good, lies are bad', or 'the world is beautiful' cannot be included amongst those affirmations which can be usefully discussed with people who do not accept them. However, if a man is prepared to accept the first affirmation then he will be unable to deny logically that dishonesty, theft, deceit, defalcation and quite a number of other similar things are also bad. It is possible to discuss the necessary relationship even with someone who does not regard dishonesty as bad. That is what I meant when I described *Weltanschauung* as a self consistent intellectual basis. However, the usual methods of proof are not sufficient to persuade anyone that the first affirmation is true should he dispute it. It is here we find the bridge between *Weltanschauung* and character as an ultimate, no further explainable, element of a human being.

There are other ultimate bases which a man is ready to accept without requiring that they should be proved to him; for example, the basis of logic. If he refuses to recognize and accept this basis he

[1] *The Philosophy of Bertrand Russell*, p. 720.

runs the risk of ending in a lunatic asylum. There are quite intelligent people who are prepared to say that the difference between a lunatic and someone who is normal is merely that one lives inside a lunatic asylum and the other outside; and that this distinction is entirely due to exigencies of space: because there's no room for the majority on the inside, it determines that the minority shall live inside whilst itself shall live outside.

With regard to this second kind of ultimate basis, which we will discuss later, the point is that a man is prepared to accept it, but not necessarily to acknowledge or confess it. The German scholar Karl Jaspers has expressed ideas which make this distinction very clear: 'The radical difference in the nature of truth can be seen very clearly in the difference between the truth which I accept with my understanding, but which to acknowledge would be pointless, and the truth which exists only if I live my life in accordance with it, and which disappears in the absence of such acknowledgement. To understand the meaning of acknowledgement must illuminate an essential difference in the nature of truth. When under pressure Galileo denied the accuracy of his astronomical knowledge he did not call that accuracy into question, just as he could not have made it any the more accurate by an acknowledgement. Socrates and Bruno died for their philosophical truth because they were identical with it; their deaths brought their truth to completion. In the arguments of a philosophy which regarded itself as a science, the silent assumption was made that truth must be unique and generally valid and conclusively demonstrable. And this unique truth was assumed to be so essential that a man can live and die for it. But once the multidimensional character of the nature of truth has become clear, thus securing an insight into the nature of philosophy, which with the aids of science is more than science, it also becomes clear that what is conclusively demonstrable is not the kind of truth for which it is worth dying.'[1]

For Galileo what was at stake was not his philosophy but his picture of the world, but with Socrates and Bruno it was a question of their *Weltanschauung*. Bertrand Russell has been in prison on more than one occasion for his *Weltanschauung*, but there would have been no sense in his doing so in order to prove that universals exist as Platonic ideas. And in any case, he himself abandoned this doctrine later on in life without in the least compromising himself. As far as I can see, Russell has never changed his *Weltanschauung*, whereas he has constantly tried to improve the content of his philosophy.

It is clear from a passage in which, significantly, Russell deals

[1] Karl Jaspers, *Von der Wahreit*, p. 651. (Piper, München 1947).

with the philosophy of Marx that he, Russell, is quite well aware of the double meaning of the word 'philosophy': 'What is conventionally called "philosophy" consists of two different elements. On the one hand, there are questions which are scientific or logical; these are amenable to methods as to which there is general agreement. On the other hand, there are questions of passionate interest to large numbers of people, as to which there is no solid evidence either way. Amongst the latter are practical questions as to which it is impossible to remain aloof. . . . A "philosophy", in a very usual sense of the word, is an organic whole of such extra-rational decisions.'[1] This last sentence of Russell's is in such close accordance with the explanation of the German expression *Weltanschauung* that I gave earlier on that obviously in both cases the same is meant. Thus there is then a connection between philosophy and *Weltanschauung* when a philosophic teaching contains an ethical theory as a scientific element, such as has been the case with almost all philosophers who have constructed philosophical systems; whether we hark back to Plato, Kant, Descartes or Hegel. It is different where those philosophers are concerned who can be termed sceptics or analysts. Their teachings in various spheres are less closely connected because they do not represent a system when taken together. One might say perhaps that the first group of philosophers build up a system of views which generally supplement and go beyond generally accepted opinions, whereas the analytical philosophers of the second group are more inclined to attack generally accepted prejudices and destroy them. Thus philosophy and *Weltanschauung* can be very closely connected, but it is not essential that they should be—with the systematic philosophers in the first group they usually will be closely connected, whereas with the analytical philosophers in the second group they will rarely be closely connected.

Hume and Russell are fundamentally quite close together in their philosophic convictions, but Hume was a Tory whilst Russell is a convinced Democrat. Writing of platonic Socrates, Russell says: 'His merits are obvious. He is indifferent to worldly success, so devoid of fear that he remains calm and urbane and humorous to the last moment, caring more for what he believes to be truth than for anything else whatever. He has, however, some very grave defects. He is dishonest and sophistical in argument. . . . There is something smug and unctuous about him which reminds one of a very bad type of cleric. . . . He was not scientific in his thinking, but was determined to prove the universe agreeable to ethical standards. This is treachery to truth, and the worst of philosophic sins. As a man we may believe

---

[1] *History of Western Philosophy*, p. 815.

him admitted to the communion of saints, but as a philosopher he needs a long residence in a scientific purgatory.'[1] Russell appreciates the man who chose death rather than deny his *Weltanschauung*, but—exactly the opposite of his behaviour where Spinoza is concerned—he does not call him a good philosopher. Writing of Rousseau he says: '. . . though a philosophe in the eighteenth-century sense, (he) was not what would now be called a "philosopher". . . . Whatever may be our opinion of his merits as a thinker, we must recognize his immense importance as a social force.'[2] And referring to Nietzsche, Russell says: 'though a professor, (he) was a literary rather than an academic philosopher.'[3]

It cannot be denied that Russell adopts various standards in judging the greatness and significance of philosophers; and as far as I can see this depends on whether at the moment Russell happens to be closer to the border line of science or of theology in his no-man's-land. When he condemns Socrates to a spell in purgatory he is obviously closer to the scientific border line. If he had judged Rousseau and Nietzsche from this same position then he would probably not have been prepared to regard either of them as a philosopher at all.

From the admissions of the young Russell and the confessions of the old one—not that Russell has ever entirely lost his youth even in his eighties—it is quite clear that he had originally hoped to become a systematic philosopher, and that he has, in fact, become an analytical one. It is this that allows him to make intellectual honesty on the one hand, and the consonance of doctrine and behaviour on the other, the two cardinal virtues of a philosopher in his basic judgement of them.

3. FROM PHILOSOPHY IN THE LARGER SENSE TO PHILOSOPHY IN THE MORE RESTRICTED SENSE

It strikes me as thoroughly justified when Russell takes philosophy in the larger sense as the basis for his historical review of Western philosophy, since it allows him to include men and ideas which have contributed little or nothing to philosophy in the narrower sense. Only on this account can one possibly explain that, for example, a whole chapter is devoted to Byron. And what Russell himself writes in the preface to this book can apply only to this philosophy in the broader sense: 'Philosophy from the earliest times has been not merely an affair of the schools, or of disputation between a handful

[1] *History of Western Philosophy*, p. 164.   [2] *Ibid.*, p. 711.
[3] *Ibid.*, p. 782.

of learned men. It has been an integral part of the life of the community, and it is as such that I have tried to consider it. If there is any merit in this book, it is from this point of view that it is derived.'[1] Men who can be described as philosophers in the more restricted sense of the term have often also developed theories concerning the State and Society, and it may be due to this that one speaks of their political philosophy. We know, for example, what an important role reflection on the State played with Plato and Aristotle; whilst Machiavelli has been included into the ranks of the philosophers purely on account of his ideas concerning government; and Locke's thoughts on government are hardly less important than his contribution to philosophy in the more restricted sense. On the other hand, Montesquieu receives only scant mention by Russell, whilst the name of Lenin is mentioned only in a parenthesis, although he certainly wrote one book that can be counted, as far as its intention is concerned, to the narrower sphere of philosophy. Referring to Coleridge and Carlyle, Russell writes that they 'were profoundly affected by Kant, Fichte and the German Romantics, but they were not philosophers in the technical sense'.[2] Referring to Marx, Russell declares that he does not propose to deal with his general economic and political ideas, and that 'it is only as a philosopher, and an influence on the philosophy of others, that I propose to deal with him'.[3] Referring to Kant, Russell says that his ethical system 'has considerable historical importance. This book contains the "categorical imperative", which, at least as a phrase, is familiar outside the circle of professional philosophers.'[4] But there is nothing in his book about the extraordinary influence that this concept has had in connection with the word 'duty' in Hohenzollern Prussia, with all the advantages and disadvantages connected with it, and this part of Kant's philosophical activities is treated very briefly by comparison with his teachings on the basis of the sciences.

When we ask ourselves about the more restricted sense of Russell's philosophy then obviously the theory of knowledge and the investigation into first principles represent its central point. It was philosophy which first created all other sciences, and then dismissed them from its sphere as soon as they were able to stand on the firm basis of facts. Mathematics and logic have also become independent sciences, but they have remained in a closer relationship to the theory of knowledge than the other sciences because they are analytical sciences and thus essential instruments within the framework of all other sciences dependent on reality. It is no accident that Russell's achieve-

---

1 *History of Western Philosophy*, p. 6.   2 *Ibid.*, p. 801.
3 *Ibid.*, p. 810.   4 *Ibid.*, p. 736.

ments in the sphere of mathematics and logic are no less than in the sphere of the theory of knowledge and in a certain sense his work presents mathematics as practically a branch of logic.

4. MATHEMATICS AND LOGIC

The role played by mathematics in philosophy is very ambiguous: 'Mathematics is, I believe, the chief source of the belief in eternal and exact truth, as well as in a super-sensible intelligible world.'[1] And: 'It might seem that the empirical philosopher is the slave of his material, but that the pure mathematician is a free creator of his world of ordered beauty.'[2]

Referring to Pythagoras, Russell says: 'Mathematics, in the sense of demonstrative deductive argument, begins with him, and in him is intimately connected with a peculiar form of mysticism. The influence of mathematics on philosophy, partly owing to him, has, ever since his time, been both profound and unfortunate.'[3] Mathematics has again and again deceived philosophers into the belief that all the questions man is capable of asking can be answered either by pure thought, or at least brought into a complete system based on a few completely perceptible principles. From Pythagoras to Plato, and from Euclid to Kant there has been an exaggeration of the insight mathematics is able to offer, and only the discovery of non-Euclidean geometry has made it clear that mathematics have nothing to teach us about nature, but merely provides us with the means for classifying our observations of nature, thus persuading us to believe that we 'understand' nature too. This clearly revealed the analytical character of mathematics, but at the same time it seemed to open up the way by which mathematics could once again be restored to that unconditional certainty which had been shattered when it became clear that its axioms could no longer be regarded as the undesirable basis of the real world. But just when the mathematicians of the nineteenth and twentieth centuries were about to place mathematics on a new and what seemed a completely secure basis, because the mathematician seemed to be 'the free creator of his world', the whole structure was shattered by Russell's discovery of the famous paradoxy of the theory of classes, a discovery named after him. The German mathematician Frege had hoped to make the theory of classes the ultimate basis of all mathematics, but whilst the book in which he presented this to the world was still in the process of printing its basis was shown to be untenable.

[1] *History of Western Philosophy*, p. 55. [2] *Ibid.*, p. 52.
[3] *Ibid.*, p. 48.

Philosophy—and in this connection it is very difficult to say where the dividing line between philosophy and mathematics lies—had intervened so radically in the development of mathematics that down to our own day there is still talk of a crisis of mathematical fundamentals. The revelation of a paradox is an achievement of logic. There was thus a clash between mathematics and logic, but what logic destroyed it had to try to put together again. Thus this joint root field of the two analytical sciences certainly belongs to the sphere of philosophical research in the narrower sense. But logic has also been put into movement from philosophy through mathematics. Right up to the days of Kant the logic of Aristotle commanded the field. Like mathematics it also seemed to be an independent science which had so far released itself from the original basis of all sciences, philosophy, that it no longer needed any assistance from that direction. But then the mathematicians intervened and gave logic a form which called the philosophers on the scene again, who saw through the new form and opened up the way to an amalgamation of the two sciences which had come so close together. In his *Introduction to Mathematical Philosophy* Russell deals very clearly with the connection between mathematics and logic: 'Mathematics and logic, historically speaking, have been entirely distinct studies. Mathematics has been connected with science, logic with Greek. But both have developed in modern times: logic has become more mathematical, and mathematics has become more logical. The consequence is that it has now become wholly impossible to draw a line between the two; in fact, the two are one. They differ as boy and man: logic is the youth of mathematics and mathematics is the manhood of logic. This view is resented by logicians who, having spent their time in the study of classical texts, are incapable of following a piece of symbolic reasoning, and by mathematicians who have learnt a technique without troubling to inquire into its meaning or justification. Both types are now fortunately growing rarer. So much of modern mathematical work is obviously on the borderline of logic, so much of modern logic is symbolic and formal. . . .'[1] This passage makes it quite clear what the nature of philosophical thought is for Russell. Science proceeds from a basis which is regarded as fixed and certain; it constructs; philosophy proceeds from this same basis into the depths; constantly re-examining fundamentals. It may well prove that the basis is by no means so reliable as the builders of science thought it was, and in that case their work will have to be supplemented by philosophy. It is therefore understandable that there is a kind of research work which operates

[1] Bertrand Russell, *Introduction to Mathematical Philosophy*, p. 194.

with scientific methods and is nevertheless not a science. From this point of view it is not the subject that determines the philosophic work, but the direction or tendency. In this way philosophy remains related to all the sciences, but it does not conflict with them—unless it has to point out that the basis on which a science is built up is actually untenable, and that therefore there is, in fact, no such science.

5. ETHICS

Such a decision applies in particular to ethics, and with it all other normative scientific effort, thus including, for example, aesthetics in so far as it proposes to determine what is to be regarded as beautiful along scientific lines and with scientific reasons. Aesthetics has certainly never troubled men so profoundly as ethics has. In our own day, of course, artists, amateurs and art experts dispute as to the nature of real art. But if anyone comes to the conclusion that art and beauty cannot be reduced to any generally valid law there is hardly any need for him to fall into despair. The situation is very different with regard to ethics. The question that faces all men, 'What shall I do?', is a much more urgent matter, because a man must act, and even if he were to attempt to remain inactive his very inactivity would be an attitude for which he is responsible. Because of the urgent necessity of providing men with rules to guide their conduct, men who have learnt to use their brains have from the very earliest times given a great deal of thought to whether it is possible—and if so how—to draft rules of a general nature for man's behaviour, rules which will be valid for all men, and which all men will recognize and accept. It is at this point that the danger mathematics represents to philosophy becomes apparent. Because mathematics seemed to lead to indubitable results, many philosophers felt that it must in the same way be possible on all other fields, including ethics, since ethics is regarded as a recognized sphere of philosophy, to find the ultimate answer to all questions. It is here that the desires and the need of man for certainty collide most violently with the objection of reason. Spinoza tried to develop a system of ethics according to mathematical principles. And after him Russell hoped in this same way to attain the objectives he had set himself in youth: 'I was kept going in these years by the desire for knowledge and for intellectual achievement. . . . I hoped sooner or later to arrive at a perfected mathematics which would leave no room for doubts, and bit by bit to extend the sphere of certainty from mathematics to other sciences.'[1]

[1] *My Philosophical Development*, p. 36.

It was certainly no easy thing for him to have to dismiss such efforts from the philosophical sphere once and for all. But philosophy does at least one thing for those who approach it with ethical questions: 'from the point of view of philosophy, however, the discovery that a question is unanswerable is as complete an answer as any that could possibly be obtained'.[1] And 'To teach how to live without certainty, and yet without being paralysed by hesitation, is perhaps the chief thing that philosophy, in our age, can still do for those who study it'.[2] With these observations Russell very clearly and definitely draws the line of demarcation between philosophy on the one hand, and theology and *Weltanschauung* on the other.

6. PHILOSOPHY AND MAN'S VIEW OF THE WORLD

But what about the line of demarcation between philosophy and the empirical sciences, which one can divide into natural sciences and the sciences of civilization. Here, too, as in the analytical sciences, the line of demarcation is variable. These sciences always proceed from assumptions that appeal as a matter of course to common sense. The necessity of common sense for everyday life is confirmed again and again, but so also is its unreliability as the basis for any science. Prior to Einstein no one doubted that time was the same for the whole universe, and that clocks had to adapt themselves to it. But physical considerations and the effort to fit them into a theory compelled Einstein to question this 'matter of course', and ultimately to abandon it and show that, on the contrary, time adapted itself to clocks; and that time depended on the position and the movement of the basis from which it was determined. These ideas of the physicist Einstein are regarded as philosophical. The discovery of quantum mechanics then demanded that common sense should accept even more radical changes in its view of the world, though physics was founded on that very common sense in the first place. The traditional axiom *natura non facit saltus*, or nature makes no jumps, had to be abandoned, and it was seen that there was a limit to the extent to which our observations could be fitted into a general picture of the world. In Newton's days scientists disputed as to whether light was a wave or a corpuscular movement, but neither side doubted that it was one or the other. But nowadays, after long disputations between philosophers and physicists—in which the physicists also thought philosophically—we have come to the conclusion that it is permissible to regard this 'either or' as not inevitable,

[1] Bertrand Russell, *Mysticism and Logic*, p. 118.
[2] *History of Western Philosophy*, p. 11.

and that, in fact, it is possible to study physics on the assumption that light can present itself to us in the one case as a wave movement and in another case as a corpuscular movement. Thus although philosophy has no right to lay down laws for physics or for any other science, and can certainly not say, as Hegel did, if reality seems to contradict philosophy so much the worse for reality, and although its task is more modest, it is nevertheless much more difficult: it has a share in the development of man's 'view of the world'.

Cosmology, or the science of the universe, was formerly a part of philosophy. The limits to which the sciences could pursue their investigations were quite narrowly drawn; and questions such as whether space is finite or infinite, limited or unlimited, whether the earth or the sun is the centre of the universe, or whether, indeed, the universe has no central point at all, were reckoned to the sphere of philosophy. Today, however, all questions relating to the astronomical universe are not longer regarded as philosophical. Philosophy has already performed its task on this field by freeing us from the prejudice that the earth could not be regarded in any other way but as the centre of the universe. Philosophy has also successfully allied itself with biology. The prejudice which insisted that man was so fundamentally different from the animal that the possibility of a development of man from the animal could not even be considered, was very difficult to overcome. Again and again philosophy has had to fight for the possibility of a scientific theory. It then very easily looks as though it were committing itself to the correctness of this view of the world. But here is precisely the line of demarcation between science and philosophy: philosophy concerns itself with the possible; science concerns itself with the real. In this sense, and only in this sense, we can understand it when Russell heads a whole chapter of one of his books on natural philosophy 'Logic as the essence of Philosophy', and writes: 'Modern logic . . . has the effect of enlarging our abstract imagination, and providing an infinite number of possible hypotheses to be applied in the analysis of any complex fact. In this respect it is the exact opposite of the logic practised by the classical tradition. In that logic hypotheses which seem *prima facie* possible are professedly proved impossible, and it is decreed in advance that reality must have a certain special character. In modern logic on the contrary, while the *prima facie* hypotheses as a rule remain admissible, others, which only logic would have suggested, are added to our stock, and are very often found to be indispensable if a right analysis of the facts is to be obtained. The old logic put thought in fetters, while the new logic gives it wings.'[1]

[1] Bertrand Russell, *Our Knowledge of the External World*, p. 68.

7. METAPHYSICS

Now the philosophers also make use of these wings in order, whilst remaining within the bounds of the possible, to make assertions beyond the sphere which is confirmed by experience. The process might almost be compared with the making of reconnaissance flights over foreign territory: one side describes the process as scouting, the other side describes it as spying. The pure empiricists condemn as senseless assertions about what cannot be experienced, or at least as impossible to decide; the others regard it as possible to take one's stand on experience in order to exceed the limits of experience. This is where that sphere begins which is known as metaphysics. We can therefore say that as seen from the standpoint of the sciences, metaphysics lies still beyond the sphere of natural philosophy. I do not propose to go into the metaphysical ideas which Russell has developed, but merely to point out that he regards metaphysics as belonging to the sphere of philosophy. There are questions which can be approached with scientific caution on the basis of a reasonable examination of all possibilities, even if they cannot be finally decided. In answering such questions it is widespread usage to rely not on reason but on mental abilities of a certain kind. 'Philosophy, for Plato, is a kind of vision, the "vision of truth". It is not purely intellectual; it is not merely wisdom, but love of wisdom.'[1] Not only to Plato, but to philosophers down to our own day it seems possible to gain knowledge by means other than sensual perception and reason; and many and various are the terms used to describe the process: intuition, insight, or even instinct as against intellect. But all these words merely serve to describe a state of mind which is certain of itself. Even knowledge such as Descartes describes as *clare et distincte*, and which clashes least of all with reason, are means in an attempt to attain to complete certainty on the basis of psychical conditions. In this connection, continental European philosophy differs very considerably from that of the English-speaking countries. Generally speaking the difference is immediately visible in the style. Whereas the one aims at lucidity and definiteness of language, the other uses a form of expression which hardly allows any certain fixation on a definite content. They claim to make the inexpressible available to the reader by means of language. Russell rejects this process on principle. He does not deny the important role that can be played and often is played by intuition in the winning of insight. Reason is not a means of scientific discovery, but it is an essential means of scientific insight. Only when the result of intuition

[1] *History of Western Philosophy*, p. 144.

has stood the test of critical examination can it be regarded as an acquisition on the philosophical field as well. As far as Russell is concerned there is no difference between science and philosophy in this methodological procedure. The difficulty is only that philosophy must attempt to penetrate right into the final reasons. Scepticism alone cannot provide knowledge: 'The method of critical doubt, though Descartes himself applied it only half-heartedly, was of great philosophical importance. It is clear, as a matter of logic, that it can yield positive results only if scepticism is to stop somewhere. If there is to be both logical and empirical knowledge, there must be two kinds of stopping points: indubitable facts, and indubitable principles of inference.'[1] In this connection it is presumably also the task of philosophy to investigate whether these final stopping points offer real certainty, or are merely the only unavoidable assumptions if there is to be science and understanding amongst men. These are the ultimate assumptions whose rejection can, as I pointed out earlier, lead a man to end up behind the walls of a lunatic asylum, without his fate having contributed in the least to their confirmation. As Russell writes: 'Therefore if we are to hold that we know anything of the external world, we must accept the canons of scientific inference. Whether, when this conclusion has been reached, an individual decides to accept or reject these canons, is a purely personal affair, not susceptible to argument when once the issue has been made clear. I, as a human being, of course accept these canons, though as a professional logician I can play with the idea of rejecting one or the other of them to see what the consequences would be.'[2]

8. COMMON SENSE

By his definition of philosophy in the broader sense Russell has flanked philosophy on the one side by science and on the other by theology. One might mention common sense as a third borderline area. All philosophy begins with common sense and stops, strangely enough, at common sense. When children start asking questions they begin with 'Why?' The one putting the question and the other answering it are both of the opinion that it is not enough just to accept the things and circumstances of our life as we experience them, and that it is possible to see them in a wider relationship. We take it that we have understood a thing or a happening when we have succeeded in fitting it into such a relationship. This fitting

---

[1] *History of Western Philosophy*, p. 589.
[2] *Philosophy of Bertrand Russell*, p. 719.

of things and happenings into wider relationships has been going
on as a matter of course since the very earliest times. That a thing,
say a tree, is still there even when we do not happen to notice it,
is, basically, a metaphysical assumption, but such an essential one
that a man realizes that he does not know this, but only supposes it,
only when he begins to doubt it. Thus this belongs to the philosophy
of common sense in the same way as the conviction that other people
hear, see and feel, and not only behave as if they were hearing, seeing
and feeling. As everyday rules of conduct such convictions are adequate, even essential. However, referring to these firm convictions
Russell says that they have three defects: 'Namely, that they are cock-
sure, vague and self-contradictory. It is the business of philosophy to
correct these defects so far as it can, without throwing over knowledge altogether. To be a good philosopher a man must have a strong
desire to know, combined with great caution in believing that he
knows; he must also have logical acumen and the habit of exact
thinking.'[1]

Philosophy must not therefore accept the convictions of common
sense uncritically, but at the same time it must not stray too far
away from them either. Russell says approvingly of Aristotle that
by means of common sense he brought Plato's philosophy down
from heaven to earth; and Russell can sympathize with Locke who
hesitated to accept his own conclusions when they seemed to lead
philosophy to abstruse results. Such behaviour may offend a logician,
but it says much for Locke's common sense that he insisted that a
correct theory must not lead to consequences with which it is impossible for men to live. In Russell's view Hume has shown that so far
no one has succeeded in justifying the inductive conclusion or in
proving the validity of the causal law. He terms this the two great
scandals of philosophy. At the same time he is not prepared to admit
that, because such proof has not as yet been brought, philosophy
should therefore adopt the view that there is no causality and that
the inductive conclusion is impermissible. This is just part and
parcel of the prudence which Russell demands of philosophers in
judging what they think they know. The acknowledgement 'I cannot
see that the causal law is valid', must not be transformed into the
statement: 'I agree that the causal law is not valid.' With the first
acknowledgement a man oversteps the borders of common sense
into the sphere of philosophy; with the second statement he steps
beyond philosophy on that side which is farthest removed from
common sense.

[1] *An Outline of Philosophy*, p. 3.

9. LINGUISTIC PHILOSOPHY

Neither science nor philosophy is possible without understanding amongst men. If ideas are to be developed and brought into relation with each other, then there must be some means of giving the fugitive idea a firm form, and a form which makes it possible to transfer an idea from one man to another. This means is language. Now language did not develop in order to assist in the solution of philosophical problems, but in order to meet practical everyday needs. It is therefore not surprising to find that its construction reflects the primitive picture of the world as seen by man's common sense. In the beginning it was possible to say only the simplest things of everyday life. When a man says 'chair', 'bread' or 'rain' he has a very clear idea indeed of what it is he means, but when he uses words like 'just', 'good', impossible', his ideas are much less definite. In the simplest language, that which deals with the world of our environment, there are words which mean things, words which mean qualities, and words which mean actions. When we form new words language involves great dangers for philosophy. 'Justice', 'Liberty', 'Power' and 'Heaven' are nouns—what the Germans call 'thing words'—and in consequence they mislead men into supposing things which accord with these words. To what extent that is possible, right or necessary is also a task of philosophy to decide: 'The philosopher is faced, therefore, with the difficult task of using language to undo the false beliefs that it suggests.'[1] As language is the only means to express knowledge Russell is brought by his own investigations to recognize in its examination such an important part of philosophy that he is impelled to write: 'It gradually became clear that a great part of philosophy can be reduced to something that may be called "syntax".'[2] Now at first glance this is a very strange statement. We can divide it into two parts. The first tells us that such investigations can teach us that some sentences which are grammatically correct have nevertheless no sense; and this includes not only sentences such as, say, 'Justice sings enormous dwarfs', which anyone can see is utter nonsense, but also sentences which are regarded by many readers as particularly profound precisely on account of their incomprehensibility—and, incidentally, many books which are generally regarded as philosophical (particularly in Germany) contain numerous such sentences. This exclusion of nonsense is useful, but also relatively easily understandable. Over and above this, however, the investigation of language is said to provide metaphysical

---

[1] Bertrand Russell, *Human Knowledge*, p. 76.
[2] *History of Western Philosophy*, p. 859.

results so that the analysis of language links up directly with meta-physics: 'complete metaphysical agnosticism is not compatible with the maintenance of linguistic propositions. For my part, I believe that, partly by means of the study of syntax, we can arrive at con-siderable knowledge concerning the structure of the world.'[1]

What Russell understands by philosophy in the narrower sense is not altogether the hopeless proposition many men take it to be when they read through a history of philosophy and get the impression that it consists of nothing but the replacement of one system by another. All outstanding philosophers have left their traces in our present-day thought. 'To a great extent, the uncertainty of philosophy is more apparent than real: those questions which are already capable of definite answers are placed in the sciences, while only those to which, at present, no definite answer can be given, remain to form the residue which is called philosophy.'[2] But even for this residue of unanswered questions Russell sees a way opening which lies nearer the scientific side of no-man's-land than the theological side. Just as is the case with all other sciences, philosophy will never be able to give a final answer to all the questions which face it, but: 'the one and only condition, I believe, which is necessary in order to secure for philosophy in the near future an achievement surpassing all that has hitherto been accomplished by philosophers, is the creation of a school of men with scientific training and philosophical interests, unhampered by the traditions of the past, and not misled by the literary methods of those who copy the ancients in all except their merits'.[3]

10. THE PHILOSOPHER AND 'WELTANSCHAUUNG'

Despite Russell's optimistic views about the progress of philosophy, with which I brought the previous part of my study to a close, and which would have provided an effective end to our whole inquiry into what Russell means when he speaks of philosophy, I cannot forbear to revert once more to the question of *Weltanschauung* and its significance in relation to philosophy. For certainly Russell has excluded ethics and all statements of values from philosophy in the narrower sense, thus also separating *Weltanschauung* from philo-sophy, but he has not separated it from the philosophers. He would not suppose that a philosopher who developed and proclaimed a *Weltanschauung* ceased thereby to be a philosopher in so far as he

---

[1] Bertrand Russell, *An Inquiry into the Meaning of Truth*, p. 328.
[2] *The Problems of Philosophy*, p. 155.
[3] *Our Knowledge of the External World*, p. 246.

indulged in a kind of spare-time occupation on a different field—
as, for example, a doctor can go in for music, and to that extent
leave the sphere of medicine. On the contrary, *Weltanschauung* is the
adoption of an attitude, and an attitude to things which are of the
greatest importance for the individual and for society. Russell, in
fact, expects men, and particularly philosophers, to adopt such
attitudes. He makes a distinction between a philosopher in the technical sense, or even what the French in the eighteenth century called
a *philosophe*, both of which almost serve him as a professional
designation, and the honorary title of philosopher, which cannot be
won merely by writing books, or by good behaviour alone—I
recall once again the examples of Socrates and Leibniz—but which
can be achieved only by a combination of the urge to knowledge, a
readiness to abandon prejudices, and a keen understanding, which
is prepared not only to expose the errors of common sense, but also
to replace them by greater insight. No one who has to go about
everyday affairs can be expected to have either the leisure or the
ability to develop an independent *Weltanschauung*. If he strives for
knowledge at all it will be only within the framework of what his
environment regards as a matter of course; and it will thus be
encumbered with precisely those prejudices which can be the task
of the philosopher to overcome. For he in his own sphere is
used to putting up with the unpleasantness which usually has to be
faced by whoever takes it upon himself to attack prejudices which
people have grown accustomed to accept as the basis of their moral
attitudes. Socrates, Jesus, Bruno and Spinoza were all made to suffer
the harsh and vigorous rejection of their contemporaries. And anyone
today who is against alcohol, or is a vegetarian as a matter of
principle, or one who disapproves of our marriage laws, or is in
favour of birth control, or who sees no reason in a world threatened
by nuclear destruction to believe in the existence of an all-merciful
God, and who therefore instead takes part in demonstrations against
nuclear armaments, or perhaps against armaments in general, will
soon be made to feel the unpleasant consequences of disagreeing
with the world around him. Russell would not proclaim that it is
the duty of the philosopher to represent exactly these minority ideas,
but he certainly would expect the philosopher to have views on such
questions, and in particular on these questions, and to make them
publicly known without being intimidated by any fear of disagree-
able consequences in his social life. Of course, Russell knows that
he must accept the existence of *Weltanschauungen* of which he cannot
approve. In dealing with Nietzsche he constructs a dialogue between
Nietzsche and Buddha which comes to nothing because there is no

logical refutation of a man who regards hatred and violence as a desirable state of this world: 'The ultimate argument against his philosophy, as against any unpleasant but internally self-consistent ethic, lies not in an appeal to facts, but in an appeal to the emotions. Nietzsche despises universal love; I feel it the motive power to all that I desire as regards the world.'[1] It almost looks as though the philosopher were doomed to resignation in face of his recognition that he cannot refute the opponent of his own *Weltanschauung*. But that is not in the least Russell's own opinion. First of all, he would say, there is no reason why you cannot work with all energy for something you cannot prove. Where it is a question of will against will then the philosopher has even less reason to abandon his own position, because: 'the mind which has become accustomed to the freedom and impartiality of philosophic contemplation will preserve something of the same freedom and impartiality in the world of action and emotion'.[2] Furthermore, it is quite possible that the philosopher will be able to open the eyes of a doubter, or of one who is in error. It very often happens that men do not realize the consequences of their basic attitude, or that they have not sufficient courage to admit such questions. For example, there may well be people who share Russell's view that love is the best means of changing the world, but who are at the same time unable to see the connection between their own addiction to love of mankind and, say, the claim of a child to an education between liberty and discipline. It is probably true that the desire of a human being determines what he regards as good. This is that ultimate scientific conclusion regarding ethics which excludes ethics as such from the sphere of philosophy. It is, however, just as much true that many people do not really know what it is they do desire. Not only do various people have various desires which easily come into conflict, but this self-same conflict of desires can take place within one and the same individual. Sometimes the conflict cannot be resolved by reason and has to be settled by a blind decision of the will, but very often it can be shown that a human being is allowing his short-term desires to obstruct his long-term happiness. This clash existed long ago in Ancient Greece between the Epicureans and the followers of the hedonist schools. Philosophical contemplation will more or less inevitably bring anyone to begin at first to doubt his own aims again and again. Unlike other *Weltanschauugen*, particularly those of a dogmatic nature, the philosophic *Weltanschauung* is dynamic: 'And philosophical knowledge, or rather philosophical thought, has

---

[1] *History of Western Philosophy*, p. 800.
[2] *Problems of Philosophy*, p. 160.

certain special merits not belonging in an equal degree to other intellectual pursuits. By its generality it enables us to see human passions in their just proportions, and to realize the absurdity of many quarrels between individuals, classes and nations. Philosophy comes as near as possible for human beings to that large, impartial contemplation of the universe as a whole which raises us for the moment about our purely personal destiny.'[1] Notwithstanding all the various changes in his individual views Russell has experienced during the course of his philosophic development, he has retained certain basic traits of those things he put forward and accepted in youth as his philosophic *Weltanschauung*; and in particular that resolve as a matter of principle never to accept anything his reason is compelled to reject, and, no matter what the consequences, to abandon even his dearest prejudices rather than be guilty of intellectual dishonesty. This is the path along which in his opinion the philosopher must travel, and should he remain on this straight and narrow way he will be richly rewarded: 'Philosophy cannot itself determine the ends of life, but it can free us from the tyranny of prejudice and from distortions due to a narrow view. Love, beauty, knowledge, and joy of life: these things retain their lustre however wide our purview. And if philosophy can help us to feel the value of these things, it will have played its part in man's collective work of bringing light into a world of darkness.'[2]

[1] *Outline of Philosophy*, p. 310.　　　　　　　[2] *Ibid.*, p. 312.

15

A. J. AYER

An Appraisal
of Bertrand Russell's Philosophy

By the last quarter of the nineteenth century, British philosophy had fallen very largely under the spell of Hegel. The British Hegelians, of whom F. H. Bradley at Oxford and J. E. McTaggart at Cambridge were the most distinguished, were perhaps not very orthodox disciples of the master—Bradley in particular found it difficult to free himself entirely from the legacy of British empiricism—but with their belief in the Absolute, their characterization of the material world as mere appearance, and their denial of the reality of space and time, they committed themselves to metaphysics in a way that British philosophers have fought shy of, both before and since. That the present century has seen a return to the older and sounder empiricist tradition, and its development in a more rigorous form, is very largely due to the work of Bertrand Russell. What is called the analytical movement in philosophy, which in one form or another has fashioned the philosophical climate at least in English-speaking countries during the last quarter of a century, is in a great measure the fruit of his ideas.

As he relates in *My Philosophical Development*, there was a period in Lord Russell's youth when he himself, under the influence of Bradley's writings, was a Hegelian idealist. He was, however, very soon converted by his Cambridge friend and colleague, G. E. Moore, to a form of Platonic realism. This conversion was made easier by the fact that Russell had first been led to take an interest in philosophy by his desire to find some reason for believing in the truth of mathematics; and he soon came to see that if he was to regard the propositions of mathematics as having objective validity, he would have to reject the fundamental idealist doctrine that the objects of knowledge are conditioned by their being known. Besides, Hegelian idealism looked askance on relational judgements which it regarded as incoherent; and Russell was convinced that the propositions of mathematics are irreducibly relational. For the same reason he rejected the view which is attributed to Aristotle and to Leibniz that all propositions are of the subject-predicate form. In the earliest of his philosophical books *A Critical Examination of the Philosophy of Leibniz*, which appeared in 1900, Russell made a convincing attempt to show that the assumption of this logical doctrine can be made to account for the main features of Leibniz's metaphysics.

Two current explanations of the nature of mathematical propositions were the Kantian view that they were synthetic *a priori* truths, and at the other extreme the view of John Stuart Mill that they were empirical generalizations, which owed their security to their having been found to be supported by a very large number of instances. But neither of these explanations satisfied Russell. He did not then reject the notion of the synthetic *a priori*, as he came to do later, but the use that was made of it in this instance seemed to him not to explain enough; at the same time, the idea that the propositions of mathematics were empirical generalizations appeared to him untenable, because it implied the denial of their necessity.

Russell's own radical solution was to reduce mathematics to logic. In order to achieve this, he had to show that the fundamental terms of mathematics could be defined by means of purely logical concepts, but more importantly he had to transform logic itself. He had to elaborate a system of logic which would be rigorous and rich enough to allow the propositions of mathematics to be incorporated in it. The first part of this undertaking was carried out in the *Principles of Mathematics*, which appeared in 1903. The second led to *Principia Mathematica*, which extended to three large volumes, of which the first came out in 1910, the second in 1912 and the third in 1913. A comparatively untechnical account of the main ideas of these works was given by Russell in his *Introduction to Mathematical Philosophy*, which he wrote while in prison as the result of his agitation against the First World War, and published in 1919.

In his idea that mathematics could be reduced to logic, Russell had been anticipated by the German mathematician, Gottlob Frege. Though Frege's work had been published over twenty years before, it was very little known, and Russell arrived independently at very similar results. In their definition of the natural numbers, for example, both Russell and Frege made use of the concept of a one-one relation; that is, a relation which is such that if it holds between any two terms x and y, no other term but x is so related to y, and x bears the relation to no other term but y. Two classes are said to be similar if their members can be correlated by a one-one relation. Then the number of a class is defined as the class of all those classes that are similar to it, and a cardinal number is defined as anything which is the number of some class. This definition is not circular as the notion of a one-one relation can be introduced in purely logical terms, without any reference to numbers. On the other hand, if the definition is to apply to every cardinal number, it seems to require that there be no upper limit to the number of things that can be classified; and it may be disputed whether this is a principle of logic.

At the time that he wrote the *Principles of Mathematics* Russell was still very much of a Platonic realist. He spoke of 'whatever may be an object of thought' as a term, and maintained that 'every term has being, i.e. *is* in some sense'. This committed him to a belief in the reality not only of universals, propositions and classes, but of everything that was denoted by any substantival expression. His assumption was that if such an expression was meaningful, there must in some sense be an object to which it referred. This worked well enough in the case of proper names like 'Napoleon' or descriptions like 'the author of Waverley' which denoted objects which were known to exist: yet it hardly seems credible that there should in any sense *be* such objects as the present King of France, or the golden mountain, or the round square. At the same time, so far as the analysis of their meaning went, there appeared to be no justification for drawing a distinction between expressions like 'the present King of France' and expressions like 'the author of Waverley'. It was just a contingent, historical, fact that one of these succeeded in its reference and the other did not.

Russell's solution of this difficulty is to be found in his famous Theory of Descriptions. This theory was designed to show that even in their referential usage expressions of the form 'the so-and-so' do not function as names. It does not follow from the fact that they are meaningful that there is any object which they mean. Russell's way of showing this was to give a rule for translating sentences in which the definite descriptive phrase occurs, in such a way that the phrase no longer even looks as though it were a name. So, to take his own favourite example, the statement 'the author of Waverley was Scott' becomes in his translation a conjunction of the three statements: 'At least one person wrote Waverley': 'At most one person wrote Waverley': and 'It is not the case that anyone both wrote Waverley and was not identical with Scott'. To put it symbolically, as Russell himself preferred to do, the theory is that to say that something which has *f* has *g*, where *f* is the property concealed in the definite description and *g* is a property attributed to what it describes, is to say that there is an *x* such that *x* has *f*, and for all *y*, if *y* has *f*, *y* is identical with *x*, and *x* has *g*. Thus any description of the subject goes into the predicate, and only what Russell called a logically proper name, that is a pure demonstrative, can serve to designate the value of the variable *x*.

This theory, which the Cambridge philosopher, F. P. Ramsey, called a paradigm of philosophy, has recently had its critics. One objection to it is that there are many cases in which the literal application of Russell's rule yields unwelcome results. If I say 'The policeman on the corner told me where to go', I am surely not implying that there exists only one policeman or only one corner. The point about cases of this kind is that the definite description does not individuate the object to which it refers; it is assumed that the means of identifying the object are supplied by the context. Nevertheless the object will have a unique set of properties which could be specified: and if they are specified, then Russell's analysis will apply. Another objection is that the existence claim which is involved in the use of a definite description is not implicitly stated by it, as Russell assumes, but rather pre-supposed. It is alleged that we should not ordinarily say that a sentence like 'The present King of France is bald' was used to make a false statement: we should say rather that since there is no present King of France the question of truth or falsehood did not arise. It does not seem to me, however, that this is a question upon which the appeal to ordinary usage is at all decisive; and there are obvious advantages in construing sentences of this kind in such a way that they do make statements which have a truth-value.

A more serious criticism is that Russell starts from a false premise. The theory is intended to show how it is possible for a descriptive expression to be meaningful, even though there is nothing which it denotes: and it does this in effect by maintaining that these expressions are not referential. The underlying assumption is then that the meaning of a referential expression is to be identified with its denotation; and it is argued that, even in the case of proper names, this theory of meaning is mistaken. I agree that it is mistaken, and, therefore, that the reasoning which appears to have led Russell to the theory of descriptions can be criticized. However, the fact that it was designed to meet an avoidable difficulty does not invalidate the theory itself.

It was not only in the field of the theory of descriptions that Russell came to be sceptical of the generous ontology which he had admitted in the *Principles of Mathematics*. In his later works he thought it unnecessary to attribute real existence either to classes or to propositions: he held them rather to be logical fictions, in the sense that they could be analysed in terms of entities of a more concrete sort. On the other hand, he has always felt bound to admit the existence of universals. He has allowed, it may be wrongly, that one can go so far in dispensing with universals as to reduce them all to the single relation of resemblance; but since he takes the view that resemblance itself is a universal, he does not think that the nominalists achieve their aim.

It is not possible, within the limits of a general sketch of Russell's philosophy, to assess the scope and originality of *Principia Mathematica*. There is in any case no doubt that it played a very important part in the development of mathematical logic. The break with Aristotelian logic consisted not so much in the use of a special notation, as in the greater generality of Russell's and Whitehead's system, and above all in their attempt to make it rigorously formal. Other systems of logic have since been developed which lay claim to greater formal rigour, but they have in a large measure been inspired by Russell's and Whitehead's work.

One very important outcome of Russell's concern with the problems of mathematical logic was his invention of the Theory of Types. The need for this theory arose out of his discovery of a contradiction in the theory of classes: a discovery which made Frege say, when the news of it was communicated to him by Russell, that the whole foundation of mathematics had been undermined. This contradiction is fairly easy to set out. Most classes appear not to be members of themselves: for example, the class of men is plainly not itself a man. On the other hand, some classes do appear to be members of themselves. For example, the class of all the things that can be counted would itself appear to be a thing that can be counted. Now consider the class of all classes that are not members of themselves. Is it or is it not a member of itself? If it is, it is not, and if it is not, it is.

Similar contradictions appear in other fields. A notorious example is the paradox of Epimenides the Cretan, who said that all Cretans were liars. Another well-known paradox, which belongs to the same family as that of the liar, arises out of the fact that some, but not all, adjectives are predicable of themselves. For instance, the word 'short' is short but the word 'long' is not long. Let us call those that are so predicable 'autological' and those that are not 'heterological'. Then is the word 'heterological' predicable of itself? Once again, if it is, it is not, and if it is not, it is.

Russell's solution of these antinomies was to arrange objects into a hierarchy of types, with the consequence that what may be true or false of the objects of one type cannot be meaningfully asserted about those of another. In particular, if a given class is the extension of a given predicate, only nonsense results if the predicate is applied to that class. So, it is not false but nonsensical to say that the class of men is human: the question whether the word 'heterological' is itself autological or heterological is a meaningless question. Even when a predicate does appear to characterize objects of different types, it does not have the same meaning in each case. Thus a predicate like 'being countable' becomes, as Russell puts it, systematically ambiguous.

171

The theory of types, of which I have here given only an outline, has a certain *ad hoc* air about it. It is hard to maintain that all forms of self-reference are logically vicious: and there seems to be no sure method for deciding when it is legitimate and when it is not. For this reason attempts have since been made to find a less restrictive means of avoiding the paradoxes. All the same, the theory of types has had an important historical influence. It called attention, in a very striking way, to the fact that a sentence may be grammatically well-formed and yet fail to express a meaningful statement. Among other things, it helped to set the stage for the Logical Positivists who rejected metaphysics on the ground that metaphysical doctrines were not even false but literally nonsensical. This is indeed a view that goes back to Hume, but Russell's work was taken as giving it logical support.

It follows from the theory of types that the statements which come lowest in the hierarchy refer to individuals; and it follows from the theory of descriptions that the individuals which, in Russell's phrase, make up the furniture of the world are designated by logically proper names. But, since logically proper names are pure demonstratives, it would appear that the only individuals which they can designate are those that are directly observable. In this way Russell's logic was integrated with his theory of knowledge.

The distinction between knowledge by acquaintance and knowledge by description, which is an outcome of the theory of descriptions, was developed by Russell in his *Problems of Philosophy*, which appeared in 1912. This book was written for the Home University Library and is still as good an introduction to philosophy as there is. It approaches the theory of knowledge from an empiricist standpoint: its guiding principle being that every proposition which we can understand must be composed of constituents with which we are acquainted. Thus Russell held that we are acquainted with universals. We are also acquainted with particulars, but only with a limited class of them: namely those which are directly given to us in experience. In their case, he took it to follow from the fact that one was acquainted with a particular object, both that the object really existed and that it had the properties which it appeared to have. On this view, we can indeed surmise that particulars of other types exist: but we can only refer to them indirectly as objects which stand in certain relations to those with which we are acquainted. Thus, when an object is known by acquaintance, its existence is not open to doubt; but the existence of objects which are known only by description is problematic.

At that time Russell believed that the particulars with which it was possible to be acquainted were one's own self and one's own private thoughts, feelings, images and sense-data; these might be past as well as present, since he allowed memory to be a form of direct acquaintance. By 1921, when he published *The Analysis of Mind*, he had come round to the view that the existence of the objects, or events, which we claim to remember is not known to us directly but only inferred from our present memory-images; and he also rejected the idea that one could be acquainted with oneself, on the ground that the self did not exist as a separate entity. On the other hand, he has never given up the view that the objects with which we are directly acquainted in perception are our own private sense-data. The sense-datum theory has indeed met with considerable opposition in recent times, as part of a general reaction against allowing the existence of private entities. If Russell still adheres to it, it is mainly because he thinks that the alternative of supposing that we are directly acquainted with physical objects is obviously untenable. His main argument against naïve realism is most succinctly put in the *Inquiry into Meaning and Truth*, which appeared in 1940. 'We all start from "naïve realism", i.e. the doctrine that things are what they seem. We think that grass is green, that stones are hard and that snow is cold. But physics assures us that the greenness of grass, the hardness of stones, and the coldness of snow are not the greenness, hardness, and coldness that we know in our own experience, but something very different. The observer, when he seems to himself to be observing a stone, is really, if physics is to be believed, observing the effect of the stone upon himself. . . . Naïve realism leads to physics, and physics, if true, shows that naïve realism is false. Therefore naïve realism, if true, is false; therefore it is false.'[1]

This implies a causal theory of perception, with which Russell began and to which he has reverted. There was, however, a period in which in obedience to the principle 'wherever possible substitute constructions out of known entities for inference to unknown entities', a principle which he has called the supreme maxim in scientific philosophy, he gave up the causal theory, at any rate in its conventional form, in favour of the phenomenalist position that physical objects are logical constructions out of actual and possible sense-data. This is a reformulation of John Stuart Mill's view that physical objects are permanent possibilities of sensation; the form in which it presents it is that statements about physical objects can be faithfully translated into statements about sense-data.

Russell developed this view in *Our Knowledge of the External World*, which was published in 1914, and in two of the essays collected

[1] p. 15.

in *Mysticism and Logic* which appeared in 1918. The materials out of which he tried to construct physical objects were not limited to the actual sense-data with which any single observer was acquainted. Russell also brought in the sense-data sensed by other persons and even unsensed sense-data, to which he gave the name of sensibilia. The only way in which a sensibile was supposed to differ from a sense-datum was in its not being actually sensed. Roughly speaking, Russell's theory was that at any given moment each observer perceives a private three-dimensional world with its own private space, or spaces, since Russell distinguishes the space of sight from the space of touch. He calls these private worlds perspectives. In addition to these perceived perspectives, there exists also an infinite number of unperceived perspectives, namely all those that an observer would perceive if he were in the appropriate state and in the appropriate position. The constituents of the unperceived perspectives are sensibilia. A physical object is then defined as a class of sensibilia, where sensibilia are taken as including sense-data; it is in fact identified with those sensiblia, or sense-data, which are commonly regarded as its actual and possible appearances. Since the three-dimensional perspectives are themselves arranged in a three-dimensional order, physical space is one of six dimensions. Russell does not work out this theory in full detail, but it is clear that it encounters very serious difficulties, even if one is willing to assume that sensibilia and unperceived perspectives literally exist.

In the *Reply to Criticisms* which Russell wrote for the *The Philosophy of Bertrand Russell*, a volume in the Library of Living Philosophers, which was published in 1944, he remarked that he did not see why this theory should preclude him from regarding physical objects as causes of sense-data. His ground for this presumably is that the causal relations which are supposed to hold between physical objects and sense-data may themselves be capable of being analysed in terms of correlations among sensibilia. This is substantially the position which he took in the *Analysis of Mind*, where he develops a theory about mind and matter which is akin to the neutral monism of William James. The theory is that both mind and matter are logical constructions out of elements, primarily sense-data, which are themselves neither mental nor physical. Apart from the fact that certain elements, such as images and feelings, enter only into the constitution of minds, what chiefly distinguishes mind from matter, in this view, is the operation of different causal laws. Thus the same sense-data when correlated according to the laws of physics constitute physical objects and when correlated according to the laws of psychology help to constitute minds. In their mental aspect, they engage among other things, in what Russell called mnemic causation, a kind of action at a distance by which experiences produce subsequent memory-images. A consequence of this view is that Russell rejects the notion not only of the self, but also of consciousness, as a substantial entity. On the other hand, while he has dallied with behaviourism, he has never denied the existence of states of consciousness which are not definable in physical terms.

An interesting feature of Russell's more recent writings on the subject of perception is that he locates sense-data, or percepts as he now prefers to call them, in the percipient's brain. He does not mean by this that when we think that we are perceiving the world around us, we are, in any literal sense, really observing only our own brains. His argument is rather that an event's position in space-time is determined by its causal relations and that 'the causal and temporal connections of percepts with events in afferent and efferent nerves gives percepts a position in the brain of the observer'.[1] If this still sounds paradoxical it has to be remembered that for Russell the brain itself is a construction out of sensible events. It is one of the perspectives from which the world is viewed and it is via the perspectives which constitute their point of view, rather than the physical objects which are constructed out of them, that actual percepts acquire their own location in physical space.

The view that the world consists in the last resort of sensible events is a feature of the doctrine of Logical Atomism which Russell, under the influence of his pupil Ludwig Wittgenstein put forward in the years following the First World War. It was expounded by him in some lectures which were first published in the *Monist* in 1918 and 1919 under the title of 'The Philosophy of Logical Atomism', and have since been reprinted in a collection of essays called *Logic and Knowledge*, which appeared in 1956; and there is also an essay called 'Logical Atomism' which Russell contributed to the first series of Contemporary British Philosophy in 1924. While making a strong plea for the method of logical analysis, considered primarily as an application of Ockham's razor in accordance with the principle of substituting logical constructions for inferred entities, the lectures were largely concerned with the problem of truth. In his earlier writings on the subject of truth, at a time when he believed in the objective reality of propositions, Russell had taken the view that truth and falsehood were unanalysable properties by which propositions were simply characterized. Propositions, he held, were true or false just as roses may be red or white. It was not long, however, before he came, with reason, to regard this theory as obscurantist

[1] *The Philosophy of Bertrand Russell:* Reply and Criticisms, p. 705.

and he accordingly abandoned it in favour of a correspondence theory of truth.

In Russell's exposition of Logical Atomism, as in Wittgenstein's *Tractatus Logico-Philosophicus*, the correspondence theory is given a very literal interpretation. Russell conceived of sensible events as entering into what he called atomic facts; and these atomic facts were designated, as it were photographically, by elementary propositions. The truth of all higher-order propositions depended upon the truth of these elementary propositions and the truth of these elementary propositions consisted in their structural correspondence with atomic facts. Russell devoted much ingenuity to the elaboration of this theory, but it depends upon a pictorial theory of meaning which both he and Wittgenstein subsequently found to be untenable.

Russell has reverted to the problem of truth both in his *Inquiry into Meaning and Truth* and in *My Philosophical Development*, which was published in 1959. He still adheres to a correspondence theory in so far as he holds that propositions are made true by facts, but he no longer thinks that truth consists in a relation of structural correspondence, and he now prefers to regard the truth of propositions as derivative from the truth of beliefs. Roughly speaking, his view is that a belief is accounted true if the state of affairs which is taken as verifying it is found by observation to exist, and false if its 'verifier' is found not to exist. This is in line also with his rejection of a pictorial in favour of a causal theory of meaning.

Russell has remained a Logical Atomist in the sense of thinking that the world consists of a number of particulars. But in the *Inquiry into Meaning and Truth* he gives this position a new aspect by identifying these particulars with what are ordinarily called qualities. Here again his motive is one of economy, supported by the desire to eliminate the dubious notion of substance. Accordingly he follows Berkeley in treating the things of common sense as collections of qualities, which are united by what he calls a relation of compresence. There are some difficulties in this theory, which centre mainly upon the interpretation of the relation of compresence: but I think it quite possible that they can be overcome.

This view of the nature of particulars is retained in Russell's *Human Knowledge: Its Scope and Limits*, which was published in 1948. Otherwise, this book is of interest chiefly for its attempt to deal with the problem of induction. Russell takes the unfashionable view that inductive reasoning stands in need of justification, and he elaborates a set of principles which he thinks would be sufficient for this purpose. He does not, however, think that any of these principles can be known to be true.

There are many other aspects of philosophy to which Russell has contributed. He has written extensively on ethics, on political philosophy, on social philosophy and the philosophy of education, on the history of philosophy and the philosophy of history. But while this section of his work contains some of the best of Russell's writing, it has not the same theoretical interest as his work in the field of logic and the theory of knowledge. In moral philosophy, he began by sharing G. E. Moore's view that 'good' was an objective unanalysable non-natural quality, but he has since been persuaded that ethical judgements are not objectively either true or false, but are rather expressive of attitudes. Though he accepts this conclusion intellectually, he confesses to disliking it on emotional grounds. His own ethical standpoint appears to be mainly utilitarian. He believes that the proper concern of ethics is to find out what people want and how their ends can be attained. At the same time it is clear that he attaches an intrinsic value to such things as justice and liberty and the pursuit of truth.

While he has an extensive knowledge of history, of which he makes effective use, Russell's approach to social questions is more moral than historical. In the *History of Western Philosophy*, which he published in 1946, he did indeed set out to relate philosophical ideas to the social conditions under which they were produced, but for the most part the exposition of the ideas and the description of the social background proceed side by side: no very serious attempt is made to integrate them. As might be expected, his history of philosophy is most illuminating when it treats of the philosophers to whom he is most sympathetic; in particular, Leibnitz and the British empiricists.

To my mind, the best of Russell's political writings is his book on the *Principles of Social Reconstruction*, which appeared in 1916 at the height of his campaign against the First World War. It is anarchist in temper and it reflects the distrust of institutions, and especially of the power of the State, that has always coloured his political thinking. Not only in politics, but also in the sphere of education, he has been a consistent advocate of liberty. Though he is more keenly aware of the irrational features in human conduct, his outlook on moral, political and social questions bears a fairly close affinity to that of John Stuart Mill.

In the course of his long career, Russell, as we have seen, has held quite a large variety of philosophical opinions. This has sometimes been used as an argument against him, especially by those who publish very little for fear of being discovered to be wrong. But the fact is that, while he has fairly often changed his views on points of detail, his approach to philosophy has been remarkably consistent. His aim has always been to try to find reasons for accepted beliefs, whether in the field of mathematics, the natural or social sciences, or common sense. He has been a consistent sceptic, not in the sense that he denies our claims to knowledge, but that he questions them. He has adhered also to a single method, the method of starting with propositions which are the least susceptible to doubt, and trying to reconstruct the edifice of knowledge on this basis, with as few assumptions as possible. When he has changed his views, the reason has usually been either that he thought he could make do with even fewer assumptions, or else that he had pared them down too far, that the basis from which he was working was not adequate to the facts. The result of his using this method has been that his justifications usually take the form of analyses; it is thus that he has come to furnish so much of the inspiration for the analytic movement in contemporary philosophy. Even so, he himself has not been interested in analysis for its own sake, but only as a method of proof. In this, as in the power and elegance of his literary style, he continues the main tradition of British Empiricism. He is, and is likely to remain, its outstanding representative in the twentieth century.

IV

MATHEMATICIAN AND LOGICIAN

16

DANA SCOTT

Existence and Description in Formal Logic

The problem of what to do with improper descriptive phrases has bothered logicians for a long time. There have been three major suggestions of how to treat descriptions usually associated with the names of Russell, Frege and Hilbert-Bernays. The author does not consider any of these approaches really satisfactory. In many ways Russell's idea is most attractive because of its simplicity. However, on second thought one is saddened to find that the Russellian method of elimination depends heavily on the scope of the elimination. Further, the semantical meaning of Russell's transformation is not all that clear; although it could be made quite precise. Frege's use of a null entity for the denotation of an improper description has of course an immediate semantical interpretation, but the arbitrary choice of a null entity in each domain is really not very natural. In many axiomatic theories, Euclidean geometry for example, the choice of a distinguished point is not possible or even very desirable. Bernays in [1] used Fregean descriptions with a kind of 'local' null entity carried along in the notation itself. This idea, though clear and workable, is not very elegant in the author's opinion.

It is curious that in ordinary mathematical practice having un-defined function values, a situation close to using improper descrip-tions, does not seem to trouble people. A mathematician will often formulate conditionals of the form

$$\textit{if } f(x) \textit{ exists for all } x < a, \textit{ then} \ldots$$

and will not give a moment's thought to the problem of the meaning of $f(a)$. More careful authors never use a description or a function value unless it has been previously proved that its value exists. This style led Hilbert-Bernays in [3] to the point of requiring such a proof before a formula containing the description can be considered as well formed. This suggestion is to be rejected on many grounds. As has often been pointed out, the class of well-formed formulas will hardly ever be recursive. Also the class of well-formed formulas will change upon the introduction of additional axioms. More serious is the fact that it is quite natural to employ descriptions *before* they have been proved to be proper. In axiomatic set theory in the discussion of recursive definitions, it is very tempting to give an explicit definition of the required function by means of a description and then prove a theorem of the form:

for all a in a set well-ordered by <,
if f(x) exists for all x < a, then f(a) exists.

It will then follow by transfinite induction that $f(a)$ exists for all a in the well-ordered set. Only a logician would have objections to this use of the 'exists'. It is the purpose of this paper to lay these objections to rest by presenting a formal theory of descriptions that corresponds quite faithfully to such natural modes of reasoning.

After the author had explicitly formulated his plan (December 1963), he discovered that around 1959–60 several other logicians had come to nearly the same idea: notably Hailperin and Leblanc in [2], Hintikka in [4] and [5], Rescher in [8] and Smiley in [10]. These papers have not received the attention they deserve; thus a complete exposition including a full discussion of the semantics required seems desirable. Further the author wishes to show how the idea can be applied to a theory like Quine's system of virtual classes in [7]. Quine, following Russell, employs contextual definitions which avoid giving an independent meaning to the virtual classes. The author will replace Quine's definitions by axioms and present a simple semantical interpretation for the theory. The paper will conclude with a model-theoretic discussion of eliminability of notions by contextual definitions. There is an interesting problem here that is left open.

The author is indebted to Professors Hintikka, D. Kaplan, Kreisel, Mostowski, Quine, A. Robinson, Suszko, Suppes, and Tarski who were kind enough to comment on earlier versions of this paper.

1. *Descriptions*

To simplify matters let us consider a first-order logic with just one non-logical constant: a binary predicate symbol R. The logical symbols are ¬ (for negation), → (for implication), ∀ (for universal quantification), = (for equality) and I (for description). Note that I is an *inverted* capital I, which the author prefers to Russell's inverted iota. The other propositional connectives ∧, ∨, ↔, and the quantifier ∃ should be considered as introduced by definition, or better, the formulas involving them may be taken as abbreviations of formulas containing only the basic symbols. The individual variables are $v_0, v_1, \ldots, v_n, \ldots$. In the metalanguage x, y, z, w are metavariables ranging over the individual variables of the object language.

We define the notion of *term* and *formula* in the usual way:

(i) all variables are terms;
(ii) if α and β are terms, then $\alpha = \beta$ and $\alpha R \beta$ are (atomic) formulas;
(iii) if Φ and Ψ are formulas and x is a variable, then $\neg \Phi$, $[\Phi \rightarrow \Psi]$ and $\forall x \Phi$ are formulas; while $I x \Phi$ is a term.

The precise definition of *free* and *bound* variables need not concern us here, and it may be assumed as known.

To give a semantical interpretation of this language one first gives a structure $\langle A, R \rangle$, where A is a set (the domain of individuals) and R is a binary relation (the interpretation of the predicate symbol R). Then relative to the given structure one defines the *values* of formulas (they will be truth values) and terms (they will be objects) corresponding to the values given to the free variables. Before presenting this definition, it will be wise to consider some informal, motivating principles that have guided the choice of our precise formulation. Above all we wish to follow:

> *Principle 1. Bound individual variables should range only over the given domain of individuals*

The author will not attempt to define what he means by 'range over' since he is sure everyone understands this statement. In case someone does not, he should wait to see the formal definition of value for the quantified formulas and for the descriptive phrases. The second principle is not so important, but the author wishes to include it with an eye to future applications:

> *Principle 2. The domain of individuals should be allowed to be empty*

Finally, and very important for the basic idea of the paper, we have:

> *Principle 3. The values of terms and free variables need **not** belong to the domain of individuals*

To see in a simple example the usefulness of Principle 3, consider the question raised by Mostowski in [6] in connection with the empty domain. Namely, it is 'clear' that the formula

$$x R x \rightarrow x R x$$

is valid in all domains including the empty one. Similarly the sentence.

$$[x R x \rightarrow x R x] \rightarrow \exists y [y R y \rightarrow y R y]$$

is valid, because if x is given a value in the domain, then there is some

183

value of y to satisfy the formula within the quantifier. On the other hand, the formula

$$\exists\, y[y\; \mathsf{R}\; y \to y\; \mathsf{R}\; y]$$

is *not* valid in the empty domain; hence, the valid formulas are not closed under the rule of modus ponens when the empty domain is included. The fallacy (or better inconvenience) here lies in allowing the second formula to be valid. The first formula is completely valid no matter what value we assign to x. The second formula will fail in the empty domain, however, if we recognize Principle 3. To have a valid formula we must modify the implication to read:

$$[x\; \mathsf{R}\; x \to x\; \mathsf{R}\; x] \;\wedge\; \exists\, y[x = y] \to \exists\, y[y\; \mathsf{R}\; y \to y\; \mathsf{R}\; y]$$

We can make this point better after the precise definition of value is given.

Before presenting the definition of value, we must still decide what to do with the improper descriptive phrases. Under the guidance of Principle 3 we are no longer required to give such terms values *within* the given domain. Indeed, it seems much better to give an improper description a value definitely *outside* of the domain, thereby emphasizing its impropriety. The way to do this is to assign to each domain A a null entity $*_A$ such that $*_A \notin A$. This is much easier than trying to make the null entity belong to A as Frege wished (especially when A is empty!). Assuming a reasonable set theory, we could let $*_B$ be the set of all sets belonging to A which are non-self-members. Thus $*_A \subseteq A$ but $*_A \notin A$. Assuming the so-called Axiom of Regularity we could even take $*_A = A$. The exact choice is quite irrelevant as long as we agree $*_A \notin A$. Now we are ready for the definition of value.

In the following we shall write $\mathfrak{A} = \langle A, R \rangle$ for short; while s will denote an *assignment* which is simply a function whose domain is the set of integers $N = \{0, 1, 2, \ldots\}$. For $i \in N$, $s(i)$, or simply s_i, is the value we wish to assign to the variable v_i. We define

$$s(i/a) = (s \sim \{\langle i, s_i \rangle\}) \cup \{\langle i, a \rangle\},$$

in other words $s(i/a)$ is like s except the ith value s_i has been replaced by a. We shall read

$$\models_{\mathfrak{A}} \Phi[s]$$

as: the (truth) value of the formula Φ is *true* for the assignment s relative to the structure $\mathfrak{A}$, or better, s *satisfies* Φ in $\mathfrak{A}$, or also, Φ is *true* at s in $\mathfrak{A}$. The symbol

$$\| \alpha\, [s] \|_{\mathfrak{A}}$$

is read: the (object) value of the term α for the assignment s relative to the structure $\mathfrak{A}$, or better, the value of α at s in $\mathfrak{A}$. (Maybe the use of 'in' is bad here, because in view of Principle 3 $\| \alpha [s] \|_{\mathfrak{A}} \in A$ need not be so.) The exact clauses of the recursive definition of these notions are as follows:

$$\| v_i [s] \|_{\mathfrak{A}} = s_i$$

$\models_{\mathfrak{A}} \alpha \; R \; \beta[s] \; iff \langle \| \alpha [s] \|_{\mathfrak{A}}, \| \beta [s] \|_{\mathfrak{A}} \rangle \in R$

$\models_{\mathfrak{A}} \alpha = \beta[s] \; iff \| \alpha [s] \|_{\mathfrak{A}} = \| \beta [s] \|_{\mathfrak{A}}$

$\models_{\mathfrak{A}} \neg \; \Phi[s] \; iff \; not \models_{\mathfrak{A}} \Phi[s]$

$\models_{\mathfrak{A}} [\Phi \rightarrow \Psi] [s] \; iff \; if \models_{\mathfrak{A}} \Phi[s], \; then \models_{\mathfrak{A}} \Psi[s]$

$\models_{\mathfrak{A}} \forall \; v_i \; \Phi[s] \; iff \; for \; all \; a \in A, \models_{\mathfrak{A}} \Phi[s(i/a)]$

$$\| I \, v_i \, \Phi[s] \|_{\mathfrak{A}} = \begin{cases} a & \text{if } a \text{ is the unique element of } A \text{ such} \\ & \text{that } \models_{\mathfrak{A}} \Phi[s(i/a)]; \\ \ast_A & \text{if there is no such element.} \end{cases}$$

We say that Φ is *valid* in $\mathfrak{A}$ and write $\models_{\mathfrak{A}} \Phi$ to mean that $\models_{\mathfrak{A}} \Phi[s]$ holds for all assignments s. We say that Φ is *universally valid* and write $\models \Phi$ to mean that $\models_{\mathfrak{A}} \Phi$ holds for all structures $\mathfrak{A}$.

The question now is to find an eximatization of the universally valid formulas. Note first that these two rules are correct:

(MP)   *If* $\models \Phi$ *and* $\models [\Phi \rightarrow \Psi]$, *then* $\models \Psi$.

(UG)   *If* $\models [\Phi \rightarrow \Psi]$ *and* x *is not free in* Φ, *then*
        $\models [\Phi \rightarrow \forall \; x \Psi]$.

Next note that these schemata comprise only valid formulas:

(S0) Φ, *if* Φ *is a tautology*,

(S1) $\forall \; x [\Phi \rightarrow \Psi] \rightarrow [\forall \; x \; \Phi \rightarrow \forall \; x \; \Psi]$,

(S2) $\forall \; y \; \exists \; x [x = y]$,

(S3) $\alpha = \alpha$,

(S4) $\Phi(x/\alpha) \; \wedge \; \alpha = \beta \rightarrow \Phi(x/\beta)$,

where $\Phi(x/\alpha)$ is the result of substituting α for all the free occurrences of x in Φ rewriting bound variables if necessary.

In as much as $\exists \; x \; \Phi$ abbreviates $\neg \; \forall \; x \neg \; \Phi$, it is easy to see that the rule (UG) includes the rule

(EG)   *If* $\models [\Psi \rightarrow \Phi]$ *and* x *is not free in* Φ, *then*
        $\models [\exists \; x \Psi \rightarrow \Phi]$.

Also using the schemata, especially (S1), we can show that

$$\models \forall x\, \Phi \wedge \exists x\, \Psi \to \exists x\, [\Phi \wedge \Psi]$$

and

$$\models \forall x\, [\Phi \to \Psi] \to [\exists x\, \Phi \to \exists x\, \Psi].$$

Using these together with (S4) we establish easily the validity of the schema

(UI) $\quad \forall x\, \Phi \wedge \mathsf{E}\, x\, [x = \alpha] \to \Phi(x/\alpha),$

where x is not free in the term α. This is the correct version of the law of universal instantiation which is valid not only when the domain is empty, but also when the values of terms are allowed to be outside the domain. Using (S2) we can also show

$$\models \forall y[\forall x\, \Phi \to \Phi(x/y)],$$

which some authors would take as an axiom but which is superfluous when principles of equality are available. On the other hand (S2) is practically a special case of this last schema. Replace Φ by the formula $\neg\, x = y$ obtaining

$$\models \forall y[\forall x[\neg\, x = y] \to \neg\, y = y],$$

from which we derive

$$\models \forall y[y = y \to \exists x[x = y]],$$

and then

$$\models [\forall y[y = y] \to \forall y\, \exists x[x = y]].$$

In view of (S3), we can now easily obtain (S2). So it is really just a matter of taste as to which schemata are chosen as the fundamental ones.

To understand better what is going on here, consider the meaning of

$$\exists x[x = \alpha]$$

under our semantical rules. When x is not free in α, then

$$\models_{\mathfrak{A}} \exists x[x = \alpha]\, [s]$$

holds if and only if $\|\, \alpha[s]\, \|_{\mathfrak{A}} \in A$. Let us call the elements of A the (properly) existing individuals (of the particular structure $\mathfrak{A}$). Then to say that $\exists x[x = \alpha]$ is true means that the value of α exists (properly). Is that not exactly what $\exists x[x = \alpha]$ ought to mean? Thus if $\forall x\, \Phi$ is true, it is not correct to conclude that $\Phi\ (x/\alpha)$ is true *unless* the value of α exists. Again, is that not quite reasonable? 'To be is to be the value of a bound variable', as Quine would say.

Turning now to the descriptive operator we have first of all this valid schema:

$$(I\ 1)\quad \forall\, y[y = \mathbf{I}\, x\, \Phi \leftrightarrow \forall\, x[x = y \leftrightarrow \Phi]],$$

where y is not free in Φ. In words: an existing individual is the value of a descriptive phrase if and only if it is indeed the unique individual satisfying the formula of the phrase. As a consequence of (I 1) we have at once:

$$\models \exists\, y[y = \mathbf{I}\, x\, \Phi] \leftrightarrow \exists\, y\, \forall\, x[x = y \leftrightarrow \Phi];$$

that is, proper phrases are the only ones whose values exist. What of improper phrases? According to our definition of value they are all given the same value $*_A$. Now the term $\mathbf{I}\, v_0[\neg\, v_0 = v_0]$ clearly is an improper descriptive phrase; call it $*$ for short. The rest of the definition of value for descriptive phrases can be expressed by the schema:

$$(I\ 2)\quad \neg\, \exists\, y[y = \mathbf{I}\, x\, \Phi] \to * = \mathbf{I}\, x\, \Phi.$$

The converse of this implication already follows from (I 1).

One important reason for insisting that improper descriptions all assume the same improper value is to have this highly useful law of extensionality:

$$\models \forall\, x[\Phi \leftrightarrow \Psi] \to \mathbf{I}\, x\, \Phi = \mathbf{I}\, x\, \Psi$$

This would not be valid if one wanted 'the golden mountain' and 'the round square' to have different values. While making unkind remarks about 'the golden mountain', Russell also rejected this law of extensionality, which this author considers an unfortunate choice. Of course, Russell was particularly interested in eliminating descriptions altogether, and we now must discuss that question.

Using (I 1) and (I 2) we can almost completely eliminate descriptions, because we have the schema of elimination:

$$(IE)\quad \Psi(y/\mathbf{I}\, x\, \Phi) \leftrightarrow \exists\, y[\forall\, x[x = y \leftrightarrow \Phi] \wedge \Psi] \vee$$
$$[\neg\, \exists\, y\, \forall\, x[x = y \leftrightarrow \Phi] \wedge \Psi(y/*)],$$

where the variable y is not free in Φ. Several applications of (IE) will confine all occurrences of the descriptive operator to the following contexts:

$$v_i\, \mathsf{R}\, *, \quad *\, \mathsf{R}\, v_i, \quad *\, \mathsf{R}\, *,$$
$$v_i = *, \quad * = v_i, \quad * = *.$$

Now, assuming that a formula Θ has no free variables, the equality formulas can be eliminated, because the last one is true, and the first two are always false in contexts where the variable v_i is bound. To be able to eliminate descriptions completely we would have to add a new schema such as:

$$(\text{I } 3) \quad {\ast} = \alpha \lor {\ast} = \beta \to \neg\, \alpha \,\mathsf{R}\, \beta.$$

However, this schema is not valid with our present semantics. It *is* valid in those structures $\mathfrak{A} = \langle A, R \rangle$, where $R \subseteq A \times A$. This restriction that the relation of a structure should be confined to existing individuals is not at all desirable, as we shall see when we discuss Quine's virtual classes.

We could have validated (I 3) by choosing ${\ast}_A$ to lie outside the field of the relation R. Again this is not too desirable, because it is often felt that the valid formulas should be closed under substitution of formulas for predicate symbols. Clearly (I 3) becomes invalid when R is replaced by $=$. So for pure logic we reject (I 3). When giving axioms for a theory on the other hand, a schema like (I 3) might be very reasonable. Then in that theory complete elimination of descriptions from sentences would be possible.

In summary the author feels that it is fair to say that the theory of descriptions presented here combines the best features of Russell's and Frege's theories. With Frege, we preserve the laws of identity and the extensionality of the descriptive operator without giving improper descriptions an unintended proper designation. Assuming the very reasonable (I 3), we would be in complete agreement with Russell in non-equality atomic contexts, for from (I 3) we could derive:

$$\models \alpha \,\mathsf{R}\, \mathbf{I}\, x\, \Phi \leftrightarrow \exists\, y[\forall\, x[x = y \leftrightarrow \Phi] \land \alpha \,\mathsf{R}\, y].$$

This possibility is of course excluded by Frege.

We shall not pause here to give the proof that every valid formula can be derived from (S0)–(S4), (I 1)–(I 2) by the rules (MP) and (UG), because in Section 3 a more general completeness proof will be presented in full.

2. *Virtual Classes*

In his new book [7] Professor Quine makes thorough use of what he calls *virtual classes* to simplify the development and comparison of various systems of set theory. For example, the different kinds of existential assumptions about the real classes can be presented in a uniform manner in Quine's notation. More than that, with mild assumptions on real classes, the reduction of arithmetic to class theory can be very conveniently described in Quine's style; so the device has considerable appeal.

In the author's opinion, the only thing missing in Quine's presentation is a semantical analysis of the notion of virtual classes. No doubt Quine feels no need for such an analysis, since his class symbols are all eliminable by design. Virtual classes function mainly as an aid in condensing long formulas; the programme is successful owing to the transfer of standard set-theoretical notions from the real to the virtual. Nevertheless, semantical insights can be helpful in understanding a formal system; especially when one can check formulas without having to first eliminate the contextually defined notions. In the presentation to be given here, virtual classes will be treated axiomatically, Quine's contextual definitions will be proved as theorems, and the model theory for the system will naturally suggest itself along the lines of what we did for descriptions.

Our language will be much like the first-order language of Section 1, except we replace the predicate symbol R by the symbol $\in$ for membership. Further we drop the descriptive operator for the time being and use instead the operator of class abstraction; thus the terms are now either single variables or expressions of the form

$$\{x : \Phi\}$$

where x is a variable and Φ a formula. The construction of compound formulas proceeds as before.

As axioms and rules of inference for the theory we use (MP), (UG), and (S0)–(S4) as before, except the notions of terms and formulas must be understood in the new sense. In addition we employ three principles governing the behaviour of membership and abstraction:

(Q 1) $\forall y[y \in \alpha \leftrightarrow y \in \beta] \to \alpha = \beta$,

(Q 2) $\alpha \in \beta \to \exists y[y = \alpha]$,

(Q 3) $\forall y[y \in \{x : \Phi\} \leftrightarrow \exists x[x = y \land \Phi]]$,

where the variable y is not free in α, β, or Φ. The last schema could also have been written in the form

(Q 3′) $\forall y[y \in \{x : \Phi\} \leftrightarrow \Phi(x/y)]$

Combining (Q 2) and (Q 3) note that

(Q 3″) $\alpha \in \{x : \Phi\} \leftrightarrow \exists x[x = \alpha] \land \Phi(x/\alpha)$

is a consequence, where x is not free in the term α.

It is quite easy to see that every theorem provable in the present theory is provable in Quine's theory. Note that (S3) and (S4) are Quine's 6.4 and 6.6. Next (Q 1) follows from Quine's 2.7; (Q 2) follows from 6.9 and 6.12; and (Q 3) is given on p. 17 of [6]. Conversely, except for our allowing the empty domain of (real) individuals, all of Quine's theory can be deduced from ours. In particular, the contextual definitions 2.1, 2.7, and 5.5 are provable at once as biconditionals, and the lone axiom 4.1 is a special case of (S4). We are not concerned here with the additional axioms on the existence of real classes.

To discuss the models of Quine's theory, we first remark that having virtual class forces us to contemplate *many* improper individuals and not just *one* as was the case for descriptions. However, a virtual class is completely determined by its real members. So let us take as models structures of the form $\mathfrak{A} = \langle A, E \rangle$, where $E \subseteq A \times A$, and where the relation E is *extensional* in A. In other words the structure $\mathfrak{A}$ must satisfy the sentence

$$\forall x \, \forall x'[\forall y[y \in x \leftrightarrow y \in x'] \to x = x']$$

in the usual sense. The *elements* of A will correspond to the real classes; while the *subsets* of A will correspond to the virtual classes—well, not quite. We must identify the real classes with the virtual classes having the same members. This is best done by making the values of terms *always* be subsets of A. To get the correspondence between the elements of A and the subsets of A we define a function $\dot{E}$ on A such that for $a \in A$,

$$\dot{E}(a) = \{b \in A : \langle b, a \rangle \in E\}.$$

By virtue of the extensionality of E, this is a one-one correspondence between elements of A and certain subsets of A. Next in the definition of value we make these changes:

$$\models_{\mathfrak{A}} \alpha \in \beta[s] \textit{ iff for some } a \in \|\beta[s]\|_{\mathfrak{A}}, \dot{E}(a) = \|\alpha[s]\|_{\mathfrak{A}}.$$
$$\models_{\mathfrak{A}} \forall v_i \, \Phi[s] \textit{ iff for all } a \in A, \models_{\mathfrak{A}} \Phi[s(i/\dot{E}(a))]$$
$$\|\{v_i : \Phi\}\|_{\mathfrak{A}} = \{a \in A : \models \Phi[s(i/\dot{E}(a))]\}$$

All the other clauses remain the same. In the definition of validity we make the restriction that assignments should have *only* subsets of A as values. Even if A is empty there is one subset of A; so this restriction does not cause any trouble.

Note that if $a, b \in A$ and $s_0 = \dot{E}(a)$ and $s_1 = \dot{E}(b)$, then

$$\models_{\mathfrak{A}} v_0 \in v_1[s] \textit{ iff } \langle a, b \rangle \in E,$$

and

$$\models_{\mathfrak{A}} v_0 = v_1[s] \textit{ iff } a = b.$$

Hence, if Φ is a formula without free variables and without the abstraction operator, then Φ is true in $\mathfrak{A}$ in the new sense if and only if it is true in the sense of Section 1.

It is easily checked that all the schemata (S0)–(S4) and (Q 1)–(Q 3) are valid in all extensional structures. The converse, that all formulas valid in all extensional structures are provable in the present theory, will follow from the completeness theorem of Section 3. Thus we have a full explanation of the model theory for Quine's system.

When he introduced the descriptive operator into his system, Quine, the modern day champion of contextual definition, abandoned the Russell approach in favour of Frege's idea. That seems a bit odd, does it not? The explanation is probably this: with Russell's elimination the formula $\alpha = \alpha$ is not always valid, whereas Quine wants this law of equality. Besides, it is a waste of effort to introduce new operators by contextual definition when an explicit definition is at hand. Quine chose this definition (more or less):

$$\mathbf{I}\, x\, \Phi = \{x : \exists\, y[\forall\, x[x = y \leftrightarrow \Phi] \wedge z \in y]\}.$$

Thus when $\neg\, \exists\, y\, \forall\, x[x = y \leftrightarrow \Phi]$ holds, $\mathbf{I}\, x\, \Phi$ denotes the empty class. Since Quine wants the empty class to be a real class, we see that the improper description is behaving in the Fregean manner.

Another definition was open to Quine, however, namely:

$$\mathbf{I}\, x\, \Phi = \{z : \exists\, y[\forall\, x[x = y \leftrightarrow \Phi] \wedge z \in y] \vee$$
$$[\neg\, \exists\, y\, \wedge\, x\, [x = y \leftrightarrow \Phi] \wedge \neg\, z \in z]\}$$

If we let Δ be the term $\{z : \neg\, z \in z\}$, then by the argument of the Russell paradox we can prove that

$$\neg\, \exists\, y[y = \Delta].$$

Hence, with the revised definition we prove exactly (I 1) and (I 2) with $*$ replaced by Δ. Of course $* = \Delta$ is at once provable, so the former theory is recaptured. The author strongly feels that this path to descriptions is much more in harmony with the concept of virtual classes than is the version adopted by Quine.[1]

Let us see now what happens to the elimination of descriptions with the definition just proposed. In view of (Q 2) we have first:

$$\mathbf{I}\, x\, \Phi \in \beta \leftrightarrow \exists\, y[\forall\, x[x = y \leftrightarrow \Phi] \wedge y \in \beta],$$

where y is not free in Φ or β. That would please Russell. In the other argument place we have:

[1] See, however, Professor Quine's remarks quoted at the end of this section.

$$\alpha \in \mathbf{I} \, x \, \Phi \leftrightarrow \exists \, y[\forall \, x[x = y \leftrightarrow \Phi] \wedge \alpha \in y] \vee$$
$$[\neg \, \exists \, y \, \forall \, x[x = y \leftrightarrow \Phi] \wedge \exists \, y[y = \alpha \wedge \neg \, y \in y]].$$

That would probably confound followers of Russell or Frege; the author hopes it is not too displeasing to the Quine school, however.

Parallel to the revision of the definition of descriptions, the author would like to also suggest a revision of Quine's definition of *function value*. Let us assume along with Quine enough axioms to guarantee the existence of ordered pairs of real classes. In the author's notation, the definition of function value will read:

$$\phi(\xi) = \mathbf{I} \, y \, \exists \, x[x = \xi \wedge \langle y, x \rangle \in \phi],$$

where x and y are variables not free in ϕ and ξ. Quine gave as his definition:

$$\phi(\xi) = \mathbf{I} \, y[\langle y, \xi \rangle \in \phi].$$

This is 'defective' not only because the wrong kind of description was used, but because when ξ does not exist (i.e. $\neg \, \exists \, x[x = \xi]$), then

$$\langle y, \xi \rangle = \{\{y\}, \{y, \xi\}\} = \{\{y\}\} = \langle y, y \rangle.$$

By chance there might be a unique y with $\langle y, y \rangle \in \phi$, and we are uncomfortable. Now Quine avoids this unpleasantness by restricting attention to the class

$$arg \, \phi = \{x : \exists \, z \, \forall \, y[y = z \leftrightarrow \langle y, x \rangle \in \phi]\}$$

Using the proposed *new* definition we can simplify this last equation to:

$$arg \, \phi = \{x : \exists \, y[y = \phi(x)]\}.$$

Further, there is no need to avoid unintended function values, for we can prove quite generally:

$$\exists \, y[y = \phi(\xi)] \leftrightarrow \xi \in arg \, \phi.$$

This last biconditional reads so well that it seems justification enough for the revised definition. (This discussion of function value is improved over an earlier version at the suggestion of David Kaplan.) The general principle to be applied to such questions is this: things should exist only when it is intended that they exist. It seems quite remarkable to the author that there is a flexible enough formalism that actually allows us to follow this principle.

In connection with these suggestions, Professor Quine wrote to the author on May 3, 1965, as follows:

'The redefinition of description and of function value that you propose sacrifices an advantage that I had gone out of my way for: the freedom to substitute descriptions for bound variables without regard to special existence premisses. This freedom, touched on in pp. 58, 68, and 107 of *Set Theory and Its Logic*, covers a lot, since so many notations are defined as function values and ultimately as descriptions. It even covers function values where function and argument are rendered by Greek letters, without presumption of existence; cf. p. 68. Also it covers arithmetical expressions containing Greek letters; cf. p. 107. Without this freedom the book would be appreciably more laboured. Perhaps you could devise alternative conventions, on your basis, that would work smoothly too; but then I'd want to see some trial runs for comparison.'

Professor Quine is quite justified in asking for trial runs for comparison, and the author will try to apply these comparisons in future publications. For the time being the reader is asked to consider the merits of the proposal on the grounds of 'naturalness' as indicated above. He should also imagine having to make all existential assumptions explicit, and ask himself whether unrestricted substitution is to be preferred over the gain of information obtained by using formulas with explicitly displayed assumptions.

3. *General operators*

The system that we shall treat here will be of the same type as the systems of Sections 1 and 2. The language will involve a binary predicate symbol R and a variable binding operator O of the same syntactical category as the operators of description and abstraction. Thus

$$O \, x \, \Phi$$

is a term when x is a variable and Φ is a formula. As before we shall not assume that the values of terms are necessarily in the range of the individual variables. A convenient way to express this is to consider structures of the form

$$\mathbb{A} = \langle A, A_*, R, O \rangle,$$

where A is a set (the domain of properly existing individuals), A_* is a *non-empty* superset of A (the domain of 'improper' individuals), R is a binary relation where $R \subseteq A_* \times A_*$, and O is a function defined on *subsets* of A taking values in A_*. The definition of value is now modified in this particular:

$$\| \, O \, v_i \, \Phi[s] \, \|_{\mathbb{A}} = O(\{a \in A : \, |=_{\mathbb{A}} \Phi[s(i/a)]\})$$

193

Further, the definition of validity is changed so that $\models_{\mathfrak{A}} \Phi$ means that $\models_{\mathfrak{A}} \Phi[s]$ only for assignments s where the values of the function s are *all* in the set A_*. When the set A_* is explicitly mentioned it is not reasonable to allow the values of assignments to the free variables to be completely arbitrary.

If $\mathfrak{A} = \langle A, R \rangle$ is a structure in the sense of Section 1, then we can correlate with it a structure in the new sense, namely:

$$\mathfrak{A}_* = \langle A, A_*, R, I \rangle,$$

where

$$A_* = A \cup \{ *_A \} \cup \text{field } (R),$$

and where I is defined on subsets $X \subseteq A$ so that:

$$I(X) = \begin{cases} a & \text{if } X = \{a\}, \\ *_A & \text{if } X \neq \{a\} \text{ for all } a \in A. \end{cases}$$

It is then easy to prove that for an assignment s with values in A_*, $\models_{\mathfrak{A}} \Phi[s]$ holds in the old sense if and only if $\models_{\mathfrak{A}*} \Phi[s]$ holds in the new sense, and that $\| \alpha[s] \|_{\mathfrak{A}} = \| \alpha[s] \|_{\mathfrak{A}*}$. Of course the symbol O should be replaced by $\mathbf{I}$ to make sense of this last statement.

If $\mathfrak{A} = \langle A, E \rangle$ is a structure in the sense of Section 2, then the correlated structure is

$$\mathfrak{A}_0 = \langle A_0, A_*, E_0, J \rangle,$$

where $A_0 = \{ \dot{E}(a) : a \in A \}$, A_* is the set of all subsets of A, J is the identity function on A_*, and the relation E_0 is defined for $X, Y \in A_*$ so that:

$$X E_0 Y \text{ iff for some } a \in Y, \dot{E}(a) = X.$$

Again, for assignments with values in A_*, the old and new definitions of value agree completely. Therefore, the structures considered here do properly generalize those used in earlier examples.

Aside from (S0)–(S4) which are all valid in the present sense, we have also

$$(O1) \qquad [\forall x [\Phi \leftrightarrow \Psi] \to \mathsf{O}\, x\, \Phi = \mathsf{O}\, x\, \Psi],$$

and

$$(O2) \qquad \mathsf{O}\, x\, \Phi = \mathsf{O}\, y\, \Phi(x/y),$$

where the variable y is not free in Φ.

These kinds of schemata were not needed explicitly in Sections 1 and 2 because the required formulas were in each case deducible

194

from the others given. In the general case they are the only schemata required that involves the operator O in a special way. We want now to show that a formula is universally valid if and only if it is deducible from (S0)–(S4), (O1), (O2) by the rules (MP) and (UG). Let $\vdash \Phi$ mean that the formula Φ is so deducible. All we need to prove is that if not $\vdash \Phi$, then there is a structure $\mathfrak{A}$ and an assignment s such that not $\models_{\mathfrak{A}} \Phi[s]$.

To this end let Φ_0 be a particular formula such that not $\vdash \Phi_0$. Let

$$\Psi_0, \Psi_1, \ldots, \Psi_n, \ldots$$

be a list containing *every* formula at least once such that Ψ_0 is $\neg \Phi_0$, and if Ψ_n is of the form

$$\neg \forall v_i \Phi$$

then Ψ_{n+1} is of the form

$$\exists v_{j+1}[v_{j+1} = v_j] \wedge \neg \Phi(v_i/v_j),$$

where v_j is the first variable not free in $\Psi_0, \Psi_1, \ldots, \Psi_n$. It is easy to show that such a sequence exists. We define by recursion the sequence of formulas

$$\Psi_0', \Psi_1', \ldots, \Psi_n', \ldots$$

where Ψ_n' is $\neg \Psi_n$ or Ψ_n according as

$$\vdash [\Psi_0' \wedge \ldots \wedge \Psi_{n-1}' \to \neg \Psi_n]$$

or not.

We let

$$M = \{\Psi_n' : n \in N\}.$$

Clearly $\Psi_0' \in M$ and the set M of formulas has these properties:

(i)   if $\vdash \Phi$, then $\Phi \in M$,

(ii) $\neg \Phi \in M$ iff $\Phi \notin M$,

(iii) $[\Phi \to \Psi] \in M$ iff $\Phi \notin M$ or $\Psi \in M$,

(iv) $\forall v_i \Phi \in M$ iff for all j if $\exists v_{j+1}[v_{j+1} = v_j] \in M$, then $\Phi(v_i/v_j) \in M$.

So far the details of the proof are just as in any standard version as the completeness proof for first-order logic based on the method due to Henkin.

Let T be the set of all terms, and define an equivalence relation $\equiv$ on the set T by the condition that

$$\alpha \equiv \beta \ \textit{iff} \ [\alpha = \beta] \ \epsilon \ M$$

The equivalence class of a term α is denoted by $\alpha/\equiv$. We define

$$A = \{v_j/\equiv \ : \ \exists \ v_{j+1}[v_{j+1} = v_j] \ \epsilon \ M\},$$

and

$$A_* = \{\alpha/\equiv \ : \ \alpha \ \epsilon \ T\}.$$

The relation $R \subseteq A_* \times A_*$ is defined by the equation

$$R = \{\langle\alpha/\equiv, \beta/\equiv\rangle : [\alpha \ R \ \beta] \ \epsilon \ M\},$$

and the operator O is defined for $X \subseteq A$ so that:

$$O(X) = \begin{cases} \mathsf{O} \ v_i \ \Phi/\equiv \ \textit{if} \ X = \{v_j/\equiv \ \epsilon \ A : \Phi(v_i/v_j) \ \epsilon \ M\} \\ v_0/\equiv \ \textit{if there is no such formula} \ \Phi. \end{cases}$$

For the particular assignment s where $s_i = v_i/\equiv$, we wish to show that $\models_{\mathfrak{A}} \Phi_0[s]$ does not hold where $\mathfrak{A} = \langle A, A_*, R, O\rangle$ is the structure just defined. This cannot be done quite directly: one must prove by induction that if Φ is a formula, α is a term, and s is an assignment where $s_i = \alpha_i/\equiv$, then

$$\models_{\mathfrak{A}} \Phi[s] \ \textit{iff} \ \Phi(v_0/\alpha_0, v_1/\alpha_1, \ldots, v_n/\alpha_n, \ldots) \ \epsilon \ M,$$

and

$$\| \ \alpha[s] \ \|_{\mathfrak{A}} = \alpha(v_0/\alpha_0, v_1/\alpha_1, \ldots, v_n/\alpha_n, \ldots)/\equiv,$$

where the notation on the right-hand sides indicates simultaneous substitution of terms for free variables. Again this step is just like the corresponding step in the usual proofs, and conditions (i)–(iv) on M were explicitly chosen so that the argument would work out.

In case the additional axioms of Sections 1 or 2 were added, the structure $\mathfrak{A}$ just obtained could be modified directly to obtain the structure in the earlier sense that is required.

4. *Eliminability*

A *sentence* is a formula without free variables. A *theory* is a set of sentences containing all universally valid sentences and closed under the rule of *modus ponens*. The operator O is *eliminable* in a theory T, if for each formula Φ there is a formula Ψ not containing O such that

$$\forall \ v_0 \ \forall \ v_1 \ldots \forall \ v_{m-1}[\Phi \leftrightarrow \Psi]$$

belongs to T, where the free variables of Φ and Ψ are among v_0, $v_1, \ldots, v_{m-1}$.

The theory based on schemata (I 1)–(I 3) from Section 1 (where O replaces the symbol I) is a theory in which O is eliminable. Similarly for the theory based on (Q 1)–(Q 3) (where O replaces the abstraction operator). The purpose of this section is to give necessary and sufficient model-theoretic conditions for O to be eliminable in a theory T. The conditions found will be very close to those of Beth's Definability Theorem (cf. [9]).

If $\mathfrak{A} = \langle A, A_*, R, O \rangle$ and $\mathfrak{A}' = \langle A', A'_*, R', O' \rangle$ are two structures, we say that $\mathfrak{A}$ and $\mathfrak{A}'$ are *weakly isomorphic* if there is a one-one function mapping the set A on to the set A' such that for all $a, b \in A$,

$$\langle a, b \rangle \in R \text{ iff } \langle f(a), f(b) \rangle \in R'.$$

When s is an assignment with values in A, we let $f((s))$ denote the assignment with values in A' such that

$$f((s))_i = f(s_i).$$

The condition of f to give a weak isomorphism can be equivalently stated as:

$$\models_{\mathfrak{A}} \Phi[s] \text{ iff } \models_{\mathfrak{A}} \Phi[f((s))]$$

for all assignments s with values in A and all formulas Φ not containing the operator O. We shall say that f gives a *strong isomorphism* if this last biconditional holds for *arbitrary* formulas Φ.

A *model* for a theory is of course a structure for which all sentences of the theory are true. We can now state the theorem on eliminability:

The operator O is eliminable in a theory T if and only if whenever two models of T are weakly isomorphic by a certain one-one function, they are also strongly isomorphic by the same function.

If O is eliminable in T, then it is clear that weak isomorphism implies strong isomorphism. The converse will be proved by applying Beth's theorem to a suitable first-order theory with many predicate symbols but without operators.

Let T be a theory for which weak isomorphism implies strong isomorphism. Introduce new predicate symbols S^Φ corresponding to each formula Φ in the original sense. The predicate S^Φ will be a m-place predicate, where m is the least integer such that the free variables of Φ are among $v_0, v_1, \ldots, v_{m-1}$. Consider the extension of T obtained by adjoining these sentences as axioms:

$$\forall v_0 \, \forall v_1 \ldots \forall v_{m-1} [S^\Phi(v_0, v_1, \ldots, v_{m-1}) \leftrightarrow \Phi].$$

The theory T_0 is the set of sentences of the extension of T involving

197

the predicates R and S^Φ but *not* O. It is obvious that O is eliminable in T if and only if *all* the S^Φ are definable in T_0 in terms of the predicate R in the ordinary sense of first-order definability.

According to Beth's theorem, to show that the S^Φ are definable in terms of R it is enough to show that two models

$$\mathfrak{A}_0 = \langle A, R_0, \ldots, S^\Phi, \ldots \rangle$$

and

$$\mathfrak{A}_0' = \langle A', R_0', \ldots, S'^\Phi, \ldots \rangle$$

of T_0, where $\langle A, R_0 \rangle$ and $\langle A', R_0' \rangle$ are isomorphic by a function f, are also isomorphic by the same function f. To prove this we will construct structures

$$\mathfrak{A} = \langle A, A_*, R, O \rangle$$
$$\mathfrak{A}' = \langle A', A_*', R', O' \rangle$$

such that for all assignments s with values in A and for all formulas Φ

$$\models_{\mathfrak{A}_0} S^\Phi(v_0, v_1, \ldots, v_{m-1})\,[s]\ \textit{iff}\ \models_{\mathfrak{A}} \Phi[s];$$

similarly for $\mathfrak{A}_0'$ and $\mathfrak{A}'$. Now by assumption $\langle A, R_0 \rangle$ and $\langle A', R_0' \rangle$ are isomorphic. Hence $\mathfrak{A}$ and $\mathfrak{A}_0'$ are weakly isomorphic; therefore strongly isomorphic. But this means that $\mathfrak{A}_0$ and $\mathfrak{A}_0'$ are isomorphic, all by the same function we started with. It will be enough to show how to construct $\mathfrak{A}$ from $\mathfrak{A}_0$; actually it will be easier to construct a structure $\bar{\mathfrak{A}}$ which is strongly isomorphic to the structure we want.

First let U be the set of all pairs $\langle \alpha, s \rangle$ where α is a term of the original language and s is an assignment with values in A. We define an equivalence relation $\equiv$ on the set U:

$$\langle \alpha, s \rangle \equiv \langle \beta, t \rangle\ \textit{iff}\ \models_{\mathfrak{A}_0} S^{\alpha = \beta'}(v_0, \ldots, v_{m-1}, v_m, \ldots, v_{m+n-1})\,[u],$$

where m is the least integer such that the free variables of α are among $v_0, \ldots, v_{m-1}$; n is the least integer such that the free variables of β are among $v_0, \ldots, v_{n-1}$; β' is the term $\beta(v_0/v_m, \ldots, v_{n-1}/v_{m+n-1})$; and u is the assignment where

$$u_i = \begin{cases} s_i\ \textit{if}\ i < m, \\ t_{i-m}\ \textit{if}\ i \geqslant m. \end{cases}$$

We let $\langle \alpha, s \rangle/\equiv$ be the equivalence class of $\langle \alpha, s \rangle$ in U and put

$$\bar{A}^* = \{\langle \alpha, s \rangle/\equiv\ :\ \langle \alpha, s \rangle \in U\}.$$

and

$$\bar{A} = \{\langle v_0, s \rangle/\equiv\ :\ \langle v_0, s \rangle \in U\}$$

We note that A and $\bar{A}$ are in a one-one correspondence by the function e such that for $a \in A$,

$$e(a) = \langle v_0, s \rangle / \equiv$$

for all assignments s with $s_0 = a$. The relation $\bar{R}$ on $\bar{A}_*$ is such that

$$\langle \langle \alpha, s \rangle / \equiv, \langle \beta, t \rangle / \equiv \rangle \in \bar{R} \text{ iff}$$
$$\models_{\text{ZO}} S^{\alpha R \beta'}(v_0, \ldots, v_{m-1}, v_m, \ldots, v_{m+n-1}) [u],$$

where m, n, β' and u are determined as before. Finally to define $\bar{O}$, we let r be a fixed assignment with values in A and for $X \subseteq \bar{A}$ we set

$$\bar{O}(X) = \begin{cases} \langle O v_i \, \Phi, s \rangle / \equiv & \text{if } X = \\ & \{e(a) \in \bar{A} : \models_{\text{ZO}} S_\Phi (v_0, \ldots, v_{m-1}) [s(i/a)]\} \\ \langle v_0, r \rangle / \equiv & \text{if there is no such formula } \Phi \text{ and assignment } s. \end{cases}$$

The desired properties of the structure

$$\overline{\mathfrak{A}} = \langle \bar{A}, \bar{A}_*, \bar{R}, \bar{O} \rangle$$

will be established by proving for all formulas Φ, all terms α, and all assignments s with values in A that

$$\models_{\overline{\mathfrak{A}}} \Phi[e((s))] \text{ iff } \models_{\text{ZO}} S^\Phi(v_0, \ldots, v_{m-1}) [s],$$

and

$$\| \alpha[e((s))] \|_{\overline{\mathfrak{A}}} = \langle \alpha, s \rangle / \equiv.$$

This result on eliminability is not very satisfactory. The operators of Sections 1 and 2 are eliminable in a much stronger sense: for example, the schema (IE) gives practically a wholesale way of eliminating the descriptive operator. Similar things may be said for Quine's abstraction operator. In other words to eliminate an occurrence of $I\,x\,\Phi$ we need only examine the context in which this term is found; we do not have to make our elimination depend on any peculiarities of the formula Φ within the scope of the operator. The author has no idea what kind of model-theoretic conditions would correspond to this *uniform* eliminability that we always have when operators are introduced by contextual definitions. It seems like an interesting problem.

BIBLIOGRAPHY

1. P. Bernays and A. A. Fraenkel. *Axiomatic set theory*, Amsterdam (1958), 226 pp.
2. T. Hailperin and H. Leblanc. 'Non-designating singular terms.' *The philosophical review*, vol 68 (1959), pp. 239–243.

3. D. Hilbert and P. Bernays. *Grundlagen der Mathematik*, Bd. I (1934), Bd. II (1939), Berlin, 471 + 498 pp.
4. J. Hintikka. 'Existential presuppositions and existential commitments.' *The journal of philosophy*, vol. 56 (1959), pp. 125–137.
5. J. Hintikka. 'Towards a theory of definite descriptions.' *Analysis* (Oxford), vol. 19, no. 4 (1959), pp. 79–85.
6. A. Mostowski. 'On the rules of proof in the pure functional calculus of the first order.' *The Journal of Symbolic Logic*, vol. 16 (1951), pp. 107–111.
7. W. V. Quine. *Set theory and its logic*, Harvard (1963), xv + 359 pp.
8. N. Rescher. 'On the logic of existence and denotation.' *The philosophical review*, vol. 69 (1959), pp. 157–180.
9. A. Robinson. *Introduction to model theory and to the metamathematics of algebra*, Amsterdam (1963), ix + 284 pp.
10. T. Smiley. 'Sense without denotation.' *Analysis* (Oxford), vol. 20, no. 4 (1960), pp. 125–135.

17

GEORG KREISEL

Mathematical logic: what has it done for the philosophy of mathematics?

It is a common place that there are two aspects to mathematical logic. It is a part of (pure) mathematics: the theory of formal systems belongs to combinatorial arithmetic, model theory to set theory. But also, perhaps primarily, it is intended as a tool in the philosophy of mathematics; just as other mathematics, for example the theory of partial differential equations, is a tool in what used to be called natural philosophy. The mathematical apparatus is not only used for solving advanced problems, but (as in the case of physics) for the very formulation of philosophical views. The views to be discussed concern this question:

In what terms is our mathematical experience to be analysed? What is significant in this experience and what are its basic elements? The answers will determine what grammatical rules are valid (i.e. lead to meaningful assertions according to our analysis) and what principles of evidence hold.

In speaking of *philosophy* of mathematics as distinct from technical mathematics one supposes that the kind of analysis here required differs seriously from everyday reflection of the mathematician: it is more *fundamental or basic*. Philosophical views differ on what is regarded as fundamental; whether there is such a thing will be discussed in §0(*a*) and throughout the essay.

§1 treats an analysis in terms of basic *objects* and the view which, roughly, says: Y is more basic than X if X is *built up* from Y by means of *basic* operations, which are taken to be the operations of set theory. (This is one—rather sharp—formulation of a traditional *realist* view.)

§2 treats several analyses in terms of *knowledge* where, roughly, one says: (the object or assertion) X is more basic than Y if X is closer to *immediate experience* than Y. The views considered differ in what they regard as *given in experience*. Strict or old fashioned formalism develops a traditional *mechanistic* or *nominalistic* view, finitism a view of mathematical knowledge based on *pure intuition*, and intuitionism a wider traditional *idealistic* or *psychological* view.

Throughout, some kind of *formalization* turns out to be an

important tool: for instance so-called first order formalization in §1(a), higher order in §3. This plays the same sort of double role that mathematics plays in the sciences: it describes in compact form the (external) facts of mathematics as it presents itself to us, that is to the more or less experienced mathematician; but also it formulates our views on, sometimes called: theories of, the basic objects, whether the latter are thought of realistically or as elements of immediate experience.

Successes of mathematical logic. What seems to me most striking (*and often overlooked*) is this: Time and again it has turned out that traditional notions in philosophy have an essentially unambiguous formulation when one thinks about them—certainly no less so than, for instance, such traditional conceptions of physical reality as atomism (of the Greeks). And also, when so formulated by essential use of mathematical logic, they have non trivial consequences for the analysis of mathematical experience. This discovery conflicts with one's naïve impression: for, a first examination of the traditional notions almost always reveals *some* unexpected ambiguities, and the shock leads one to suppose that further examination might produce an *endless* chain of ambiguities: in other words, that there is nothing behind these notions. Instead, in many cases relatively few basic distinctions were enough to get decisive results (unaffected by possible ambiguities); for the general principle, cf. §0(c), examples occur throughout the text. Among them are the well known cases (i) the notion of mechanical process, its stability in the sense that apparently different formulations lead to the same results, its use for stating precisely the formalist position and the notion of *formal rigour*: all this is done in the theory of recursive functions; (ii) the notion of aggregate which is analysed by means of the hierarchy (theory) of types, and, of course, (iii) the notions of logical validity and logical inference which are analysed, at least for an important class of formulae, by means of (first order) predicate logic, §3(a). Less conclusive, but not negligible results have been obtained on the notions of finitist, predicative and intuitionistic proof, §2.

Besides their intrinsic interest, the results are important as *object lessons*: once one has seen, for instance, the simple considerations in §3(a) (concerning Gödel's completeness theorem), *one cannot doubt the possibility of philosophical proof* or, as one might put it, of *informal rigour*; the somewhat more sophisticated considerations in §3(b) (concerning Gödel's incompleteness theorem supported by an analysis of mechanical processes) leave *no doubt about the possibility of refuting rigorously a philosophic position*, here: mechanism, from general, essential features of the position (and not on the basis of some unfortunate formulation!). More specifically, Hilbert's programme as formulated in §2(b) shows once and for all: *no crude argument can establish the* (positivist-pragmatist) *contention that questions of evidence are inherently arbitrary.* Further (this is perhaps a matter of personal taste) I am much impressed by two more isolated conclusions. First, the role of empirical (statistical) support. In 1930 (I believe) the 'statistical' support for each of the following propositions was overwhelming:

Every (intuitively) valid first order logical formula is formally derivable by means of the formal rules of predicate logic.

Every (intuitively) provable arithmetic formula is formally derivable by means of the formal rules of set theory.

§3(a) establishes the first (1930), §3(b) refutes the second (1931). Second, the role of scientific experience in taking ideas seriously. There is the old and familiar idea, or: idealization, which regards a *thought* and, in particular, a *proof* of a general proposition as an infinite object. Could one fail to take the idea seriously, at least in the sense that infinite objects are better *representations* of proofs than the words we use to communicate proofs, after having seen the wonderfully efficient and elegant theory of infinite proof figures?, cf. §2(b).

Failures of mathematical logic. Time and again mathematical logic (or: the community of logicians) *has failed to build on its own discoveries.* Certainly, the first discovery, namely formalization, was built on; it is the basis of all the detailed work in §1, 2. But when the first naïve ideas (assumptions) turned out to be wrong people essentially gave up and turned to mathematical 'refinements': there is no evidence that conceptually fruitful ideas were suggested by this (though there is, I think, no *a priori* reason why this should not be so); and, despite the undoubted interest of these refinements, there is, I think, little doubt that, for instance, *sub specie aeternitatis* the completeness of predicate logic is more interesting than all its applications put together. The following startling failures are both connected with Gödel's incompleteness theorems. His first incompleteness theorem makes clear that the known axioms (of arithmetic or set theory) leave many problems formally undecided; and recent results of Cohen and others show that several quite familiar problems are among them. The process, whatever it was, which led to the known axioms is relevant to the technical progress of mathematics. Instead of taking this question more seriously after Gödel's discovery, most logicians took it less seriously! The second incompleteness theorem makes clear, as will be explained in detail in §2(b), that questions of mathematical evidence are more difficult than, for instance, Hilbert thought, just as the first showed that questions of mathematical truth, even in the domain of arithmetic, are more difficult than a good number[1] of mathematicians thought. Here again the reaction seemed to be: if one can't get one's philosophy cheap one doesn't want it at all. But is this all?

Discussion of the failures. One view is this (in accordance with the parallel between mathematical logic and mathematical physics). What mathematical logicians, respectively applied mathematicians like are philosophical, respectively physical problems where it is easy to see (i) what formal problem constitutes the correct formulation and, preferably, difficult (ii) to solve the formal problem. It is clear that (i) is not (primarily) solved formally. A pretty example in physics is Galileo's first theory of freely falling bodies: the velocity is proportional to the distance fallen. If this were true ($s = Ae^{Bt}$) a body at rest would never start to fall; at least for his time the mathematics involved was sophisticated. But very little experience of the physical world is enough to reject the theory! An example in logic is in §3(*a*), as already mentioned. So, truly unless God is a mathematician, one has little reason to suppose that all interesting philosophical questions would have the property above. I think that the refutation of the formalist position in §2(*a*) is an intermediate case because it needs a careful analysis of what a formal system is. Finally, it looks as if Hilbert's consistency problem does not have this property at all.—A mathematician will find parallels to the contrasts between (i) and (ii) in mathematics itself: (i) corresponds to the choice of problems and conjectures, (ii) to their formal decision. [That there is rhyme and reason in (i) has a kind of magic quality for the tame mathematician; and even more so the fact that, for a given formal problem, a philosophically inspired interpretation may actually provide the solution. An example (though perhaps not the most important) is provided by questions of *formal* independence in intuitionistic systems; the formal independence of a statement may be evident simply because it is not valid on the intended intuitionistic interpretation, but a purely combinatorial independence proof may be tricky.]—The view just discussed is particularly persuasive if one returns to the parallel between mathematical logic and mathematical physics already mentioned. The successful formulation of philosophical views by use of the mathematical methods of mathematical logic is naturally compared to the use of the calculus, for example, for

---

[1] In this article, there will be much more on evidence than on truth. First, because these questions interest me more; but also, objectively, there is more need for explanation because the literature concerned with mathematical truth, i.e. set theoretic semantic interpretations, is more familiar.

formulating consequences of traditional views on the continuous nature of matter; the flight of mathematical logicians into rigid mathematical forms corresponds then to certain phases of applied mathematics of which the old fashioned Cambridge Tripos is typical, notoriously lacking in physical interest. Even the stereotyped application of modern concepts which have been fruitful in algebra or topology, has its parallel in mathematical logic and mathematical physics. Looked at this way, the failures would appear to be a passing phase: and one would expect a thoughtful application of modern mathematical methods to be profitable also in logic, provided it is combined with respect for the philosophical problems involved, *i.e. with informal rigour*.

The other view regards the failures as inherent (permanent) and gives *theoretical* reasons for them, roughly these. The traditional philosophical questions are so ill defined that there is no possibility of a precise solution. This view, familiar from pragmatist or positivist doctrines, rejects the parallel with natural philosophy used above. It takes seriously what is traditionally counted as experience of the physical world (experiment and observation), but not what is counted as experience in traditional mental philosophy, namely insights into such intuitive concepts as logical validity, mechanical process, elementary proof, to name a few which are relevant to the present article. Consequently it does not accept as meaningful the question whether certain axioms (laws) for such concepts are *correct* as an analysis of the understood concepts and thus rejects the possibility of informal rigour. Instead it speaks of *replacing* these concepts by formally introduced concepts which are supposed to be useful or adequate for certain (more or less unspecified) purposes: clarification or explication (*sic*) are favourites.

Personally, I believe the first view is correct, as is implicit in the way I spoke of the successes of mathematical logic. I do not think that the talk about 'adequacy' is well thought out: the only *obvious* purpose of introducing the concepts mentioned in a *formally* rigorous way is as a correct analysis of the given intuitive concept! Just as in topology the obvious purpose of introducing a *definition* of dimension in topological language is as a correct analysis of an intuitive notion of dimension. I believe the examples collected together in §3 show, contrary to what is sometimes asserted, not only does technical mathematical logic not support pragmatist and positivist against traditional views, but discredits the former.

If one accepts the first view, the problems which were mentioned above in connection with the incompleteness theorems, will probably be regarded as the most natural ones at the present time. My general impression is that the fruitful problems are *among* the traditional ones: *originality is needed in selecting those that are ripe for solution.* Also I believe (though this view is not shared widely) that the decision between different traditional positions, for instance realism and idealism, will be greatly helped by technical development: their current formulations are so rudimentary that our present experience does not allow us to decide between them nor do they tell us what new experience to look for. I return to this matter on p. 211, and in more detail on p. 223.

To avoid misunderstanding: while I do not find antitraditional arguments persuasive, the tendency behind them seems quite natural (even if mistaken). Progress with traditional questions *was* slow: so one looks for a reason; and, quite frequently when one has succeeded in formulating a question in 'positivistic' terms, *initial* progress is quite staggering; this applies as much to the introduction of formalist methods in mathematics as to molecular physics in biology. So I discuss doubts about traditional questions in §0. The rest of the article is independent of §0, and some readers may find the list in §3 of positive achievements along traditional lines more satisfactory.

§4 is, I think, of interest even if one regards traditional philosophical questions as significant, but specially so if one has doubts. What can mathematical logic contribute to a more empiricist approach to questions of knowledge, that is, to an understanding of actual reasoning? Or, as one sometimes puts it, to a descriptive rather than primarily normative science of reasoning. In particular: is actual reasoning mechanical? (in the sense made precise in recursion theory). I discuss the relation of this question to the place of Church's thesis in intuitionistic mathematics. It is of course clear that this question could not even be properly formulated without the machinery of mathematical logic.

0. DOUBTS

If one does not have general doubts about philosophical questions one should omit this section: for

(Lord Melbourne) If it is not necessary to do a thing it is necessary not to do it.

(Talleyrand, when told that a certain stupid personage did not think much). *'Le prince pense beaucoup trop pour son intelligence.'*

(*a*) Technical and fundamental analysis: is there a genuine subject of philosophy of mathematics? or is it simply the kind of clarification and reflection which everybody has to do for himself anyway? If there is, what distinguishes it from technical subjects?

First, a point of principle. Even if there is a clear distinction one cannot hope to formulate it well at the present time. Compare physics and chemistry: it was clear from the beginning that there was some sort of distinction (and perhaps one even overestimated it); I believe that one nowadays says this: if intra atomic forces are dominant (in an atomic description of, possibly, macroscopic phenomena) it's physics, if molecular forces are dominant it's chemistry. So, *a high level of development of the subjects was needed to give a good characterization*. Similarly, to distinguish technical and fundamental analysis may well be a major problem of fundamental analysis itself.

But, granted this, is there a sensible working distinction? It's fundamental when one is breaking new ground. Specifically, suppose we have a well established domain of science with tried out principles of evidence. One may go beyond it by *extending* the frame work or by *scrutinizing* it. The former corresponds to *speculative*, the latter to *critical* philosophy; or, perhaps better, to *ontology* (what else is there between heaven and earth than thought of in our philosophy?), respectively to *epistemology* (is what we accept really given?).— Within mathematics the distinction is well illustrated by considering questions of the form: what is X? It is technical if the answer is given in terms of the subject, i.e. X is *defined* from the primitive notions already in use; for instance, if, in geometry, X ($=$ a circle) is defined in terms of *point* and *congruence*. It is fundamental if the definition is given in terms of new primitives, not already in use. If a wide and diverse area of experience is studied and one looks for *few* basic elements one is often forced to a fundamental analysis in the sense above: for, the very meaning of diversity is that one does not expect a reduction to a few *familiar* elements.

The working distinction is relative to an existing state of knowledge. I think Russell implied that there really isn't more to the distinction when he said the progress of philosophy consists in removing questions from itself to technical domains. This opinion is not universal; for instance, in [3] Gödel calls logic a science prior to all others: *this* difference in degree is surely enough to make it a difference in kind!—I am sure I don't know, but there seems a strong case for an *objective* distinction between technical and fundamental analysis.

The paradigm is physics (cf. Dirac's introduction to his book), where an analysis of X in terms of Y is fundamental if Y is much *smaller* than X. This is not some kind of scientific fashion, but expresses a view on the nature of the physical world: if one thought field theory was basic, one would certainly not accept the principle above. However, the distinction is not merely relative to existing knowledge.

The following points are clear.

Though one may *regard* a fundamental analysis, for instance in terms of fundamental particles, as a 'convenient' description of the (macroscopic) facts one will hardly take it seriously unless one thinks there are such particles. For otherwise one would have no particular reason to think that this kind of analysis will also be 'convenient' for the next phenomenon we encounter.

One would not expect the same notions and questions to arise in practice (the description of the phenomena) and in the fundamental analysis. In fact, if the latter did not contain new notions, one would hardly speak of an analysis! Cf. Dirac's remark on what makes an explanation satisfactory. This is borne out in §1, 2: In the practice of mathematics one speaks of sets and eliminates 'unnecessary' axioms such as the axiom of regularity; in foundations one uses types and *ordinals* (for which this axiom holds): in mathematics one looks for what is needed for a result, in foundations one makes the notion as specific as possible to gain evidence. Even in intuitionistic mathematics we find that the notion of *proof* is not used explicitly in practice, but that it is basic in foundations.

Fundamental analysis does not necessarily make experience more intellible (one does not expect to describe a shockwave intelligibly by giving atomic wave functions).

Regarding critical and speculative sides of philosophy: it *may* happen that the same fundamental analysis serves both sides, but there seems (at present) no reason to expect it.

(*b*) Traditional philosophic questions: basic or naïve? By definition, old questions were formulated at a stage of very limited experience; are they not suspect because of this? As traditional concepts of space and time were, presumably, affected by lack of experience with speeds near the speed of light.

I am impressed by the evidence to the contrary. It is a fact that most elementary mathematics, for instance what is familiar to the bulk of philosophers, is (easily codified in systems which are) decidable. A pretty example, noticed by Wang, is the part of predicate logic developed in *Principia Mathematica*: the theorems given belong to a decidable class. This accidental feature of elementary mathematics was not noticed and traditional doctrines were hardly affected by it. Note, in contrast, the 'plain man' is much more affected by limitations of his own experience; every mathematician has been asked with wide eyed innocence (at a party): but what else is there to do in mathematics? I am equally impressed by the good sense on foundational questions shown by mathematicians *without* logical indoctrination: they may be dreadfully wrong on details, but sound on principles; cf. §2(*a*), §3.

Naturally, one does not expect *all* traditional questions to be fruitful, any more than all modern ones. And one certainly must not assume that the first questions which come to mind in a subject are the first to be solved! Thus, several thousand years ago one could have asked (and probably did): (i) Why does it take the moon about 30 (solar) days to go round the earth? (ii) Why is glass transparent? Who would have thought that (i) is easier than (ii)? A significant answer to (ii) requires a fundamental theory which relates structural and optical properties of matter. It might be remarked that it stands to a linguistic answer ('because one can see through glass') perhaps like a good solution to a philosophical problem stands to a linguistic analysis.

(*c*) Precision: Is lack of precision not the main reason for slow progress in philosophy? It seems to me the accent is in the wrong place. For, of course when there is progress, in particular a successful analysis of what is involved in a problem, precision results: but finding the analysis is part of the solution, it is not given with the problem. In fact, one of the most important uses of the *axiomatic* method is just to deal with 'imprecise' notions (which have not been formally introduced). What makes Riemann's *definition* of area good is, of course, not that it is precise but that it is derived from a few properties of the intuitive notion of area: the achievement was to have found 'partial' information (in practice most information is partial!) which is sufficient to determine for instance numerical values for the area of many figures. §3(*a*) does for logical validity what Riemann's axioms do for area [and §3(*b*) does for arithmetic truth what proofs of Riemann-non-measurability do for certain geometric figures].

The assumption is that, as one goes on formulating 'partial' properties of philosophic notions, one will not get into hopeless contradictions: this conviction is expressed in (*b*). (One must expect some initial errors of formulation, even if not contradictions, just as one generally has to look twice at a thing to get reliable information.[1])

(*d*) Philosophical analysis: does it affect practice? Here a distinc-

[1] It is this kind of parallel between things and notions which is rejected outright in anti-philosophical doctrines, cf. p. 205. I see no evidence for this assumption that notions are not objective: there is certainly more agreement between people on Riemann's axioms being correct for the notion of area, than, for instance, on most 'empirical' matters such as the number of leaves on some tree (to use agreement as a criterion!).

tion is needed. Perhaps analysis does not affect much the way we *see* the world: the physical world does not look very different to us after we find out that it has atomic structure and we don't think of natural numbers very differently after we have a set theoretic definition. But analysis affects very much first what questions we can hope to treat (What is matter made of? What are the essential properties of the number series?), and, second, the way we *handle* the world. As is to be expected this distinction applies especially to an ontological analysis.

In mathematics it has often been stressed that analysis in set theoretic terms (§1) has led to axioms and notions which allow one to solve problems which could not be, or, at least, were not, solved without them. But also—this is not so often stressed—philosophical doctrines can shape the whole style of mathematics, as, for instance formalism [for details cf. §2(*a*)] shaped modern axiomatic mathematics. First of all, formalism is responsible for the ideal of formal rigour, so much so that a text book like Bourbaki begins with a set of formal rules of inference; this is not very serious because these rules are never mentioned in the later development which shows that the evidence of the proofs in the main text depends on an *understood* notion of logical inference. But second, by formulating theorems for axiomatic notions instead of others one brings mathematical truth and formal provability closer together (in accordance with formalist doctrine). If we know that a theorem about addition and multiplication of rational numbers is true, we know really nothing about its proof; if we know that (formally) the (same) theorem is true in all real fields we know of course more, since the rationals are such a field, but, in addition, *we can always find a formal proof by trial and error* (namely by means of the formal rules mentioned). In a sense, by stating the more general theorem we make it in principle easier to remember the proof!

So even if the field of rationals were to remain the formally real field *par excellence* to the end of time, the latter (formally introduced) notion would still be useful.

There is one respect in which mathematical practice is far ahead of systematic (philosophical) analysis. Some branches, in particular category theory, specialize in formulating theorems whose proof cannot only be found in principle by trial and error, *but leaps to the eye.* Does this mean that *our present mathematics in future will be expounded as a series of decidable systems?* I know nothing in logic which bears on this possibility.

(*e*) Philosophical disputes: Why not compromise? As a student I was attracted by the heuristic value of philosophical questions and notions [cf. (*d*) above], but felt: Why all the fuss about philosophical issues? Why not accept the pragmatist's position who rejects the issues as meaningless, but will judge by *fruitfulness*? The pragmatic position would be refuted on pragmatic grounds; this was to be expected since the pragmatic position is well known to be unstable; what is fruitless within 1 year, may be fruitful in 5. Of course I could see no *a priori* reason why all that is true should be fruitful; but if it should happen to be so, life would simply be nicer in this best of all possible worlds.

The pragmatic approach is not particularly natural, at least to the working scientist. Thus the possibility of using mathematical logic for the simplification or sharpening of results in algebra has not been especially impressive; independence and incompleteness results in arithmetic and set theory (which, so far, have had no impact on mathematical practice) have hit the headlines.

But a more objective weakness is that the whole business of fruitfulness does not seem to be well thought out. Put precisely, it means that one confines oneself to applications formulated in the frame work of concepts used by the pragmatist. In particular, if he is a positivist, this framework is limited to 'concrete' matters; if he is an old fashioned pragmatic mathematician it is limited to problems in the theory of numbers or of a real variable. Is it really the business of philosophy to perpetuate limitations of the existing framework of concepts (by judging everything in relation to it)? *Should it not extend the range of experience which we can understand theoretically?*

In practice there might be a case for restrictions if one finds the philosophic notions difficult and nothing in experience that becomes intelligible through them. This happened to me in connection with intuitionistic notions in the constructive analysis of existing mathematics: the parts that could be made constructive at all only needed very elementary, so-called finitist methods, §2(*b*). But later I saw how the use of intuitionistic interpretations made consistency proofs intelligible which previously consisted of *ad hoc* tricks, and particularly the theory of recursive ordinals, which previously teemed with *ad hoc* applications of the so-called recursion theorem. Somebody less short sighted might have suspected the value of intuitionistic notions even from the very fragmentary development before, say, 1940. What is absurd (and often merely affected) is to reject these notions as 'unintelligible' simply because they do not fit into a customary framework. Coming back to fruitfulness the lesson is this: to be useful these notions had to be developed to a fairly advanced level; propositional logic was not enough. *During* the development they could of course not be used: so at that time they would have failed the test of fruitfulness, which shows that it is not a good test.

The point here made is a straightforward transfer to philosophical issues of a perfectly common place view, somewhat colourlessly described as the intrinsic interest of pure research. For instance, when abstract methods were introduced in algebra or analysis one could recognize them as an extension of our horizon of knowledge long before they could be applied to simplify old proofs or give proofs of new results in non-abstract mathematics. In fact, even to this day I find these applications less interesting than the original purpose for which the abstract methods were introduced, namely to answer such questions as: what is *essential* to some given group of constructions which we could (or could not) see to have something in common, without having the notions needed to formulate this insight.

It is sometimes claimed that pragmatic tests are needed to stop people from talking nonsense about things they do not understand: one wonders if one really needs a false doctrine to achieve this. But, after all, may be one does: apparently false medical doctrines have been used to stop little boys from being naughty.

(*f*) A kind of paradox: high hopes for (the subject of) Philosophy, especially of Mathematics, and little trust in (the profession of) philosophy. Thus despite the enthusiasm of (*a*)–(*e*) there is hardly a reference to the work of contemporary professional philosophers. In particular, there is no trace of the logic chopping and obviously minor distinctions of which contemporary (Anglo-Saxon) philosophy is full. The technique of these professionals is by now suspect for two reasons: First it is intended to clarify ideas in the Socratic manner; but it only keeps the outer forms including the banter of Plato, not the substance, namely the serious search for general definitions. Second there is no evidence that careful work on *insignificant* aspects leads one, even indirectly, to recognize what is essential. This applies not only to philosophical analysis, but for instance to the axiomatic analysis of insignificant variants which is often done after a new concept is introduced in abstract algebra or topology. If an endless list of variants for some notions or position occurs to one—as, possibly, significant—one simply has not understood the notion sufficiently to make work on it worth while. More generally, it is the hallmark of significance that not too much care is needed! It is worth considering here the case of mineralogy [though, by §0(*a*), it would be wrong to apply uncritically experience from the natural sciences to foundational studies]: information on significant features such as molecular structure to an accuracy of 30 per cent is more informative than painstaking description of insignificant, external features of a crystal.

A real paradox. I see no evidence that the formulations (*a*)–(*f*) above really satisfy the principles formulated in (*a*)–(*f*); for instance: is the talk about significance in (*f*) significant? It seems to me that this question makes perfectly good sense; in particular, that *self application* need not be excluded for the notions occurring in (*a*)–(*f*). To speak of (*a*)–(*f*) as *meta* philosophy is a thoughtless transfer to abstract ideas of the type distinction which is properly used in the analysis of (the extensional realist conception of) aggregate (in §1). After all, type distinctions do not apply to the external form of our *thoughts*: we give syntactic instructions for giving syntactic instructions and so forth (in the theory of partial recursive functions). But remembering Talleyrand I shall stop here.

1. BASIC OBJECTS. MATHEMATICAL REALISM

This section considers the analysis of mathematical experience in terms of the notions of set theory. Sets and the membership relation are the basic elements in terms of which one can answer such questions as: what is a natural number? (As a physicist answers the question: what is iron? in terms of atomic theory.) The contact with mathematical realism is, of course, the assumption that there are basic elements with the properties assumed in the analysis, that is *the existential assumptions of set theory are valid*. For general comments on fundamental analysis see §0(*a*), for specific comments on the present assumptions see §1(*d*) below.

(*a*) *An example*: *how it all began*

In the last century Dedekind, Frege and Peano asked themselves: what is essential about the series of natural numbers (for pure arithmetic)? If one thinks of this structure as an object at all the following properties are clear:

A universe N of objects and a relation S (the successor relation: $S \subset N^2$) and a distinguished element u (the first element: $u \in N$) are involved. They satisfy the well known conditions, known as Peano's axioms, which are expressed in the vocabulary of pure set theory (the notion of set and membership relation $\in$).

The striking result is that if $\langle N', S', u' \rangle$ satisfy the same axioms, the structures $\langle N, S, u \rangle$ and $\langle N', S', u' \rangle$ are isomorphic, that is there is a 1–1 correspondence $f : N \leftrightarrow N'$ such that $f : u \leftrightarrow u', f : S \leftrightarrow S'$. The *obviously* valid axioms of Peano determine the structure $\langle N, S, u \rangle$ uniquely up to isomorphism.

Other characterizations of this kind (for the continuum, for the finite type structure) will be given in §3(*b*).

This kind of analysis may be properly compared to a fundamental analysis in physics such as the kinetic theory of gases. Peano's axioms about the intuitive concept of number correspond to macroscopic laws relating volume, temperature, and pressure of gases. The use of the set theoretic vocabulary corresponds to the theory that the macroscopic laws are to be explained in terms of the motion of molecules, and the set theoretic laws to the laws of molecular motion. Finally, the characterization of the set theoretic structure (the so-called abstract structure up to isomorphism) corresponds to determining the statistics of the collisions of molecules from the macroscopic laws. The comparison suggests the (very instructive) question:

What *might* be the limitations of a set theoretic analysis of mathematical experience? We might have *conflict* with experience, that is intuitive arithmetic notions which satisfy laws that can be proved not to be realizable by means of sets: this is the usual fate of physical theories which contradict experience; or the laws of arithmetic notions cannot be proved from recognized set theoretic laws: in short, the set theoretic laws leave part of experience *unexplained* and questions about it undecided. Here it is to be remarked that a delicate question arises: *what experience is to be regarded as* (physically, respectively, mathematically) *significant?* For instance, a physical theory is not regarded as inadequate because it leaves unexplained so-called particular or accidental facts. A very interesting example from arithmetic concerns so-called *intensional* aspects which are involved in *decision procedures*: for instance, the order relation is (mechanically) decidable if the natural numbers are given (or: described) by numerals $1, 1 + 1, (1 + 1) + 1, \ldots$, but evidently not if they are described in a crazy fashion (we take an undecided sequence of problems P_n and describe the numbers by the expressions a_0, i.e. the number X such that $X = 0$ & P_0 or $X = 1$ & $\sim P_0$, a_1, i.e. $X = 1$ & P_0 or $X = 0$ & $\sim P_0$, $\ldots$ and a_{2n}, i.e. $X = 2n$ & P_n or, $X = 2n + 1$ & $\sim P_n$, a_{2n+1}, *i.e.*, $X = 2n + 1$ & P_n or $X = 2n$ & $\sim P_n$, $\ldots$). If one is interested in decision procedures, the characterization up to isomorphism is not adequate because two systems of notations may be isomorphic, but the isomorphism does not preserve decidability: special conditions would have to be imposed on the kinds of isomorphism.[1]

---

[1] Tame mathematicians sometimes have a rather soft conception of mathematical significance: if they know how to fit the intuitive notion into an existing frame work such as set theory, they call the notion significant and not otherwise.

(b) Systematic theory

Two essential elements are involved in the reduction of mathematics to set theory:

(i) A basic language (with an interpretation), namely the language of predicate logic of first and higher order. One of the remarkable discoveries of the last century, clinched by the work of *Principia Mathematica*, is this: the bulk of the properties of mathematical objects which strike us as significant, can be expressed in this language. This is quite surprising because this language has a precise grammar and few primitives and casual inspection of common usage (even in mathematics) suggests that the complexity of ordinary language is quite essential to its expressive power and flexibility. It is easy to forget this striking discovery when one finds that *some* significant distinctions cannot be expressed in predicate logic.

It has often been stressed that this discovery is not a formal linguistic matter. What is formulated or approximated is the *meaning* of assertions of informal mathematics, not their external syntactic form: fortunately, since otherwise there would be little hope of simplification! For these reasons I said 'with an interpretation' above. Here the realist view of the nature of mathematics enters in the use of so-called classical or two valued logic, when for instance the operations: *there is* and: *not for all not* of common usage are treated as interchangeable, that is, not as *significantly* different. It is well known that the description of our experience of the physical world is equally determined by our view of the nature of the physical world: we describe differently what we see in the heavens if we think of the stars as bodies (as we do) or as holes in the sky (as the old Greeks did). At this *very* basic level analysis does affect the way we see the world, in contrast to §0(*d*).

By the note p. 214, the development of mathematics *since* the discovery can hardly be regarded as supporting it. Personally, I should be very much surprised if, for instance, the so-called continuum problem (is $2^{\aleph_0} = \aleph_1$) were to be solved as long as one operates only with assertions formulated in the language of set theory: the problem concerns all *possible* subsets of the integers; why should the relevant properties (which are also evident to us) be expressible in the language of set theory? Considering the poverty of results in the theory of *cardinals* one can hardly say that mathematical experience makes this plausible!

A more delicate point concerning the expression of properties of mathematical objects is this. Even granted the restriction to a limited language, *what properties of an object* in mathematical experience *are essential*? This is well illustrated by *Souslin's problem* on the continuum. Granted that the continuum is to be conceived as a set theoretic structure $\langle L, O \rangle$ $(O \subset L^2)$ we would all agree that the line L is totally ordered without first or last element, and that every cut in L is determined by an element of L (Dedekind's continuity condition). Now, it is known that $\langle L, O \rangle$ is determined up to isomorphism by these conditions if, in addition, (α) There is a denumerable D $(D \subset L)$ which is dense in L, i.e. between any two elements of L lies an element of D: this D has necessarily the order type of the rationals.

How *essential* are the rationals to the intuitive continuum?

Souslin noticed that the additional condition implies (β) Every set of non-overlapping intervals in L is denumerable.

There seems little doubt that *this* condition is essential. So, just as in the natural sciences one tries to make one's conclusions independent of dubious observations, so here one asks whether (β) (together with the evident conditions) implies (α). Here 'implies' is to be understood in its intuitive sense, cf. §3(*b*).

It would be a good test of one's mathematical insight to ask oneself whether (α) requires a 'different kind of evidence' from (β), and to compare the answer with the logical relationships between (α) and (β) as follows: if the answer is positive but (α) and (β) are logically equivalent than one has bad insight [NB. if the answer is positive, but (α) and (β) are not formally equivalent, nothing follows: cf. §3(*b*).]

(ii) Existential assumptions. In (*a*) above the *uniqueness* of the characterization of the structure of natural numbers was emphasized. Naturally, in the analysis one will also consider the *existence* of sets N, S, u with the properties demanded by Peano's axioms. Here the principal axioms are the so-called axiom of infinity, and, for the justification (derivation) of the principle of induction the comprehension axiom:

$$\forall X \, \exists Y \, \forall Z \{ Z \in Y \leftrightarrow [Z \in X \,\&\, \mathsf{P}(Z)] \}$$

where P is an arbitrary property of Z. The requirement $Z \in X$ is imposed if one wants set to be understood as: sets in the hierarchy of types obtained from a collection C_0 of individuals by taking $C_1 = C_0 \cup \mathfrak{P}(C_0)$ ($\mathfrak{P}$ denoting the operation of taking all subsets of C_0), $C_2 = C_1 \cup \mathfrak{P}(C_1)$, etc. For technical details, cf. [10].

If one thinks of set as an object in the hierarchy described, the principal axioms concern the existence of sets of large (transfinite) type, or, in other words, of large ordinals. In this connection two points should be noticed.

First, if one describes an ordinal abstractly, e.g. the first non-denumerable ordinal (the first ordinal not in one-one correspondance with ω by means of a mapping in a class of mappings satisfying explicit axioms) there will be a *denumerable* model of the axioms with a suitable interpretation of $\mathfrak{P}$. However, in general, the only evidence for the existence of such a model will be the existence of C_2 above with $C_0 = \omega$ or, equivalently, $C_{\omega+2}$ with $C_0 = \phi$ (the empty set).

Second, there is a more delicate reduction to the basic structure of ordinals instead of sets, in terms of the so-called ramified hierarchy, due to Poincaré and Russell, and developed into a powerful tool by Gödel. This requires the ordinal $\aleph_\omega$ (the ωth infinite cardinal) for the reduction of Zermelo's set theory [10]: these axioms are satisfied by C_ω if $C_0 = \omega$ above, and it is this structure that provides the obvious evidence for the existence of $\aleph_\omega$, namely the union of all well orderings in C_ω. Cf. [10a]

The two observations above will be used in:

(c) General theory and mathematical practice

The two main questions are: do the existential assumptions affect practice? does practice support the existential assumptions?

(i) Gödel's incompleteness theorem. The first point to notice is that very strong existential assumptions can be formulated in the language of set theory, on so-called inaccessible or measurable ordinals [10]. This is as remarkable as the fact that $10^{10^{10}}$ is defined by a short expression in our ordinary notation, but of course not all integers less than this number. Next, whatever axioms we may put down there will be an ordinal α_0 such that C_{α_0} satisfies them, as $C_{\omega+\omega}$ (with $C_0 = \phi$) above satisfies Zermelo's axioms. [Here 'satisfaction' is understood in its intuitive sense, namely, *all* properties P are considered in the comprehension axiom above; for more precise details on this so-called second order notion of satisfaction, cf. §3(b).] Then the existence of such an α_0 does not follow from the axioms given. Hence, without further technical details we have this:

Any axiom system for set theory is inadequate or unjustified set theoretically. For, either we do not recognize that the axioms are satisfied at any C_{α_0}; then they are not justified. Or else α_0 cannot be defined in the language of set theory [for instance, if all true set theoretic statements are taken as axioms; cf. also (b) (i) above]; then the expressive power of this language is inadequate. Or finally the existence of this α_0, though recognized intuitively, does not follow from the axioms.

Gödel analysed his argument further, for the case of so-called *formal* logical consequence, and found roughly [for precise statements, cf. §2(a)]: a certain purely arithmetic statement is formally undecided by the axioms, namely the statement expressing: the system of axioms is formally consistent! It is proved from the existence of α_0!

Thus *even if mathematical practice is confined to arithmetic, existential assumptions*, namely on the existence of α_0, *affect the body of provable theorems.*

(ii) Eliminating existential assumptions for the analysis of *actual* practice. One of the more remarkable discoveries of mathematical logic is this [in contrast to (*b*) (ii), first comment]: Though we *think* of the hierarchy described in (*b*) (ii) when setting up the set theoretic axioms, we only *use* very weak forms in actual practice. For instance, in a good deal of arithmetic we do not use the axiom of infinity, in a good deal of analysis [so-called predicative analysis of §2(*b*)] the comprehension axiom is used with properties P defined by means of formulae with *bounded* quantifiers [10] and the power set axiom not at all. This constitutes a real reduction of existential assumptions: the first only assumes the existence of (so-called hereditarily) finite sets, the second can be stated in terms of the ramified hierarchy of (*b*) (ii): instead of the existence of $\aleph_1$, the first non-denumerable ordinal, one only needs ω_1 (the first non-*recursive* ordinal). As a corollary: actual practice of arithmetic constitutes only support for the existence of finite sets, and actual practice of analysis for the existence of ω_1, not for $\aleph_1$!

My impression is that the state of actual practice is a passing phase: mathematicians have simply not learnt how to use the existential assumptions. (For an attempt at an explanation of this psychological fact, see §4 below.) But it is still possible that the problems in arithmetic or analysis which actually interest mathematicians at present, can be decided without these assumptions.

(*d*) Traditional mathematical realism and set theory

Before reviewing the problems it is necessary to make some elementary

(i) *Distinctions.* It is sometimes claimed that the *paradoxes*, obtained by formulating the comprehension axiom in (*b*) (ii) without the restriction $Z \in X$, refute the realist view of mathematics; for, the unrestricted axiom is supposed to follow from the realist view. I think this is not justified, at least if one considers sets as external to ourselves, something not too different from abstract objects realized in the physical world, like the number 4. For, then the most obvious interpretation of set is in terms of a hierarchy of types, and for this interpretation the unrestricted comprehension axiom is *obviously* false. (What instances of the comprehension axiom lead to contradictions is merely of technical interest since an assertion may well be false without leading to a formal contradiction. A more interesting problem is to find syntactic conditions on properties P for which $\exists\, y\, \forall\, x[P(x) \to x \in y]$ is a theorem). Unless I am suffering from wishful hindsight, the unrestricted comprehension axiom is plausible only for a quite different *idealistic* interpretation of set in terms of arbitrary, not necessarily well defined properties for which the laws of classical logic are certainly not plausible. It seems certain that the paradoxes will be useful for the discovery of such laws.

The realist position is here taken in its *strong* form, namely a involving the existence of sets of high ordinal, and not merely a involving the existence of *some* mathematical objects. Too many ambiguities in this latter idea occur to me: by §0(f) I do not yet understand the question. For instance I do not see at all that in an assertion about 4 yellow apples, the number 4 enters less objectively than the colour yellow. But there may be a problem.

The realist position is not here interpreted in its *strict* form, namely that *all* mathematical notions are built up from the notion of set by means of logical definitions in the language of pure set theory ($\in$); for specific criticisms of this form, cf. (*b*) (i). It is a striking psychological fact that here, as in the formalist and intuitionistic positions below, people are often attracted by the (implausible) strict form, and have doubts about the strong form! these doubts may even be responsible for the facts reported in (*c*) (ii) though §4 gives another explanation. I see nothing objective to this preference; only a faintheartedness which wants to restrict problems, and a kind of cunning: for, if one is convinced that *only* the notions one uses oneself make sense, one need not scrutinize them too much; they can't be worse than the rival notions which (are supposed to) make no sense at all!

(ii) *Taking realism seriously.* Two things stand out. First, the way we think of mathematical objects when we do arithmetic or geometry or set theory (not so much in numerical analysis) is realistic. Whatever alternative analyses are proposed, as in §2, the obvious source of the mathematical properties used are insights which we interpret as being about external objects. The reliability of these insights is quite overwhelming, not ignoring the paradoxes: they not only can be 'analysed away' as in (i) above, but even first reactions of mathematicians were reliable! After all, their prejudice against the introduction of *naïve* set theoretic methods is legendary. [I mean here 'naïve' in the sense of thoughtless; so 'naïve notion of set' does not mean (intuitively) understood notion of set, but simply: misunderstood notion of set.]

219

The second thing is, as (c) (i) shows, that the realistic interpretation *can* be exploited even to affect elementary mathematical practice, if one only sees how. The difficulty involved should not be underestimated: in [3], p. 127, Gödel criticizes Russell for starting off with a pronouncedly realistic attitude but not keeping it up when confronted with a specific problem. I am sure this was not lack of moral fibre on Russell's part: he simply did not see how to exploit this realistic attitude. And (c) (iii) shows that the same is true of present-day mathematicians. *Added in proof.* The situation is changing, cf. [11].

But granted the principle that one can take realism seriously, the question is how to do it in practice. Gödel faces the problem squarely in [5] (and was, I believe, the first to do so). His main suggestions are to use so-called axioms of infinity (existential assumptions of objects of high type) and to judge between alternatives by their 'fruitfulness', specifically by what number theoretic propositions they settle. Now, first, the continuum problem, which, by §3(b), is decided in the sense of second order implication, is formally not affected by the strongest existential assumptions so far proposed, namely the existence of so-called measurable ordinals [7]. Next, the majority of formally undecided propositions do not affect number theoretic propositions at all; this applies both to the true axiom of choice and the dubious continuum hypothesis. However, there may be something to the criterion mentioned: I do not know a reasonable proposition A which is formally undecided, true on the intended interpretation, but $\sim A$ decides more number theoretic propositions than A; (in view of §0(e) it would be curious if *this* kind of fruitfulness were to be a principal consideration). As to the use of axioms of infinity rather than the use of new primitive notions which are not expressible in pure set theory [cf. (b) (i)], the former have the advantage of being more specific. Also, at the present time, mathematicians accustomed to the language of set theory would find it difficult to operate with new notions confidently.

It should be remarked that most other systematic ways of extending axiom systems S (for set theory) are reducible to the addition of axioms of infinity; for instance, adding the relevant consistency statement or the assertion: the axioms S have a model, etc.

Concerning the general problem of criteria for finding new axioms, one would like to use simple and unsophisticated considerations: not because (as far as I can see) the truth is necessarily simple but because one just hasn't much chance of understanding those aspects of experience which are not simple. But I can't help feeling that such criteria as fruitfulness are too rough. It is all very well to stress the objective character of mathematics, and for instance, the common aspects of physical and mathematical objects. But is it not about time that one is forced to look at the *differences* between these objects more closely in order to make progress? [One can acknowledge such differences without becoming a complete obscurantist like the formalist of §2(*a*).] What I find really marvellous is how many axioms we have found without closer analysis of the

(iii) *Nature of mathematical objects.* There is a *broad* distinction between views which hold that all mathematics is purely 'conventional' or, more precisely, depends on human reactions incapable of *a priori* explanations and those which hold that there is something 'objective' about mathematics. As stated in the Introduction, and developed in §2, I believe the former views are simply wrong. But it would seem that there are quite basic distinctions between different views of the second kind, for instance those that stress the objective aspects which are *external* to ourselves and those which do not. (Trivially, everything has an aspect not external to ourselves simply by virtue of being perceived or understood.) It might well be that the methods needed to extend known axioms depend on whether or not mathematical objects are (primarily) external to ourselves. Perhaps there is a prejudice against taking seriously the existence of infinite sets not external to ourselves: there wouldn't be enough room in our heads! But here it should not be overlooked that relations between *finite* objects may well involve the infinite: for instance, the relation between finite expressions A and B (of second order predicate logic): A is a second order consequence of B. The existential question is then replaced by: is this relation objectively determined?

2. MATHEMATICAL EVIDENCE

Questions of evidence have already turned up in §1, particularly (*b*) (i) and (*d*) (ii); both, for instance in (*b*) (i), to make results independent of dubious assumptions, and more theoretically to find *evidence* for the basic assumptions; in §1(*d*) one of the principal questions was to find evidence for existential assumptions, and, in particular, for new ones, i.e. for new axioms. This kind of problem has its analogue in all sciences.

(i) *Is there something special about mathematical evidence?*
The traditional idea is this. What is essential and even character-istic for mathematics is *specifically* mathematical evidence, namely proof, more so than subject matter, in particular more so than mathematical objects. Even if the existence of mathematical objects external to ourselves is not rejected it is often held that whatever is

specifically mathematical in our evidence does not apply to them but to something else, for instance to our ideas of them. This would be analogous to Einstein's *aperçu* concerning certainty in geometry; he did not deny certainty of our geometrical assertions interpreted formally, nor the existence of space-time, nor the possibility that his theory of space-time was true; but he denied that the geometrical assertions *interpreted as being about objective space-time* were certain. One simple minded thought on why there might be something special about mathematical evidence (even for an objective view of mathematics) was mentioned in §1(*d*) (iii): if mathematics is (interpreted as being) about objects *not* external to ourselves. Then mathematical objects would be sufficiently different in degree from, say, physical objects to make the need for different kinds of evidence plausible.

Two things stand out. First, the realist view of mathematics is so natural that one would not question it if one did not also take seriously the idea of specifically mathematical evidence: the more radical the difference between what mathematics is about, and what, for instance, physics is about, the more plausible is the specific character of mathematical evidence. This seems to be borne out historically: philosophers interested in mathematical evidence tended to finish up as anti-realists. Second, as I stressed above, a non-realist view of mathematical evidence is not directly *inconsistent* with the existence of mathematical objects. But it obviously cannot support realist, for instance existential assumptions, and so has a *negative* consequence for the realist view: for if it is shown to 'account' for our mathematical experience, then (perhaps contrary to first impressions) mathematical experience does not *force* one to adopt a realist interpretation.

The present section describes some of the work done on *specifically mathematical evidence*. Roughly, *one tries to find this evidence in what is given directly in experience. Three different views on what is so given are considered. Not surprisingly, the technical apparatus for stating and developing these views is complicated because the phenomena studied are complicated.*

(ii) *Sense and significance of questions of evidence*

As stated in the introduction, the work below leaves in my opinion no shadow of doubt that traditional notions of different kinds of evidence are essentially unambiguous; at least, different formulations turn out to be equivalent. Here it is to be remarked that this view conflicts with a commonly held view; namely, inspection shows (incontestably) that there are *border line* cases, for instance between

222

mathematical and physical evidence; one then concludes (superficially) that the notions of evidence are not capable of precise study. What would have become of physics if one had refused to take seriously the distinctions between solid, liquid and gaseous state because there are border line cases? Actually, it turns out that the distinctions between different kinds of evidence are sharper than distinctions between the phases.

What was said in footnote, p. 217, about tame mathematicians, applies *mutatis mutandis* to tame philosophers who think that if certain distinctions cannot be formulated in a familiar frame work they have no sense.[1]

But even granted that different kinds of evidence can be *formulated* precisely, is the distinction significant? To take a rough parallel: we hardly doubt that we can distinguish between visual and auditory experience (evidence); but is it of importance for objective knowledge of the physical world that we have learnt a fact by visual rather than auditory means? It seems to me that this question of significance is itself a subject for research. Furthermore, *such research may provide criteria for deciding between philosophical positions* (cf. p. 206). Consider §1(*d*) (iii) concerning the nature of mathematical objects. I do not think that we can expect to decide the matter merely by agreement or conflict with our present experience; least of all [recall §0(*d*)] if we confine ourselves to aspects of experience significant for a particular philosophical view! (cf. p. 245 and 251 below). Instead I should look for a parallel to the well known argument for physical realism (for instance, in Gödel [3]):

The existence of physical objects is supported by the simplicity of the analysis of our physical experience in terms of physical objects. Perhaps it should be added: and analysis in terms of the kind of evidence employed does not seem to make this experience more intelligible.

Now, suppose—in contrast—that mathematical experience does become more intelligible when analysed in terms of the evidence employed. Would this not constitute at least the beginnings of a case against mathematical realism? at least as long as the impasse of p. 220 remains closed? And to take this possibility seriously, one is forced to develop the notions of evidence in a sophisticated way.

Just what mathematical experience has to be appealed to is discussed in §2(*c*), especially §2(*c*) (iv); §2(*c*) treats intuitionism, which is the most sophisticated theory of mathematical evidence studied so far.

---

1 There is a remarkable cult of impotence, *a quiet pride* in not being able to make sense of a question.

Marginal comments. The choice between a classical and romantic approach is especially important in the early stages of a theoretical treatment (here: on evidence or immediate experience in mathematics). Should we formulate our views sharply and generally, and confine ourselves to questions strictly significant for the particular view? Or should we pursue questions that arouse our curiosity and let our general views grow? Evidently, when a subject is developed the two approaches would not be expected to conflict because both one's curiosity and one's theoretical views are influenced by detailed experience of the subject.—As is to be expected from §0(*f*) I shall try to give a classical exposition. The view expressed above is contrary to common practice where sharp formulations are generally given only when the subject is highly developed. I think this practice is adopted merely because it is easy and not because it has been fruitful; in any case progress in our subject has been too slow to create much confidence in common practice.

Note that what is to be formulated sharply and coherently are the *informal* views; by §0(*c*) there is little evidence that formal precision alone will be fruitful.[1]

(a) Formalism: *the evidence of the multiplication table*

The present view considers as given in mathematical experience (or: as specifically mathematical) the recognition whether or not a sequence of symbolic expressions is formed according to some given finite number of mechanical rules. A typical instance of applying mechanical rules is a numerical computation carried out according to the rules of the multiplication table; but, at least *prima facie*, numerical arithmetic is a particularly restricted part of mathematics. Formalism can be considered at all only because of the discovery of formalization, mentioned in §1(*a*), but now sharpened and interpreted differently; sharpened because mathematical notions cannot only be *expressed* axiomatically but the relation: (the formula) *A* is a logical consequence of *B*, can be defined by means of purely mechanical rules [see (ii) below] (formalization of predicate logic);

[1] For the specialist. Consider early studies on the role of the axiom of choice (*AC*). The problems were perfectly precise: can a given statement *X* be proved from given axioms (of set theory) without use of *AC*? Even quite elementary results *X* in the semantic development of predicate logic, such as Skolem normal forms for satisfiability, are most naturally proved by use of *AC*.—Now, either one does not understand the notion of set: why should one bother to give a semantic treatment? or one does: since (I believe) the one and only notion of set which is really clear is the cumulative hierarchy described in §1, why should one eliminate *AC*, *AC* being valid for this notion?—Satisfyingly enough, many of these problems were even formally pointless: cf. footnote, p. 261.

and now the axioms are not interpreted as true about abstract objects, but the whole deductive system consisting of axioms and rules of inference is regarded as a compact *description* of linguistic behaviour; specifically, of the outward (syntactic) forms of mathematical language, separated from their meaning and informal uses. The most important point of the formalist doctrine is this: all questions which go beyond such elementary acts of recognition are regarded as outside mathematics.

(i) *Generalities about the formalist position.* Concerning the new interpretation of formalization recall §1(*a*): what the formal rules describe is not *actual* linguistic behaviour, but its significant aspects, namely meaning. The formalist contention is (at least) that it is fruitful to *separate* problems connected with equivalence of meaning, for instance between ordinary mathematical language and a formally introduced one, from syntactic questions.

The description has not been found by empirical (statistical) analysis of, say, records of mathematical lectures or texts, but by analysing their meaning. What is essential to the formalist position is first, that the description is given by means of *mechanical* rules (and not, for instance in geometry, by the rule: take as axioms all statements true in our universe) and second, that a *few* such rules are enough to codify the bulk of mathematical practice [this is tacitly understood whenever one speaks of formalizing an argument; one does not mean the (mechanical) rule: write down the words of your argument and nothing more!]. As already mentioned in §0(*d*), while the properties of the objects, namely the axioms, are constantly referred to in mathematical practice, the description of logical inference is not.

A possible ambiguity in the general formalist position is this: What is a mechanical rule? As long as only positive, i.e. formalizability, results are considered, no general answer is needed provided we understand this notion well enough to recognize that we have to do with mechanical rules. Actually, by (ii) below, it turns out that a general analysis of the notion of mechanical process is not too difficult. It is needed for negative results.

The most serious and basic questions are these: First, *what is gained by such a* (mechanical) *formalization of a branch of mathematics*? or, what is gained by the separation mentioned above which is recommended by formalists. Second, *how does one decide whether a formalization is correct*? Concerning the second question a believing formalist really need only consider: How does one know that a formalization is correct, not that it is not correct. The general belief was this: the formal rules decide every question in the language considered, i.e. for every sentence (closed formula) A either A or $\neg\, A$ is formally provable, so-called: saturation [provided A expresses a mathematically well defined assertion; examples of such A are arithmetic propositions, propositions about real numbers, for details see §3(*b*)]. The property of saturation refers only to the formal rules; *if* one has an interpretation of the formal rules in mind at all, one can verify that the rules are valid; and saturation assures one that the formal rules are complete, i.e. settle every question in the language treated.

Concerning the first question, even when there is no doubt that the formalization is correct, it is not easy to say in advance what is gained. But the discovery itself is sufficiently astonishing to be interesting. In a very superficial way, cf. (iv) below, one might expect that questions of *reliability* lend themselves to a more systematic treatment when one has mechanical rules, for instance for logical consequence, rather than an understood notion of consequence used in practical mathematics. Probably the major attraction of formalization was that it suggested the possibility of a *mechanistic theory* of human reasoning, in particular, that the propositions A above not only can be decided by means of the formal rules, but that something like repeated application of such rules is all that goes on even if we consciously think of reasoning differently; more precisely, that the higher nervous system consists of a *mechanism* whose behaviour is given by the formal rules, as an electronic computer is a mechanism whose physical behaviour realizes certain mechanical laws (the 'instructions' which it is given); cf. also §4. Some psychological reasons for wanting the separation were mentioned in §0(*d*). In a vague way an analogy between applications of mathematics to physics, and applications of formal results to intuitive mathematical notions suggests itself: since the separation between mathematical questions and their physical interpretations seems to have been, by and large, useful, one asks here for a similar separation. Thus, consider the application of mathematical theorems *within* mathematics. On the formalist view, we have the following separation. The sequence of 7 symbols $a + b = b + a$ has been derived in one of the usual systems (as we would say: systems for arithmetic): this is a mathematical fact. The inference from this to the assertion: when the elementary computation rules are applied correctly to, say, 5 and 2 in different order then they give the same result, is empirical and our confidence in it is (or: should be?) based on long experience with formal rules. This suggestion will be examined in (iv) below. The whole business is not very plausible because the methods used in verifying physical interpretations, for instance by means of observations from rockets that go round the moon, are patently different from the usual activities of mathematicians while the actual conviction in the so-called empirical inference above is got by inspecting the mathematician's proof of $a + b = b + a$ itself. Again, returning to *saturation* above, the proof of saturation is given a special status (it is called: metamathematical) although when we do have such proofs they show no apparent difference from any other arithmetic proof (of a relatively simple kind, so-called $\forall\exists$ statements).

If, however, we have a branch of mathematics for which no complete formalization is known, only partial ones, then the interest of the separation is vanishingly small for the general formalist position, although it may be of use in solving specific mathematical problems as in §0(*d*). For, either the particular formalization is an historical accident, in future one will add new axioms or rules by methods which are not determined by mechanical rules; then we don't have a formalization. Or the partial formalization is distinguished by subtler qualities than mere saturation; then the heart of the epistemological problem lies in the discovery of these subtler qualities and not in the formalization itself. For this latter possibility, see §2(*b*), (*c*).

(ii) *Successes*. The existence of correct formalizations of several parts of mathematics is known; for a more detailed discussion of correctness of predicate calculus, perhaps the most important case, see §3(*a*).

The possible ambiguity concerning the notion of mechanical procedure, mentioned in (i), has been investigated in the theory of recursive functions. The principles to be used in analysing such a notion as mechanical process are necessarily more delicate than those used in §3(*a*), but Turing's analysis is quite convincing. The notion is certainly *stable* for quite a spectrum of alternatives: the mathematical results which can be used to establish this are strong *closure* properties of the class of recursive functions. Thus the basic concept of the formalist doctrine, that of formal system, has not only a clear meaning, but a *precise extension*: we can see what sort of thing can be done by use of the particular kind of evidence admitted or, at least preferred, by formalism.

In consequence, one also has a (stable) notion of *formal rigour*: a formulation of (properties of) a concept is called formally rigorous if it is given by means of a formal system. The importance of this notion does not, of course, depend on the rejection of informal rigour but may have led to the rejection: it is a common place, in philosophy and elsewhere, that people get a thrill out of a thing not because it is satisfactory, but because they believe it is the only thing in the world.[1]

Finally, formalist researches have corrected *false impressions*. For instance, Poincaré argued that in the development of Euclidean geometry from Euclid's axioms one needs more than purely logical inference. It is perfectly possible that the actual evidence used is other than logical inference, and, moreover, that not every formal derivation would be accepted, for instance if it is too complicated to be graspable: $A \rightarrow \neg \neg A$ is accepted, but $A \rightarrow \neg \neg \neg \neg \neg \neg \neg \neg A$ probably not. Also, in a sense, Poincaré was right in principle because, by (iii) below, this kind of mechanical axiomatizability no longer applies to richer geometric languages. But the fact remains that, before the formalistic researches, one really did not know that Poincaré was wrong on the particular issue mentioned, nor in what respect there is a *need* for non-mechanical rules; in fact, one probably would not even *state* the different senses above, if one did not have a firm notion of formal rigour as an anchoring point. (It seems to me premature to ask whether the alternatives are 'minor': as Feynman emphasizes in his lectures on physics, in a *fundamental* theory the explanation of a small point may require a total revision of the theory.)

(iii) *Failures*. A variant of the incompleteness result of §1(*b*) for set theory is Gödel's famous *first incompleteness theorem*. Supported by an analysis of the notion of mechanical rule, cf. (ii) above, it shows:

Every consistent formal system F obtained from a certain well established part of current mathematical practice by adding a (mechanically generated) set of rules, is unsaturated. Specifically, a certain purely arithmetic identity F_U (obtained from the description of the rules), can neither be formally derived by these rules nor refuted. Moreover, F_U is quite elementarily recognized to be true if the system is consistent.

This means that *there is no saturated* (consistent formal) *system for arithmetic which can even be described with formal rigour*. All the difficulties mentioned at the end of (i) above concerning the significance of the formalist separation have to be faced: Gödel's theorem provides a straight refutation of the assumptions which made the formalist view even remotely plausible.

It is rare, not only in philosophy but in practical applications of

---

[1] Here it is to be remarked that the so-called principle of *tolerance*, emphasized by formalists like Carnap or Curry, really preaches tolerance with respect to *content*, i.e. is easy going on informal rigour, but not with respect to *form*.

mathematics in science or engineering, that a simple result has such clear cut consequences as Gödel's result has for the formalist position. It may be instructive to list some delicate considerations that *might* have been needed in a discussion of the formalist position, but are superfluous. First, suppose our usual formal systems had turned out to be saturated, but either our (arithmetic) proof of this fact had been abstract or we could not find any reasonable 'empirical' explanation of the success of these systems. Second, they are unsaturated, but we could find saturated extensions: however, the added axioms were chosen for 'metaphysical' reasons, for instance axioms concerning the set theoretic continuum introduced for geometric reasons. Third, they are saturated for arithmetic statements, but not analytic ones. [Cf. §3(*b*) for a discussion of attempts to reinterpret the incompleteness theorem as showing that, contrary to common sense, the formally undecided arithmetic propositions involved are not well defined.]

(iv) *Revisions and refinements.* Of course the most obvious revision of the formalist view is simply to *enlarge* the area of what is regarded as given in mathematical experience. After having checked that it is so given! This will be done in §2(*b*) and §2(*c*) for three well known views. Here an interesting, but still fragmentary, revision due to Lorenzen should be mentioned, which is about formalist mathematics (though an extension of it): we are not only supposed to be capable of following mechanical rules, but of certain reflections about such rules and so forth (and these reflections may or may not be adequately represented by mechanical rules).

As to a mechanistic theory of reasoning, and, in particular, of learning (which was regarded above as one of the attractions *behind* formalism) nothing positive seems to be known; see also §4 below.

Formal results and their applications. As I have emphasized in (i) the relation between formal mathematics and its applications, in particular a sharp separation between them, is one of the essential elements of the formalist view. By excluding non-formal aspects (mathematical truth, or: truth for an interpretation) from mathematics, the formalist cannot explain the *choice* of our usual formal systems in the obvious way, namely by their validity for the intended (abstract) meaning. The usual proposal is to explain it in terms of applications of formal systems. Since 'validity for the intended meaning' is not counted among the applications, one must be prepared for a delicate analysis of what applications are to be considered [cf. the difficulties about fruitfulness in §0(*d*)]. As a corollary:

without such an analysis the whole talk about applications may be one big cheat.[1]

A concrete example of such an analysis of *applications of formal results within mathematics* concerns purely numerical results. Consider a formal system F (the reader can take any system of arithmetic which he knows: it will be typical), in which some elementary arithmetic is developed, such as the commutative law mentioned above. If $P_F(\mathfrak{a}, \ulcorner A \urcorner)$ means: the sequence $\mathfrak{a}$ of formulae in F is a derivation according to the rules of F of the formula A (corners emphasizing that the syntactic object A is meant and not the assertion expressed by A); then the validity of the 'empirical' inference on p. 226 is expressed by

$$(\ast) \qquad \forall\, \mathfrak{a}\, \forall\, n, m[P_F(\mathfrak{a}, \ulcorner a + b = b + a \urcorner) \to n + m = m + n].$$

The very meaning of formal system requires that for any given sequence $\mathfrak{a}$ one can verify by a (finite) series of mechanical acts whether or not $P_F(\mathfrak{a}, \ulcorner a + b = b + a \urcorner)$ is correct; note that $\ulcorner a + b = b + a \urcorner$ is a fixed expression of F with 'formal' variables a and b. The letters n and m are variables over the natural numbers. Since finite sequences $\mathfrak{a}$ can be numbered, $(\ast)$ *is essentially an arithmetic identity*. For the case of the commutative law, $(\ast)$ is not problematic because we know $\forall\, n, m(n + m = m + n)$; but suppose the expression $C(a, b, c, d)$ in F is used to express Fermat's conjecture: $q > 2 \to n^q + m^q \neq p^q$; then the assertion corresponding to $(\ast)$

$$\forall\, \mathfrak{a}\, \forall\, n, m, p, q[P_F(\mathfrak{a}, \ulcorner C(a, b, c, d) \urcorner) \to (q > 2 \to n^q + m^q \neq p^q)].$$

is really problematic if we do not know whether the rules of F are correct.

Thus, *the validity of the empirical inference of* (i) *is nothing else but the truth of the arithmetic identity* $(\ast)$.

The obvious way of establishing $(\ast)$ is to give a mathematical proof using as evident principles as possible. Since $(\ast)$ is to be a general assertion its content cannot be expressed in terms of what the formalist accepts as given in mathematical experience; for instance,

[1] It is probably rather more difficult to analyse the formalist proposal than to analyse so-called metaphysical assertions. Personally I think that something quite definite and important is meant, and that *certain* choices of formal systems are best understood in terms of applications. One reason why formalists have done so little towards analysing their notion is this: they realize the interest of formal systems (and even informal notions) which cannot be explained in terms of their applications in the sense in which *application* is originally meant, and so they water down this sense. This refusal to commit oneself has probably been a much greater obstacle to progress in philosophy than any *inherent* vagueness in traditional (or other informal) notions.

suppose ($*$) is in turn to be interpreted in terms of formal derivations in a system F' of (the formula, say, S used to express) ($*$): then this would have to be supported by establishing

$$\forall \, \mathfrak{a}'[P_F{}'(\mathfrak{a}', {}^{\ulcorner}S^{\urcorner}) \rightarrow (*)],$$

and so forth. Thus, on the *formalist* analysis of what is specifically mathematical evidence there is no means of doing the obvious thing. But, at least for particular F, cf. §2(*b*) (ii), the obvious approach can be carried out.

What is much more difficult is to think of another approach which is coherent (and really establishes the validity in question)! There is a proposal (for instance, in Bourbaki): the assertion ($*$) *is to be established statistically* (empirically after the fashion of the natural sciences). It would be very interesting if somebody gave it a second thought! I have never seen even a broad discussion of the following questions: what statistical principles should be used in evaluating our experience of whatever formal system F is considered, for instance current set theory? does our experience really support the reliability of F and not only the reliability of some weak subsystem of F? since by p. 218, in actual practice the full force of F is not used. And, above all, how one does statistics without assuming *a priori* at least inferences of the form ($*$)?

Marginal comments. The explanation of the successful application of mathematical results, not only within mathematics, is generally regarded as a crucial question for the theory of knowledge. If one accepts explanations in terms of abstract objects the natural approach is this: The objects and situations to which we apply mathematics possess certain abstract properties; mathematics is the theory of such properties, and therefore provides the means of formulating the relevant facts. In other words, abstract truths are used to explain the applications; the limit to our ability of forming mathematical theories is then the limit of our ability to recognize the abstract properties possessed by the objects we study. (This is just the reverse of the formalist's aim to reduce abstract truths to applications.) From this point of view the formalist procedure seems even pragmatically hopeless, because of the following parallel with the sciences: there we study objective physical properties, for instance the atomic structure of matter, and find that we are able to understand the uses of physical objects in terms of their structure: but we'd have a hard time to get the structure from the uses which people happen to make of the objects. (Of course, by footnote 1, p. 209, the formalist would reject the parallel: on theoretical, certainly not on pragmatic grounds!)

A question suggested by the Bourbaki proposal above. While it seems pretty hopeless to develop it for its intended purpose, can we use it to distinguish formal systems F, we actually use, from possible variants ? for instance from extensions by adding the undecided formula F_U in (iii). In other words, is there something special about our traditional systems? (Obviously one will assume some statistical principles, much more than the commutative law!) The naïve procedure does not work provided our statistical principles include the little bit of mathematics needed to infer the consistency of $F \cup \{F_U\}$, say F', from the consistency of F (this shows how statistical evaluation is sensitively related to what mathematics we accept). Perhaps a more hopeful approach is to consider lengths of proof. Evidently, at any given moment t, the statistical reliability $\rho_t(l)$ of proofs in F depends on the length l of the proofs considered, and, presumably, $\rho_t(l) \to 0$ as $l \to \infty$. Now, there are theorems of F' which have quite short proofs in F', but long ones in F, and so the functions ρ' and ρ need not be of the same order of magnitude. F might be regarded as statistically distinguished for suitable distribution of the empirical data; if for (reasonably chosen) subsystems F_1, F_2 of F, ρ_1 and ρ_2 were of much the 'same' order of magnitude: F would be a kind of natural barrier. (This problem is a bit far fetched: it is suggested by natural barriers in so-called autonomous progressions [2], considered in the next section.)

I should be very pleased if something of this kind could be done. For, formalist writings often talk of lengths of proofs or lengths of expressions when discussing problems of reliability. This is superficially silly because, for instance in the case of the commutative law, for quite small numbers a, b, say < 20, the computations of $a + b$ and $b + a$ are short, but the number of (different) $\langle a + b, b + a \rangle$ is quite large (190). If one has not gone through each of these cases, the validity of the commutative law even for a, $b < 20$ is problematic on the formalist view. If the question above could be solved positively, this might be taken to mean that there is a little bit of good in everything, even in formalism.

(b) *Finitism: What we can visualize* (concretely, with the mind's eye)

The present section starts where formalism leaves off. It consists of two parts. First, a general schema of analysis which can be applied provided only there are *general* assertions (like the commutative law) which are capable of a 'preferred' kind of evidence, in contrast to the formalist view, cf. (iv) above. This schema formulates a theoretical (mathematical) explanation or, as it is sometimes called, justification of mechanical rules of the kind considered in (*a*). Since the *mechanical* character is essential, at least for an important kind of preferred evidence, this approach too builds on the basic discovery of formalization. Second, a discussion of a *particular* kind of preferred evidence (from which the section gets its title), with some remarks on another kind of evidence, so-called *predicative* proofs. It is to be remarked that the two kinds of evidence have been suggested by the traditional literature on the Philosophy of Mathematics: what is done here is to sharpen the notions involved and to see whether they can be formalized, i.e. formulated with formal rigour in the sense of §2(*a*) (ii). It is to be expected that mathematical logic will not for ever limp behind traditional notions, but that the technical results will suggest new significant kinds of preferred evidence. There are indications of the basic role of *ordinals* (transfinite iteration) in such a future theory of mathematical evidence, cf. (iv) below.

(i) *Generalized Hilbert programme*: *a method of philosophical analysis*. The programme extends the discussion on p. 230 above. We suppose given some *restricted* or *preferred class* $\mathscr{P}$ of principles of reasoning which may be codified in some formal system, but need not be. The analysis applies to systems F which are *intended* to be about (abstract) objects that have no place in $\mathscr{P}$; thus not all formulae of F (are intended to) express assertions which are meaningful for $\mathscr{P}$. The general assumption is that *some* formulae of F are intended to express relations, respectively assertions, meaningful for $\mathscr{P}$. Let $A\mathscr{P}$ denote a class of such formulae. To avoid useless complications we choose a notation (for syntactic objects in F and interpreted assertions in $\mathscr{P}$) where, for $A \in A\mathscr{P}$, the formula A also denotes its interpretation in $\mathscr{P}$. When explicit distinctions are convenient, corners are used as in §2(*a*) (iv). L.c. German letters are used for variables over (finite) sequences of formulae in F, capital Roman letters for formulae of F. *Assume that the proof relation for F* ($\mathfrak{a}$ is a formal derivation in F of A) *is defined in* $\mathscr{P}$, and denote it by $P_F(\mathfrak{a}, \ulcorner A \urcorner)$. (Note that, by our convention, the formula which defines P_F on the intended interpretation of F, is also denoted by P_F. As on p. 230, the mechanical character of F implies essentially that P_F is quite elementary (primitive recursive).

Generalized Hilbert's problem: to establish, by means of $\mathscr{P}$, for all $\mathfrak{a}$ and all $A \in A\mathscr{P}$

$$(*) \quad P_F(\mathfrak{a}, \ulcorner A \urcorner) \to A.$$

This really establishes as much as could be expected, if $A\mathscr{P}$ is the largest class of formulae which we have recognized to have the same sense on the intended interpretation of F and on the interpretation $\mathscr{P}$: formal provability implies correctness.

This problem includes the problem of p. 230 (provided F contains elementary arithmetic, and $A\mathscr{P}$ includes all purely numerical expressions). Let A be a purely universal formula ($B(x)$ with the free variable x, so that, for each n, $B(0^{(n)})$ ($0^{(n)}$ denoting the nth numeral) is purely numerical). Then, if substitution of terms is a (derived) rule of F, $P_F(\mathfrak{a}, \ulcorner B(x) \urcorner) \to P_F[\mathfrak{a}* B(0^{(n)}), \ulcorner B(0^{(n)}) \urcorner]$ and so by $(\ast)$

$$P_F[\mathfrak{a}, \ulcorner B(x) \urcorner] \to B(n).$$

To appreciate the reduction effected by a proof of $(\ast)$ in $\mathscr{P}$, recall that a sequence $\mathfrak{a}$ which proves A formally in F may contain formulae not in $A\mathscr{P}$, i.e. assertions which have a sense only on the intended interpretation of F, for instance only if certain existential assumptions of §1 are made. But if $(\ast)$ is established in $\mathscr{P}$, and $\mathfrak{a}_0$ is a formal proof in F of A, then we have also a proof of A in $\mathscr{P}$: in this proof there are of course only formulae which have a meaning for $\mathscr{P}$. Thus one may properly say that *all reference to abstract meaning* (involved in the intended interpretation of F) *has been eliminated*, and, in the case of F interpreted according to §1, *the validity of* (formally proved) A in $A\mathscr{P}$ has been separated from *the existential assumptions of* §1 [if $(\ast)$ can be established in $\mathscr{P}$!].

A remark on method. Given a codification of $\mathscr{P}$ in a *formal* system, a (positive) solution of Hilbert's generalized problem for a given F is a formal result. Conversely, given F, the philosophical question is to find a $\mathscr{P}$ valid for the preferred kind of evidence and for which $(\ast)$ holds. By being *mathematically clever* one may find a very elementary $\mathscr{P}$ and an ingenious proof of $(\ast)$: then it will be easy to establish in an informally rigorous way that $\mathscr{P}$ and, because of $(\ast)$, also F is valid for the kind of evidence considered. By *searching informal understanding* of what is involved in this evidence, one may find a much stronger $\mathscr{P}$ which is also valid for this evidence, but the proof of $(\ast)$ in this $\mathscr{P}$ is easy. Conversely for negative results such an informal understanding can only be replaced by showing that $(\ast)$ is not provable for a *very* wide class of $\mathscr{P}$.

(ii) *Successes.* The following simple case shows that at least in some cases Hilbert's problem can be solved without difficult informal analysis: let F_0 be the usual formal system for classical arithmetic with the induction principle restricted to purely universal formulae; cf. §1(c) (ii) for other restricted principles. Now, the actual reason for accepting F_0 or better, the intended interpretation of F_0, is based on the idea of a well defined infinite structure, that of the natural numbers; the use of classical logic is justified because this structure is thought of as being well defined or, as one sometimes says, completed. Once this is accepted the restriction of the induction principle is wholly arbitrary (and, by the same token, one has no idea how it affects the class of theorems or, more generally, what is gained or lost by the restriction). It so happens that quite a bit of ordinary arithmetic is easily formulated in F_0. Also it turns out that

$$(*_0) \quad P_{F_0}(\mathfrak{a}, \ulcorner A \urcorner) \to A$$

can be established in primitive recursive arithmetic $\mathscr{P}_0$ for the natural corresponding class $A\mathscr{P}_0$. Intuitively, it is quite clear that $\mathscr{P}_0$ is much more elementary than the existential assumption of a structure of all natural numbers. This is reflected in the following formal fact: If F_1 is full first order classical arithmetic, which is equally justified by the existential assumption above, the corresponding $(*_1)$ cannot be proved in $\mathscr{P}_0$. It is not surprising that the proof of $(*_0)$ in $\mathscr{P}_0$ (either by means of Herbrand's ideas or Gentzen's cut elimination) requires a non-trivial combinatorial analysis [while $(*_0)$ can be established very easily by set theoretic methods]; for, without the analysis one cannot hope to see why $(*_1)$ cannot be proved in $\mathscr{P}_0$.

For the case of F_1, Hilbert's generalized problem $(*_1)$ has been carried out beautifully in [8], where now the preferred proofs are not those of $\mathscr{P}_0$, but codified in a system $\mathscr{P}_1$ of *infinite* proofs. The characteristic feature of $\mathscr{P}_1$-proofs, as in Gentzen's cut elimination, is this: all formulae that occur in a $\mathscr{P}_1$-proof of A are of 'complexity' not exceeding A, and in particular, if $A \in A\mathscr{P}$ then all formulae in $\mathscr{P}_1$-proof of A also $\in A\mathscr{P}$. Consequently, it is easy to establish: $P\mathscr{P}_1(\mathfrak{a}, \ulcorner A \urcorner) \to A$ where $\mathfrak{a}$ ranges over the infinite proof figures of $\mathscr{P}_1$, but $P_{F_1}(\mathfrak{a}, \ulcorner A \urcorner) \to P\mathscr{P}_1[\psi(\mathfrak{a}), \ulcorner A \urcorner]$ (for suitable ψ) is not so easy. There is an alternative method related to Herbrand's ideas, in which *each A* of F_1 is given a constructive *interpretation* A_1 (no counter example interpretation) such that, for $A \in A\mathscr{P}_1$, $A = A_1$, and one establishes $P_{F_1}(\ ,\ \ulcorner A \urcorner) \to A_1$ by induction.

However, in contrast to $\mathscr{P}_0$, closer analysis of $\mathscr{P}_1$ is required to establish its significance, cf. (iv) below.

(iii) *Some historical points concerning Hilbert's original programme; Gödel's second incompleteness theorem.* For the usual systems F, the *consistency* of F is a special case of $(*)$ above, i.e. of Hilbert's generalized problem. Take $0 = 1$ for A and suppose, of course, that $\ulcorner 0 = 1 \urcorner \in A\mathscr{P}$. Then $(*)$ reduces to $\neg P_F(\mathfrak{a}, \ulcorner 0 = 1 \urcorner)$, i.e. $\ulcorner 0 = 1 \urcorner$ is not derivable in F. It is well known that this implies consistency since, for a very elementary operation σ (and all F including propositional logic):

$$P_F(\mathfrak{a}, \ulcorner 0 = 1 \urcorner) \to P_F[\sigma(\mathfrak{a}, \ulcorner A \urcorner), \ulcorner A \urcorner] \text{ (for all } \mathfrak{a}, A).$$

What makes consistency important is that, for the usual F, *consistency implies* ($\ast$) *in* $\mathscr{P}$, for all formula A satisfying the following condition (roughly: formal verification of counter examples).

If the variables of A are $a_1, \ldots a_p$, say $A(a_1, \ldots, a_p)$, then

$$\neg A(n_1, \ldots, n_p) \to P_F[\pi_A(n_1 \ldots, n_p), \ulcorner \neg A(0^{(n1)}, \ldots, 0^{(np)}) \urcorner],$$

can be proved in $\mathscr{P}$ for a suitable π_A. (This says nothing else than that the computations of $\neg A$ for numerical arguments can be mimicked in F: this is assured if arithmetic can be developed in F).

To see this take $p = 1$ (as a typical case): consistency implies $P_F[\mathfrak{a}, \ulcorner A(0^{(n)}) \urcorner] \to \neg P_F[\mathfrak{a}', \ulcorner \neg A(0^{(n)}) \urcorner]$ for all $\mathfrak{a}$, $\mathfrak{a}'$, n, and so, by the condition above, $\to \neg \neg A(n)$. Thus without further assumption, for all $\mathfrak{a}$ and n

$$P_F[\mathfrak{a}, \ulcorner A(x) \urcorner] \to \neg \neg A(n).$$

Hilbert considered only *decidable* formulae in $\mathscr{P}$ [for which $\neg \neg A(n) \to A(n)$] and hence ($\ast$). (It is easy to show that for less elementary $\mathscr{P}$ the condition above is not verified: in that case, though consistency is necessary, it loses its central importance.)

Returning to the end of §2(*b*) (i) above, Hilbert almost certainly expected to avoid all *searching informal analysis* because he made the following assumption: *there is a certain* $\mathscr{P}$, *intuitively interpreted in a quite elementary way, such that for all F that we actually use,* ($\ast$) *can be proved in* $\mathscr{P}$.

In fact, he would not have been surprised if $\mathscr{P}_0$ itself were such a system; on first glance it seems not impossible that for *all* consistent mechanical F, ($\ast$) can be proved in $\mathscr{P}_0$: ($\ast$) is certainly in $\mathscr{P}_0$. There is a perfect parallel between Hilbert's view and the formalist view of §2(*a*) (i). He considers not *all* mathematically well defined assertions, but only those defined in terms of some elementary $\mathscr{P}$; and he wants not just *some* saturated formal system, but an elementary $\mathscr{P}$ in which all (elementary) ($\ast$) are formally decided. I don't think he explicitly assumed that there was *one* such $\mathscr{P}$; but it is hard to see how one could avoid informal analysis or, as he put it, remove once and for all philosophical problems of foundations unless there were one such a $\mathscr{P}$.[1] Note that the generalized problem for F leaves open the possibility that the whole of elementary evidence considered could not be formalized, but for each particular F which we encounter we find a $\mathscr{P}_F$ (a partial system for the evidence considered) in which ($\ast$)

---

[1] Also one would need one such $\mathscr{P}$ to support the following analogue to the mechanistic theory of p. 226: the true reason why we accept F is the elementary proof of ($\ast$), and derivations in $\mathscr{P}$ are what really goes on in reasoning.

can be proved. Finally, even if one did find one $\mathscr{P}$ there might still be an informal problem of analysing its validity for the kind of evidence one has in mind.

Hilbert's favourite possibility is excluded by *Gödel's imcompleteness result* [more precisely, second version of §2(a) (iii)].

If F' is a formal system of rules codifying $\mathscr{P}$ and F is a formal system which extends F' then ($*$) cannot be proved in $\mathscr{P}$.

This leaves then the following possibilities: $\mathscr{P}$ (the principles of elementary evidence) cannot be codified in any F' even in the following weak sense: not all theorems (in a given language) valid for $\mathscr{P}$ are formally derivable in F'; or else $\mathscr{P}$ can be so formulated in F' but F' cannot be recognized by means of $\mathscr{P}$ to have this property. In this case ($*'$) can be stated but not proved in $\mathscr{P}$. Finally, F' may transcend all formal systems which we actually encounter in mathematical practice, in which case one might say that Hilbert's programme can be carried out with a transcendental singularity. Finally, F' may be included in one of the usual systems.

(iv) *Finitist Proof.* I now consider a kind of elementary evidence (mentioned in the literature particularly in connection with Hilbert's original programme), and propose an analysis according to which so-called *first order* classical or intuitionistic *formal arithmetic is of essentially the same proof theoretic strength as the body of finitist arithmetic proofs*. Thus, granted this analysis, the last of the possibilities just mentioned applies, and *Hilbert's original programme cannot be carried out for first order arithmetic*.

To avoid misunderstandings, note the following points.

The *name*: finitist proof (finiter Beweis) is due to Hilbert, as a result of Hilbert's particular view of the *nature* of mathematical evidence. The facts are these. There is a type of proof, in arithmetic and combinatorial mathematics, which has always struck mathematicians as being of an especially elementary character. Up to the nineteenth century, when analysis was formulated rigorously, it was perhaps *the* method of proof and therefore not contrasted with others; but later, attention was drawn to this kind of proof, for instance by Kronecker. What (intensional object of mathematical experience) was meant by Kronecker seems reasonably clear, but not so clear how to say what is essential and significant about it. Hilbert believed that finiteness was the essential feature involved. *Prima facie* this is quite dubious because, whatever else is in doubt, this much is clear from §2(b) (i): Hilbert's programme requires that *some general* (universal) *statements about the natural numbers should be capable of elementary* preferred *kind of proof*. We therefore continue to use Hilbert's terminology but on the explicit understanding that it is not tied to his analysis. (Cf. our continued use of the words: *real* and *imaginary* or *complex* number; this doesn't mean that we share the view of the people who introduced these terms on the ontological status of the objects in question).

A typical example of a finitist proof is the use of the principle of induction applied to elementary properties: for instance, to prove $2^n > n$, one observes $2^0 = 1 > 0$, and $2^n > n \rightarrow 2^n + 2^n > n + n$; since $2^n + 2^n = 2^{n+1}$ and, for $n \geqslant 1$, $n + n \geqslant n + 1$, $2^n > n \rightarrow 2^{n+1} > n + 1$; from this and $2^0 > 0$ one concludes generally $2^n > n$. It is a common place that the words we use, the outward and visible signs of our reasoning, do not represent fully our thoughts (though for particular conclusions the words may be sufficient). When studying an intensional object such as finitist proof one must be prepared to find that the differences between thoughts and words are essential. Thus, when we are convinced by the proof of $2^n > n$ above, *is the actual evidence used finitist or not*? In particular: are we thinking of 2^n as a *set* of ordered pairs

$$\{<0, 1>, <1, 2>, <2, 4>, <3, 8>, \ldots\}$$

or as a *collection of rules* $D(0) = 0$, $D(n + 1) = [D(n) + 1] + 1$, $2^0 = 1$, $2^{n+1} = D(2^n)$ with some equation calculus? I said explicitly above that the principle of induction is to be applied to elementary (i.e. finitistically meaningful) properties: does this restriction on the principle enter consciously our heads when we have the proof above before us? In other words, it is an empirical question (possibly difficult, but I believe quite meaningful) whether any particular person who goes through the argument above at some particular time understands it as a finitist argument or as some other argument. Just as somebody who goes through a set theoretic argument which does not use the axiom of infinity, may understand it as being about, say, hereditarily finite sets, or about all sets.

What is considered below is the *notion* of finitist proof: how to find out whether a particular act (of understanding) is finitist is a separate matter; merely to ask this latter question needs of course the notion. Concerning the significance of the notion, cf. p. 223. The assumption is that we have enough mathematical experience to make an analysis of the notion profitable and let questions of empirical verification look after themselves; cf. the notion of *length* which was (profitably) analysed in geometry long before one had any idea how to measure the distance of a fixed star from the earth: in fact, one appealed to the analysis to find out whether a proposed method of measurement was *correct*. [Put 'operationally': early experience convinced us what was the proper notion to use; cf. §3(*a*), §4(*c*).]

In [10] there is a (formally) rigorous description of a proposal for analysing the notion of: *finitist proof of an arithmetic identity $A(n)$*. Essential points are (i) what kind of A are to be considered, and, in terms of this, (ii) what is the difference between the *truth* of $A(0)$, $A(1), \ldots, A(n), \ldots$ for all n and having a finitist *proof* of $A(n)$.

In view of the discussion on p. 237 the experience involved in such a proof cannot be expected to be 'strictly finite', and one would like (ii) to be so formulated that it would not even make sense to apply for instance induction to an A different from those in (i). The difference between finitist and other evidence should be as abrupt as between, say, visual and auditory!

The idea of the proposal is this: *Finitist reasoning consists of acts which enable us to visualize a whole structure of concrete configurations.* Specifically, for each n, $A(n)$ is to be an equation between terms which constitute instructions for computations, and a finitist proof of $A(n)$ should enable us to visualize the whole structure of the computations involved $(n = 0, 1, 2, \ldots)$. The technical problem is to analyse operations on structures (yielding structures) which have the property that the result of the operation can be visualized if the structure can be visualised, for example the operation of forming a tree of structures S from S:

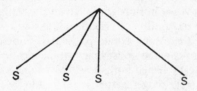

The most delicate point is the analysis of what *iterations* of the operations can still be visualized. For the analysis in [10], ϵ_0 (the limit of the ordinals ω, ω^ω, $\omega^{\omega^\omega}, \ldots$) is an upper bound to the iterations which can be (so to speak: theoretically) visualized.

The infinite proof trees which, in [8], played a purely technical role, *are* (or, at least, are typical of) the structures which are visualized. Thus, if the present approach is on the right lines it is a far cry from Hilbert's analysis.

N.B. Mathematicians sometimes speak of visualizing structures which are quite different from those here considered; for instance, in set theoretic arguments, the structure of all denumerable ordinals or of all accessible ordinals. Since their main interest is the validity of their results and not the mathematical activity itself, it does not matter whether they really visualize those structures or only analogous ones; as long as the latter are sufficiently analogous to lead to valid arguments. Therefore they would hardly go into this question and consider their use of 'visualizing' metaphorical. The situation here is parallel to the use of *construction* where one speaks of set theoretic constructions, but also distinguishes between constructive and non-constructive methods in arithmetic. When the latter become objects of study a (theoretical) notion of constructive procedure by trial and error is introduced in recursion theory. It is related to what is really effective, i.e. can be really carried out, as our intended (theoretical) notion of visualization is to be related to what one can really visualize. As in §2(*a*) (ii) (p. 228), it is a separate question whether this difference is 'minor', i.e. whether the theoretical notion provides a good theory.

(v) *Developments*. First, improvements of the analysis of finitist proof. If one finds the approach convincing at all, the first thing to do is to eliminate dubious assumptions about visualization needed in getting the bound ϵ_0. The only result on this is in [10], where the conditions on the iteration procedure are relaxed without changing the bound ϵ_0. As to possible simplifications there seems to be little hope of giving a really simple description of visualizable structures since the phenomenon described is complicated (though this is not certain because a description in sufficiently *abstract* terms may be simple; note that *some* notion going beyond visualization is in any case needed since the totality of visualizable structures is not visualizable). However there are some particularly interesting specific questions such as: can the consistency of classical arithmetic or its ω-consistency be established finitistically? By ingenious mathematics it should be possible to get a (negative) result by the use of substantially fewer properties of finitist proof than those used in the general analysis in [10], particularly in the case of ω-consistency.But the most satisfactory improvement would be provided by some axiom about finitist proof [analogous to Principle 2 of §3(*a*) for logical validity] which relates finitist proofs to something not involving this notion: roughly, an axiom which tells us what more we know (in familiar mathematical terms) if we can visualize the whole structure of computations of $A(0)$, $A(1)$, ... than if we merely know the truth of $\forall n\, A(n)$. The present axioms only provide closure conditions on the class of finitist proof. (In this respect the situation is analogous to the analysis of mechanical process by Turing, but the latter is much superior to what we have at present about finitist proofs.)

Second, once one thinks of the *generalization* of Hilbert's programme in §2(*b*) (i), one looks for significant kinds of mathematical evidence other than finitist proof. One of them is: *predicative proof* (relative to the concept of natural number) not primarily in connection with arithmetic but analysis and set theory. Both Poincaré and Russell drew attention to this area of mathematics, Feferman has given an analysis in [2], in general principle similar to the description of finitist proof in [10], but so much more thorough that the subject of predicative proofs is certainly better understood. One accidental attraction of his work (and that of Schütte working with my original proposal on predicativity) is this: he obtained a bound Γ (the so-called first strongly critical number) corresponding to ϵ_0 above; while earlier work in proof theory since Gentzen has prepared us for ϵ_0, Γ was a brand new star. A probably quite significant discovery of Feferman is an unexpected connection between his characterization of predicative proof and a famous principle in constructive mathematics, Brouwer's bar theorem: If a (decidable) ordering is well founded in the sense that all freely chosen descending sequences are finite then transfinite induction may be applied. In Feferman's work the central principle is this: If (in the bar theorem) the premise is *proved* then the conclusion may be inferred. It should be remarked that there is a characterization of finitist proofs (in [10]) where one uses Feferman's principle but with induction *restricted* to so-called constructive existential properties. So, different areas of evidence may be falling into place.

Marginal comments. As in §2(*a*) (iv) one may modify Hilbert's (generalized) programme by taking into account the *lengths of proofs.* Thus given a formal system F and an area of evidence $\mathcal{P}$, let $\psi(n)$ be the length of the shortest proof in $\mathcal{P}$ of the consistency of F restricted to proofs of length n. (If the number of proofs of bounded length in F is finite and F is consistent, there will always be a proof of their consistency.) If $\psi(n)$ is of the same order of magnitude as n we should have a 'practical' reduction of F to $\mathcal{P}$. I first heard this interesting suggestion in a conversation with Gödel.

One nowadays treats: *seeing* in geometry: and *seeing* in arithmetic, quite separately. I wonder whether some of the basic notions in topology do not really constitute an analysis of what one can *see* (though this question is of course not put in so many words): is not, for instance, *combinatorial* as opposed to topological *equivalence* an analysis of a basic element of geometric intuition? If so, we might learn something by asking what theorems a topologist would quote to justify the notion of combinatorial equivalence: these theorems should be kinds of axioms for the (hypothetical) basic intuition.

(*c*) *Intuitionism: what we can understand* (about our own mental activity in mathematics).

In contrast to §2(*a*), (*b*), one is here not interested in restricting oneself to a minimum of what is given in mathematical experience, but to study as much as possible of what is so given. Several distinctions are needed.

First, intuitionistic mathematics goes beyond finitist mathematics. Gödel [4] has characterized the difference succinctly as follows: finitist constructions operate only on concrete, that is spatio temporal, objects, intuitionistic constructions also on abstract objects. If the analysis of §2(*b*) (iv) is accepted, spatio temporal objects are not to be restricted to finite configurations, but to those structures that can be visualized. The abstract objects considered in intuitionistic mathematics are not sets of higher type in the sense of §1, but meanings, proofs, and rules (which we understand). Some examples of the latter are mentioned in (i) below: the constructions actually familiar to the majority of mathematicians are finitist.

Second, just because intuitionistic mathematics takes abstract objects seriously (unlike, for instance, §2(*a*)), one has to investigate whether given syntactic formation rules ensure that formulae are *meaningful*, (formal) inference rules are valid principles of *proof*. In this respect it is closer to §1; cf. §3(*a*) on (classical) logical validity. It should not be assumed that all legitimate formation rules or rules of inference are necessarily formal (mechanical). In particular, the validity of (a certain analogue of) Church's thesis for understood constructive number theoretic functions is an important issue, cf. §2(*c*) (vi) below.

Third, intuitionism is concerned with mathematical activity and not (only) validity. Therefore understanding is an object of (precise) analysis. As in §2(*b*) (iv), the primary interest is in a theoretical notion of understanding and its limits, and not in practical understanding, i.e. in real intelligibility. As is to be expected from pp. 239–240 in §2(*b*) (iv), the mathematician whose main interest is in validity, uses 'understanding' in a more liberal way.

The points above constitute the relatively little known *positive* side of intuitionism: it goes not only beyond finitism, but may go beyond set theory in the sense that, for instance, the intuitive notion of constructive number theoretic function may be set theoretically undefinable; even the class of recursion equations which can be *proved* constructively to define (total) functions is perhaps set theoretically undefinable.

The *negative* side of the intuitionistic position comes from the following doctrine:

If something in mathematical experience is to be really evident, it must be wholly about such experience and not, for instance, ultimately about objects external to ourselves or even about concepts of such objects, for instance of sets as conceived in §1.

As discussed in (i) below, both the positive and the negative sides are problematic; for a parallel between the negative side and *strict realism* of §1, cf. (iv). Some interest attaches to the positive side even if one does not accept the negative side, but only assumes that the area admitted in intuitionistic mathematics isolates one important area of mathematical evidence. I think the negative aspect of intuitionism constitutes a serious issue; what I doubt is that anything has ever been said in support of it that need be taken very seriously.

(i) *Generalities.* First, a *weakened* case for the negative side. Even if one expects to find in one's mathematical experience objects not treated in intuitionistic mathematics, there is always the question: which of them are most essential for the theory in hand? And if one is primarily interested in an analysis of evidence there is a *prima facie* case for the intuitionistic position. Teaching at an early stage apart, understanding is every man's own business, apparently not much helped from the outside. So it is natural as a first approximation to ignore the outside altogether. If in addition one regards understanding as a (mental) act that happens here and now one has, I think, broadly accepted the intuitionistic position. However, it may be fruitful to analyse this last step more carefully.

Next, some illustrations of the positive side: truly intuitionistic, i.e. non-finitist notions or operations. First, it is to be remarked that the gap between familiar (finitist) constructive operations and non-constructive ones is enormous: in other words, only very weak properties of constructivity are needed to establish familiar examples and counter examples. For instance, to refute the law of the excluded middle one considers the following predicate $A_0(f)$ of free choice sequences f of natural numbers x: $\exists x [f(x) = 0]$, and the obvious, *continuity* property for disjunctions: to prove $\forall f [A(f) \vee B(f)]$, one must prove that a finite number of values of f are enough to decide either $A(f)$ or $B(f)$, i.e. one must prove $(\ast)$:

$$\forall f \exists x \{\forall g[f \overline{\overline{x}} g \to A(g)] \vee \forall g[f \overline{\overline{x}} g \to B(g)]\},$$

where $f \overline{\overline{x}} g$ means $(\forall y \leqslant x) [f(y) = g(y)]$. But $(\ast)$ is refuted for $A = A_0$ and $B = \neg A_0$, by taking for f the *constant* function $f_0 \equiv 1$, and showing that there is no x that satisfies $(\ast)$. Clearly this refutation does not use the delicate element of intuitionism at all, namely the opposition between proof versus truth: roughly speaking, the latter would be needed if $(\ast)$ were true (non constructively speaking), but we could show that it could not be proved constructively. The constructive meaning has only been used to justify the implication:

$\forall f[A(f)\ B(f)] \to (*)$, but not afterwards. It would hardly be worth while to study intuitionistic mathematics at all if one believed that nothing more recondite is implied by the intuitionistic meaning. The following example may give a better idea. It concerns the area *between* finitist and non-constructive mathematics, and uses the (minimal) requirement that a constructive proof of an existential assertion must supply an effective instance. To fix ideas we consider a formal system F which we have so interpreted that every formal derivation represents a convincing proof; consider now the *rule*:

With every formal derivation D in F of an existential (numerical) formula, i.e. a closed formula of the form $\exists x A(x)$, associate *that* x which is supplied by the proof *which you understand to be represented by* D (x will, in general, be a term containing parameters).

Note that (α) there nothing objectionable to the subjective formulation! on the contrary, according to the basic intuitionistic position all mathematical assertions ought to have this kind of subjective form (when properly analysed), (β) though argument and value of the (function defined by the) rule are concrete objects, namely formal derivations and numbers respectively, there is nothing *prima facie* mechanical about the instruction, (γ) quite simple examples such as Heyting's arithmetic show that D need not *mention* this term x, i.e. need not contain a theorem of the form $A(t)$, at all and, finally (δ) there are perfectly good constructively interpreted F for which $\exists x A(x)$ can be proved formally in F, but no $A(0^{(n)})$—though, of course, for some n, $A(0^{(n)})$ can be proved in another constructive F'.

There is nothing surprising in the fact that different people *might* understand the rule differently [just as different people might understand the notion of *set* differently; cf. (iv) below]. But it is worth taking a closer look at a particular F, namely Heyting's first order arithmetic. In this case (δ) does not arise because it is a fact that, if $\exists x A(x)$ is proved there is also a number n for which $A(0^{(n)})$ can be formally proved. An immediate consequence, concerning (β), is this; there is a mechanical (formal) rule which associates with every D an x, namely: take the shortest (formal) proof which proves a formula of the form $A(0^{(x)})$ and take this x! But is it *that* x which is demanded by the rule? This cannot be expected; interestingly enough the question can be solved! It uses the machinery of infinite cut free proofs. Reflection shows that when one thinks through a formal argument D in Heyting's system, the *thought* involved is more closely represented by the cut free proof D' associated by means of so-called cut elimination [8] with $D : D'$ has the property that if it proves $(\exists x)A(x)$, it *mentions* a particular $A(t)$ from which it obtains directly $(\exists x)A(x)$. Thus, though D' may still be understood differently

244

by different people, it is a detailed enough representation of the intuitive thought to settle the particular question above (namely, what x is supplied by the proof that we understand to be represented by D?). All that is needed is this: each of us should convince himself that cut elimination provides a correct (i.e. more faithful) analysis of the proof which D represents for us.[1]

The last general point concerns the following apparent peculiarity of the intuitionistic position compared with §1, §2(a), (b): In the other proposals for a fundamental analysis, mathematical practice was accepted, and so the success of the analysis was tested by means of the practice [modulo such matters as the correctness of a formalization §1(b) (i)]; intuitionism rejects much of this practice, as one might expect from a solipsistic doctrine. Sure, all theory influences what area of experience we take seriously (cf. p. 215); but isn't intuitionism doctrinaire beyond reason, i.e. does it not cut itself off from all mathematical experience as the latter presents itself to us naturally? Two things are to be said. First, even though mathematical assertions present themselves to us as being about external objects, when *confronted with a proof* we quite naturally ask ourselves: can it be made constructive or effective? It is now the fashion to formulate the result of studying such a question or, at least, some of the knowledge so obtained, in terms of a sharper theorem. Also one treats such questions in an unsystematic *ad hoc* fashion, by 'rethinking' the proof as one says, and foregoes a general theory. (The only exception to this rule is a growing interest in recursion theory, but, as pointed out, p. 243, it uses only extremely crude properties of constructivity: in particular, it does not use specifically intuitionistic operations on proofs.) Everything in mathematical experience connected with such questions of proof is most naturally treated by use of intuitionistic notions: set theoretic interpretations are generally ill-motivated and tortuous. Second, not only is there a good deal of existing mathematical experience which is directly relevant to the intuitionistic position (though not generally isolated systematically) but one must expect this experience to grow *after* the position is developed. For the parallel with set theory, cf. (iv) below. But, quite generally, it is perfectly natural to be blind to, or at least to ignore for the time being, a part of experience about which one can do nothing (at the time). And, trivially, it is only with the help of

---

[1] The current view of cut elimination is technical; the view I propose above is probably not shared generally. But it should be noted that though it is more precise and specific (and, perhaps, wrong in detail), it is not inconsistent, for instance, with Brouwer's view, [1], footnote 8, where he speaks of fully analysed, canonical proofs and stresses that they are infinite structures.

specifically intuitionistic notions that we can understand the constructive aspects of those parts of mathematical experience which need these notions, such as analysis (and set theory, if its constructive features should be worth studying).

(ii) *Something about intuitionistic mathematics.* The present state of the subject illustrates rather well the view expressed on p. 207: there are quite a lot of ideas around, the difficulty is to know how to exploit them and which of them are really fruitful. Some technical information is in [10]; the non-specialist should not worry about it until the subject is *au point*. Some of the principal truly intuitionistic (non-finitist) notions are these: Higher type operations, first emphasized by Gödel in [4]. The great point in their favour is the extraordinary formal simplicity and elegance achieved by introducing them as primitive notions, instead of representing them by means of explicitly defined rules. As impressive as the introduction of the language of set theory in analysis, instead of specific constructions of sets. The weakness is that, up to now, all really evident properties of these notions can also be realized if one interprets the higher type operations in terms of more or less arithmetic rules. A basic notion in the subject is that of *intensional* or definitional equality between terms t and t_1 which is intended to mean that the operations which we understand to be denoted by t and t_1, are the same (intensional) objects. All axioms so far put down for this notion are also realized if one assumes that t and t_1 are interconvertible by suitable formal rules, usually those expressed by the axioms themselves; cf. (i) (δ) above. Intensional equality is used in contrast to extensional equality between (two possibly intensional objects) a and b, where, for each accepted argument x, $a(x)$ and $b(x)$ are equal: and this latter equality can in turn be interpreted extensionally or intensionally. See [12].

Generalized inductive definitions and (non-visualizable) infinite proofs. These definitions are supposed to be obtained by exploiting fully the basic principle underlying the definition of *natural munber* and their *order*: 0 is a natural number; if n is one, so in n' and $0 < n'$, and if $m \leqslant n$, also $m < n'$, and nothing more. A, perhaps the, typical case of the extension is the definition of ordinal number and their order. We assume two operations: successor and supremum (with familiar properties) and say: 0 is an ordinal number; if n is one, so is its successor, say n', and if $m \leqslant n$ also $m < n'$; and if f is a constructive operation whose values for $m < n$ are ordinals with $m < m^* < n \rightarrow f(m) < f(m^*)$ then $\sup(n, f)$ is an ordinal, and $[m < n \ \& \ m^* < f(m)] \rightarrow m^* < \sup(n, f)$. [Here higher type operations are involved since f is a function, $\sup(n, f)$ is at least of type as high as f, and then functions are introduced which take $\sup(n, f)$

246

as values]. The formal axioms which are most immediately justified if one accepts this kind of definition, go far beyond finitist and even predicative proof of §2(*b*). One is rather convinced that the definitions are justified, and, in fact, it is they which really bring out the virtue of intuitionistic logic for constructive mathematics, cf. [10], 2.16411. But there is certainly something that is not yet clearly understood: when one tries to analyse them in terms of more basic notions of constructions, one uses principles which go beyond the generalized inductive definitions, in short, one deprives the latter of any special status. (This is, of course, familiar from classical mathematics where the justification of an inductive definition is given by a formal derivation of the existence of a set with the defining property from the comprehension principle: in other words it is the latter principle which is fundamental. Actually, in contrast to intuitionistic logic, the inverse is also true in classical mathematics if one uses quantifiers over sets at all [10] 4.2121.) But I suspect this is a defect of the analyses one has so far tried.

Free choice sequences of natural numbers and of other (intensional) objects. One of the more picturesque chapters of intuitionistic mathematics concerns the idea of free choices of natural numbers. For instance, if we wish to assert that the (natural) order of the natural numbers is well founded, i.e. that every descending sequence is finite, it is completely pointless to think of sequences as completed infinite objects or as given by rules. If the sequence is $a_0, a_1, \ldots$ we need only know the value of a_0, continue the sequence to a_{a_0}, and can be sure that for some $n \leqslant a_0$, $a_{n+1} \nless a_n$. To be sure of verifying this statement, the $a_0, \ldots a_{a_0}$ must be so *given* that we can decide their order. Some obvious continuity properties of the quantifier $\forall f \exists x$ (p. 243) have already been mentioned. Brouwer analysed the quantifier further and came up with some (rather persuasive) property of possible proofs i.e. canonically analysed ones!—of $\forall f \exists x$ statements: these properties lead to the axiom called bar theorem on p. 241. I looked at another type of statement, namely those of the form $\exists f A(f)$, and formulated a (very convincing!) property of proofs of such statements. The upshot of all this is that (α) generalized inductive definitions of a certain *form* can be replaced by explicit definitions in terms of free choice sequences, by essential use of the bar theorem; (β) conversely, though free choice sequences cannot be 'defined', to each closed statement A in the usual language of free choice sequences there is a statement A' not containing them (but A' contains symbols for inductively defined properties of *constructive* functions) such that A, A' are equivalent. For the equivalence one uses the axiom about $\exists f A(f)$ when dealing with

247

formulae not containing the quantifier $\forall f \exists x$, and additional use of the bar theorem for other formulae; (γ) if one studies free choice sequences of free choice sequences, the corresponding additional axioms can be formally reduced to the ones above, and so there are at least some contexts where free choice sequences of 'incomplete' objects can be meaningfully introduced. For a new angle, cf. [13].

Logical connectives. Two rather different (but both constructively meaningful) interpretations of logical operations in terms of *constructions* and intuitive *proofs* have been given, one based on the original formulation by Heyting, one by Gödel. In both cases the proofs considered concern a very special type of assertion: for all x, $A(x)$, where A is evidently *decidable* for each x. The former interpretation is more abstract and assumes more about the notion of proof, the latter is more elementary, for instance in that it has a type distinction. The two interpretations are not equivalent, because different laws hold for them, but they are consistent with all intuitionistic practice so far formulated. Gödel's interpretation has been fruitful, for instance Spector used it for reducing classical analysis to a generalization of the bar theorem mentioned above, free choice sequences of free choice sequences of *all* finite types being admitted.

From a purely formal point of view the axioms so far formulated are extremely well understood through work by Howard, Kleene, Spector, Tait and myself: proof theoretic equivalences galore! But there are serious doubts about the informal conclusions to be drawn from them. Some of these doubts are expressed in the following

(iii) *Problems*. The proof theoretic studies have shown, broadly speaking, the formal interreducibility of the various schemas of axioms which have been isolated for the notions mentioned above. As will be discussed more fully in §3(*c*), this means no more than that the axioms so far formulated may not have expressed the really fruitful content of these notions. Two real issues seem worth pursuing.

(α) Just what kind of object are these constructive operations of higher type? and how basic is the relation of definitional equality? Certainly, one must distinguish between those operations that are *rules*, applying to rules and so forth and those that are in some sense *freely chosen*. In the latter case, one has asked oneself in what way these objects are to be *given*: for this will determine (in technical language) what continuity conditions are to be satisfied by the operations. For instance, information about freely chosen sequences of natural numbers is given in terms of a finite set of values, and hence the appropriate topology (neighbourhoods) is the usual product topology N^N. It is not a question of a 'convenient' choice of topology, but the topology is determined by the intended presentation of the objects.

Under the influence of a mechanical prejudice I once formulated these distinctions in first and second order terms, rules being interpreted as mechanical rules, and freely chosen objects as free choice sequences of neighbourhoods (with two different topologies). In all these cases some kind of extensionality was required, at least extensionality with respect to the neighbourhood functions.

The elementary axioms for higher type operations are satisfied by all these interpretations; as expected, the bar theorem is only satisfied by the freely chosen ones; but the *axiom of choice* is not satisfied by the latter kind ($\mathscr{C}$) of operations with the strong extensionality conditions. Specifically, one has a (fairly complicated) property $P(F, x)$ (F being an operation on number theoretic functions), $(\forall\, F \in \mathscr{C})\; \exists\, x\, P(F, x)$, but no Φ in $\mathscr{C} : F \to x$, such that $(\forall\; F \in \mathscr{C})$ $P[F, \Phi(F)]$. So, presumably, the wrong topology was chosen. (The topology was not derived from intuitive axioms for the higher type operations, but was simply put down as 'reasonable').

If one gives up the full extensionality condition, one can realize definitional equality as a mechanical (recursive) relation, as shown by Tait in [9] and particularly [12].

If one takes higher type operations not as primitives, but as analysed (or: defined) objects, the meaning of bar induction for higher types is expressed by a certain *extended form of the bar theorem* (wholly formulated in the language of free choice sequences of numbers x). Essentially, it allows one to consider sequences of numbers x or even sequences of free choice sequences f which satisfy some complicated condition P, provides only $\exists\, x\, P(x)$, respectively $\exists f P(f)$ holds. So, by Spector's result this form of the bar theorem is sufficient for a consistency proof of classical analysis. (The details depend on what interpretation of higher type object one uses.)

The situation calls for a philosophical analysis of notions. *Are such free choice sequences in our mathematical experience?* Tradition excludes it; cf. Kleene [6], p. 44, l. 1, who, following Brouwer, permits only sequences of objects chosen from a countable set (= decidable set). But as we saw in (ii) (γ) above, there is no reason to exclude free choice sequences of objects not satisfying this condition, namely free choice sequences of free choice sequences. Also, though Brouwer explicitly stated this condition, his arguments in connection with the bar theorem are not detailed enough to see exactly how they depend on this condition.

Of course, proof theoretically, the restriction on free choice sequences is enormous. But we have parallels in set theory, cf. (iv) below, which make one suspect an argument based on this.

(β) Just what is the role of mechanical rules among constructive rules? We can formulate this in the form:

$$(\ast) \quad \forall x \exists y\, A(x, y) \to (\exists e)\ \{e \text{ is the number of a recursion equation } \& \ \forall\, x\, A[x, \{e\}(x)]\}$$

for *all* $A(x, y)$ without free variables. (A simpler formulation is possible if one has variables for constructive functions.) More precisely this assertion says that all constructive number theoretic functions are recursive. I have called this elsewhere an expression of *Church's Thesis*; I am sure that, at the time, one would have been prepared to regard *effective, intuitionistic, constructive, mechanical, formal* as equivalent when applied to rules! after all, less than 10 years before Church formulated his thesis, von Neumann and Herbrand took it for granted that *finitist* and *intuitionistic* had the same meaning! But, perhaps, it would be historically more correct not to call it Church's thesis; for, once alerted to the difference between intuitionistic and mechanical rules, he would surely have formulated the thesis for the latter, namely that for every mechanical rule there is an e (number of a recursion equation) which defines the same function as the rule. (Intuitionistic requirements were brought in as follows: if the proposed mechanical rule simply *is* well defined then $\{e\}$ is classically well defined, and if the rule has been constructively recognized to be well defined, so is $\{e\}$.) In contrast, $(\ast)$ relates recursive functions to constructive ones that may be defined non-mechanically as in (ii) above.

One of the more interesting proof theoretic discoveries is that $(\ast)$ is compatible with most of the intuitionistic systems proposed. It seems worth while to find systems with which it is not compatible. (The only case I know is bar induction for the functionals on which excessive extensionality conditions are imposed; but just because of this the contradiction is of little interest.) Kripke has observed that it is inconsistent with some of Brouwer's 'empircal' propositions about free choice sequences by essential use of the very convincing new axiom mentioned in (ii) above. As matters stand *the refutation of* $(\ast)$ *(or, at least, of its extension to higher types) by means of suitable new axioms may be one of the more feasible problems at the present time.*

(iv) *Parallel with set theory.* Besides solving particular 'hard' problems, one also wants to learn from experience in foundational research and avoid the errors and blind spots which have delayed progress in the past. Set theory is undoubtedly more highly developed than intuitionistic mathematics; it is therefore to be expected that (if one does not pursue analogies thoughtlessly) one can learn something from the history of set theory.

First, the negative side of the intuitionistic position is parallel to strict realism, mentioned in §1(d) (i). The objection to the rival view as being unintelligible, specifically unintelligible in terms of one's own view, may be as much a proof of the inadequacy of one's own view as of defects of the other. The intuitionist has nothing to be proud of, if his notions do not allow him to draw a significant distinction between arithmetic propositions proved from the existence of inaccessible ordinals and those proved from the Riemann hypothesis: the former are true and the latter problematic. This is why it is important for the intuitionist to give a consistency proof for set theory with inaccessible ordinals! Similarly the (classical) realist has every reason to give a consistency proof for the theory of free choice sequences with continuity conditions because on the intuitionistic notions the latter is obviously correct. This is an example of the general view expressed in §2 (ii), on p. 222: for decisions between philosophical views it is not sufficient to rely on agreement with experience, one must consider which view enlarges the area of experience that can be understood; cf. §0(d).

Second, formalization plays a rather similar role both in §1 and here [§2(c)], only the ambiguity of interpretation was less obvious in the case of §1. If an axiom system is given, and only very *general* restrictions on its interpretations are imposed (such as: the interpretation of the logical symbols), the general entities that the system is about (structures in the realist case, constructions and proof of some kind or another in the intuitionist case) are unlikely to be determined. In the intuitionistic case this was quite obvious, related to the subjective nature of the interpretation, cf. p. 244. (It is in fact likely that intuitionists like Brouwer in their diatribes against formalization, overlooked the usefulness of formalization by being too much impressed by its (evident) limitations.) As is easily shown by the compactness theorem exactly the same applies to the classical case if one considers general models [Skolem–Loewenheim §3(b)]. If stronger restrictions on the interpretations are imposed, for instance principal models only are considered, more can be defined; but exactly the same is true in the intuitionistic case if for instance the notion of all possible constructive proofs is taken as determined.

Third, if an abstract notion is first talked about, it is likely to be a mixture of notions; as in the case of *set* one had the notion of

251

collection, but also of property and of abstract structure. There are two kinds of consequences. If one is not careful one will put down *obvious* axioms, only some are obvious for one notion, others for another and one gets contraditions. If one is too careful one will put down axioms which are in fact obvious for all these notions, but just because of this they are of little depth. This is clearly what has happened in the case of higher type operations above. Contradictions happened in set theory where the unrestricted comprehension axiom is obvious for properties, classical logic is not (though it is obvious for collections in the sense of the hierarchy of types); objections to the axiom of choice were introduced: the axiom is obvious for the type structure, but not for the properties; or to the power set axiom which is not obvious for abstract structures, and so forth. (For a somewhat similar situation in the intuitionistic case, cf. [13].)

Fourth, when a new notion is first introduced, even with quite weak axioms, it may lead to elegance and to the formulation of facts which one could previously only 'see', but not formulate: one needed set theoretic notions to formulate set theoretic aspects of the continuum! But it takes time to exploit the new notion: the (weak) axioms that are actually used are easily realized by structures definable in terms of less abstract notions too. If, possibly unconsciously, one has such a reducible notion in mind even when talking of an abstract notion, the only axioms that are evident will of course be reducible! There is little doubt that at the turn of the century, many mathematicians meant: predicative set (i.e. what we should now call by this name) when they talked of set. Little wonder that the axioms they used were valid for predicative sets. As far as I personally am concerned I am obviously in the analogous position with respect to higher type constructive operations; unfortunately because of lack of insight, not because of lack of good will (if, as seems reasonable, permanent defects are to be considered the really bad ones, lack of good will would seem to be minor); cf. Gödel's criticism of Russell, p. 220.

When one looks at the situation more closely, the parallel ends. On the one hand, at the present time we have nothing in intuitionistic mathematics that has the central role of the notions of *set* and *membership* from which the other notions of classical mathematics can be defined outright. Several basic notions were given in (ii) above which are, at best, interreducible by contextual definition, but in most cases not even this. There seems to be no evidence at present whether this large number of primitive notions is to be a permanent feature of intuitionistic mathematics. On the other hand, taking the rival positions quite literally, it may be expected that we can find new axioms more convincingly for the intuitionistic position since we are supposed to find them by looking at our own activity, and not by entering into a platonic heaven.

Marginal comments. By (ii) we have found new axioms: it is very pleasing to remind oneself of the process whereby this is done!

It is not surprising that formal systems which hold for intuitionistic interpretations are not only valid for different *intuitionistic* interpretations, but also for others. After all, we should not speak of, for instance, set theoretic (transfinite and impredicative) *constructions* or *processes* if they did not have something in common with constructions in an effective sense; so why not some laws of logic? This possibility is realized in Cohen's interpretation of logical constants (forcing) which was useful for his formal independence proof of the continuum hypothesis. (Cf. also top of p. 240.)

As appeared in §2(*b*), it is essential for Hilbert's *generalized* programme to find a significant area of evidence, denoted by $\mathscr{P}$ in §2(*b*) (i). It is amusing to observe that one of the major current interests in intuitionistic notions is derived from this generalized programme: it wants to use them for $\mathscr{P}$.

3. INFORMAL RIGOUR: PROOF FROM MEANING

For general observations on formal and informal rigour, cf. the introduction, §0(*d*), §2(*a*) (ii). The examples below are relatively simple, but, I think, not so simple as to make one think that informal rigour is possible *only* in simple situations.

(*a*) *Logical validity, formal derivability, and set theoretic validity*

Consider the language L of first order predicate logic and formal rules of derivation; for instance those proposed by Frege. How do we know that they yield precisely the logically valid formulae (in L)?

The so-called empirical approach is this: try and find a logically valid formula which is not derivable by the given rules. For this to make sense one must be convinced that one's understanding of logical validity is clear enough to decide whether any particular argument does or does not establish logical validity. It would generally be agreed that the rules given are valid in this sense. So, using A as a variable for formulae of L, Val(A) to mean: A is logically valid, and $I(A, B, C)$ to mean: C is an immediate consequence of A and B according to the formal rules given, we recognize

Principle 1: [Val(A) & Val(B) & $I(A, B, C)$] $\rightarrow$ Val(C).

This expresses a closure condition on logically valid formulae. [We may interpret $\rightarrow$ as an intuitive notion of implication, not necessarily as the usual truth function if we are not convinced that

Val(A) is defined for all A.] Writing $D(A)$ for: A is formally deriv-able, we get by induction applied to formal proofs:

Principle 1': $D(A) \to \text{Val}(A)$.

Actually, since A is a variable, the principle expresses a *general* insight into the notion of logical validity. It is therefore not impos-sible that another general insight will allow one to make precise assertions about *the extension of* Val *applied to L*. Write $V(A)$ to mean: A is valid in all set theoretic structures; i.e. if A has the relation symbols $R_1, \ldots, R_n, R_i$ with p_i arguments (and, to fix ideas, no function symbols) then A is satisfied by $\langle E, R_1, \ldots, R_n \rangle$ where $R_i \subset E^{p_i}, E \neq \phi$.

Principle 2: $\text{Val}(A) \to V(A)$

expresses that a logically valid formula is valid in all set theoretic structures. Note that the converse is not immediately plausible: for instance, a logically valid formula should hold when its quanti-fiers range over all sets, though the universe of sets is not a set theoretic structure.

From Principles 1 and 2 we have this: *If the purely mathematical statement* (which does not involve the predicate Val)

$$(\ast) \qquad\qquad V(A) \to D(A)$$

is established then: $V(A) \longleftrightarrow D(A) \longleftrightarrow \text{Val}(A)$: in other words, the extension of Val(A) is determined *on L*. [Note that the Principles 1 and 2 about Val(A) together with ($\ast$) imply another purely mathe-matical result: $D(A) \to V(A)$; this is one of the simplest examples of a mathematical result being established from the meaning of a notion like Val!]

($\ast$) is precisely the mathematical content of Gödel's completeness theorem. Actually he proves rather more: Let C be any collection of sets which includes the set N of natural numbers and a certain class of subsets of $N, N^2, N^3, \ldots$. Then: $V_C(A) \to D(A)$. Since evidently $C \subset C' \to [V_{C'}(A) \to V_C(A)]$, ($\ast$) *holds for a wide variety of interpretations of the notion of set* (theoretic structure). It should be remarked that it would not be sufficient to take for C the collec-tion of finite sets since A may be valid for all finite sets but not for all: for instance, if A expresses that every total ordering has a first element. The result has the same kind of remarkable conclusiveness as Gödel's result in §2(a) (ii): one might have been hard put to say if $D(A) \longleftrightarrow \text{Val}(A)$ were really established if the proof of ($\ast$) had involved the assumption that there are non-denumerable measurable sets! It should be mentioned that the known corresponding results

254

$(*_I)$ for intuitionistic logic are less elementary because, for $(*_I)$, one has to use peculiar kinds of free choice sequences (corresponding to peculiar sets; satisfyingly, the problem arises in classical second order logic, [10b]).

An historical comment. The argument involved in $(*)$ is rather simple, and the different mathematical ideas were already in papers by Skolem and Herbrand in the Twenties. I believe it would be quite wrong to say that the basic result: $\mathrm{Val}(A) \leftrightarrow D(A)$ was known before 1930. Certainly not by Herbrand because he said he did not understand what $\mathrm{Val}(A)$ or, for that matter, $V(A)$ meant! Nor by Skolem who hardly distinguished between $\mathrm{Val}(A)$ and $D(A)$. [Nor would the result be accessible to people who insist that one needs a set theoretic notion to *replace* $\mathrm{Val}(A)$ because the principal question is to see whether $\mathrm{Val}(A)$ *can* be so replaced.] But to me the most crucial point is an attempt by Hilbert around that time to replace (essentially) the principles above by others which would be meaningful to a finitist; in particular, by principles, in which the set theoretic property $V(A)$ is replaced by an assertion about *formal derivability* in a particular system Z of arithmetic. For each A, Hilbert considered all substitution instances A_i of A in the language Z, i.e. the R in A are replaced by formulae of Z. Principle 1 is unchanged, and

$$\text{Principle } 2_H: \mathrm{Val}(A) \to (\forall\, i) \vdash_Z A_i$$

Instead of $(*)$, he wanted to establish (trivially, since Frege's rules are incorporated in Z)

$D(A) \to (\forall i) \vdash_Z A_i$, but also

$(*_H)\; \neg\, D(A) \to (\exists\, i \vdash_Z)\; \neg A_i$ (with a finitist interpretation of the constants, i.e.)

$D(A) \vee (\exists i) \vdash_Z \neg\, A_i$

Now, $(*_H)$ is simply not true, not only not for Z, but for no mechanical system since the class $\{A : D(A)\}$ is not recursive. $[(*_H)$ would be analogous to Hilber–Post completeness for propositional logic.] It should be noted that Hilbert's formulation was *perfectly natural for his philosophic position*: it was a discovery that it could not be carried out.

(b) *Formally definite and mathematically definite problems*

The topics discussed here are of interest only if one has some knowledge of standard mathematics, and so standard terminology will be used without explanation.

The notion of formal definition and formally definite or formally decided problem was explained in §2(*a*). For usual axiomatic mathematics the notion is confined to first order statements as in §3(*a*) above. To explain the notion of mathematically definite problem one needs the notion of second (or higher) order statement and the corresponding notion of second order consequence. Familiar second order axiomatic theories are Peano's and Dedekind's axioms for the series of natural numbers and for the continuum respectively. A less well known axiomatic second order theory is that of Zermelo for certain sections of the *cumulative type structure*.

$\langle M, E \rangle$ is called an *extensional* relational system if and only if the following (first order) condition is satisfied:

$$E \subset M^2 \,\&\, \forall xy \,[\forall z \,(\langle z, x \rangle \in E \leftrightarrow \langle z, y \rangle \in E) \to x = y]$$

(where $x, y, z \in M$ if $\langle z, x \rangle, \langle z, y \rangle \in E$, since $E \subset M^2$).

$\langle M, E \rangle$ is *well founded* if and only if the following (second order) condition is satisfied:

$$(\forall B \subset M) \,\{B \neq \phi \to \exists x [x \in B \,\&\, (\forall y \in B) \neg \langle y, x \rangle \in E]\},$$

i.e. x is minimal with respect to E. Note that the corresponding axiom of formal set theory is a schema for all B *explicitly definable* in terms of some given language. Here the axiom is intended to state that the condition holds for *all* subsets B of M.

Note that every extensional well founded relational system is isomorphic to a subset M' of some C_α where C_α is the cumulative type structure up to the ordinal α starting with $C_0 = \phi$. The isomorphism maps E into the restriction of ϵ to M'. The argument proceeds by transfinite induction, taking $B = M$, when the corresponding x is unique since $\forall y \neg \langle y, x \rangle \in B$ and by extensionality: $(\forall y \neg \langle y, x \rangle \in E \,\&\, \forall y \neg \langle y, x' \rangle \in E) \to x = x'$.

$\langle M, E \rangle$ is *comprehensive* if and only if the following condition is satisfied:

$$(\forall x \in M)(\forall B \subset M) \,\exists y \,\forall z [\langle z, y \rangle \in E \leftrightarrow (z \in B \,\&\, \\ \langle z, x \rangle \in E)].$$

This means that if, in the isomorphism above, x' is the image of x, *every* subset of $x' \cap M'$ is also the image of some y in M.

$\langle M, E \rangle$ is *collective* if and only if the following (first order) condition is satisfied:

$$(\forall x \in M) \,\exists y \,\forall z [\langle z, y \rangle \in E \leftrightarrow \forall u (\langle u, z \rangle \in E \to \langle u, x \rangle \in E)].$$

This is, abstractly, the power set axiom for extensional well founded structures (since E is the restriction of ϵ to M').

The least system satisfying these axioms is C_ω, the collection of hereditarily finite sets built up from the empty set. The least system which contains C_ω and satisfies the axioms is $C_{\omega+\omega}$. To characterize for instance $C_{\omega+n}$, one leaves out the power set axiom and replaces it by special cases, namely: $x = C_\omega$ to yield $C_{\omega+1}$, $x = C_{\omega+1}$ to yield $C_{\omega+2}, \ldots, x = C_{\omega+n-1}$. (Note that Peano's characterization of N and Dedekind's of R is easily derived from $C_\omega, C_{\omega+1}$ respectively).

Let $Z(M, E)$ mean: $\langle M, E \rangle$ is a Zermelo system, i.e. extensional, well founded, comprehensive, collective, and containing C_ω. Note that for each of the α above, there is a formula Z_α in the language of extensional relational structures which defines $\langle C_\alpha, \epsilon \upharpoonright C_\alpha \rangle$ uniformly for all Zermelo systems.

(i) *Fundamental Definition.* A is a *consequence* of $Z_\alpha(M, E)$ means: $(\forall M, E)[Z_\alpha(M, E) \rightarrow \langle M, E \rangle$ satisfies $A]$.

Since $Z_\alpha(M, E)$ is a *second* order statement (for instance for $\alpha \leqslant \omega + \omega$) we write $Z_\alpha \vdash_2 A$.

A is *decided* by Z_α if and only if $(Z_\alpha \vdash_2 A) \vee (Z) \vdash_2 \neg A)$.

A is called mathematically definite for C_α if A is decided by Z_α.

Theorem. Every A in the language of extensional relational systems is decided by $Z_\alpha (\alpha \leqslant \omega + \omega)$.

Corollary. The continuum hypothesis is decided for all Zermelo systems. For, $2^{\aleph_0} = \aleph_1$ means that every subset of $C_{\omega+1}$ is either isomorphic to $C_{\omega+1}$ itself or to a subset of C_ω. This is a statement about $C_{\omega+2}$ and, by above, $Z_{\omega+1}, Z_{\omega+2}$ define $C_{\omega+1}, C_{\omega+2}$ uniformly for all Zermelo systems.

On the other hand, if A expresses: $\langle M, E \rangle$ contains an element isomorphic to $C_{\omega+\omega}$, A is *not* decided for all Zermelo systems, because $C_{\omega+\omega}$ is one in which A is not satisfied and $C_{\omega+\omega+\omega}$ is another in which A is satisfied.

Reflection shows that the logical undecidability results which surprise mathematicians concern mathematically *definite* problems like the continuum hypothesis, not the existence of $C_{\omega+\omega}$. Note that the latter shows that there *are* problems in the language of extensional relational systems which are *not* mathematically definite for all Zermelo systems. Thus the distinction between mathematically definite problems and others is not empty.

In terms of the notion just explained one can formulate two *defects of first order languages*:

(α) With respect to *definability*. Call a set of axioms definite if all systems that satisfy it are isomorphic. A large number of familiar mathematical structures, such as $C_\omega, C_{\omega+1}, \ldots, C_{\omega+\omega}$ are defined by definite *second* order axiom systems. In contrast (by the familiar Loewenheim–Skolem Theorem) the only structures that satisfy, or:

are defined by, definite first order systems are *finite* (and even then only if $=$ is interpreted as true identity). I do not know general limitations on structures that are defined by (finite or infinite) second order systems: of course the collection of all sets is not so definable!

(β) With respect to *truth* or *consequence*. Trivially, if arbitrary sets of axioms are considered, for any given language all statements true in a structure, for instance in C_ω, can be taken as axioms, and then all true statements are trivially decided. But if only mechanically describable, *a fortiori* if only finite first order axiom systems are considered, we have by §3(a) that all valid consequences can be generated mechanically by means of formal rules of predicate logic. So, Gödel's incompleteness theorem applies, and some *arithmetic* statement, i.e. with quantifiers restricted to C_ω, is formally undecided. N.B. *The defect mentioned does not concern some extravagantly abstract notion of set, but C_ω itself.*

Evidently, (α) is stronger than (β) in that *arbitrary* axiom systems are admitted, (β) is stronger than (α) in that *some* axiom systems A may decide every statement in some *given* language even if A is satisfied by non-isomorphic structures (real closed fields).

In the present connection one sometimes calls *part* or *subset* a logical notion if one supposes that, for a given structure $\langle M, E \rangle$, one not only knows what it means to *quantify over all elements* of M, but also over all elements of $\mathscr{P}(M)$. (Similarly, $=$ is called a logical notion if one supposes that identity is understood.)

(ii) *Are the defects* (α), (β) *real?* This question raises a point of principle which did not come up in §3(a) because the main result of (a) is *positive*: the formally introduced $D(A)$ (formal derivability) *is* equivalent to Val(A). If Val(A) is understood, the equivalence Val(A) $\leftrightarrow$ $D(A)$ is meaningful; if Val(A) is not accepted, it has to be replaced [either directly by $D(A)$, or by $V(A)$]: whatever uses one has in mind for Val(A), $D(A)$ will serve them too (for first order formulae A).

In discussing *negative* results (defects), here: of first order languages, with respect to (intuitive) notions of mathematical definiteness or decidability, one has to face the issue: *do we have a defect* or *do* (α) *and* (β) *above show that the intuitive notions are illusory* or at best highly relative? (Doesn't the diagonal of the unit square have a length because it is not rational, or are rational measures inadequate for geometry?) The traditional argument is this:

If these notions are relative there is no defect: the theorem in (i) above

$$\forall A[(Z_\alpha \vdash_2 A) \lor (Z_\alpha \vdash_2 \neg A)]$$

no more requires that either A is decided to be valid or $\neg A$ is decided to be valid than, for instance (for the group operation $\bigcirc$),

$$\forall\, xy(x \bigcirc y = y \bigcirc x) \;\vee\; \neg\; \forall\, xy(x \bigcirc y = y \bigcirc x)$$

requires that every group is commutative or every group is not commutative. All the theorem means is that for *each* notion of set involved in the definition Z_α either $Z_\alpha \vdash_2 A$ or $Z_\alpha \vdash_2 \neg A$, but the answers are different for different notions. If no 'privileged' notion of set is admitted *a priori*, in particular: not even C_ω, then (α) or (β) constitute nothing else but a proof that first order systems do not single out a privileged notion.

Now, all that this traditional argument is aimed to show is that the restriction to first order formulae and consequently first order consequence is not incoherent. This provides no objection to going beyond the restriction. One must reflect on the second order notions and see if they too make sense, though, trivially, by (α) and (β) they will not be formulated with formal rigour in the sense of §2(*a*) (ii).

But closer inspection shows that even *this limited aim is not achieved if* (first order) *consequence is interpreted set theoretically or, as it is sometimes called: semantically. Nothing short of a proof theoretic analysis like,* §2(*b*) *can make the restriction significant*, since, in a semantic analysis *some* intuitive notion of set is used, and then first and higher order notions are *both* definable. N.B. If one means by 'set': predicative set as in §2(*b*) or even finite set, the notions of first order and higher order consequence are uniformly definable. Of course, in general different logical laws will be valid: for finite sets even first order laws are different, for predicative sets only higher order laws. To spell all this out, recall the definition, say, $R(M, E)$ of: $\langle M, E \rangle$ is an extensional relational system, and $W(M, E)$ of: $\langle M, E \rangle$ is well founded. Let $A(M, E)$ be a (first order) property of $\langle M, E \rangle$, formally expressed by A. Then, A is a (first order) consequence of R means:

$$\forall\, M\, \forall\, E\{[E \subset M^2 \,\&\, R(M, E)] \to A(M, E)\},$$

and A is a (second order) consequence of W means:

$$\forall\, M\, \forall\, E\{[E \subset M^2 \,\&\, W(M, E)] \to A(M, E)\}.$$

If the quantifiers M, E are not understood this is not a definition; if they are understood, the quantifier $(\forall\, B \subset M)$ which appears in $W(M, E)$ is also understood. If the meaning of these formulae above, in particular of the quantifiers M, E, is to be 'determined' by an hypothetico-deductive axiomatic theory T of sets, then: A is a consequence of R is expressed by

$$T \to \forall\, M\; \forall\; E\{[E \subset M^2\; \& \; R(M, E)] \to A(M, E)\}.$$

Now, for the proposed interpretation the meaning of *this* formula is in turn to be 'determined' by an axiomatic theory and so we get into an infinite regress; cf. §2(a) (iv).

The point above is not an objection to the semantic interpretation, but only to a semantic interpretation which accepts first order and not second order consequence. Historically, the situation is probably quite understandable. Until Gödel's incompleteness theorem there was very general interest in second and higher order definability and validity. At that time, only thoroughly proof theoretic expositions ignored these notions: quite properly, because there was really very little evidence that these notions could be formulated with formal rigour. Gödel's result clinched this. So, *if* one aims at a mechanical proof theoretic analysis *then* (as I said above) these notions are not basic. Some time later one went back to a semantic analysis, in terms of definability, yet kept a prejudice in favour of first order notions, not for technical reasons, but as a thoughtless hangover from the days of proof theory (where the distinguished role of first order notions was *established*, not simply accepted).

In this connection the sound instinct of mathematicians, already mentioned in §0(b), should be mentioned who [as Poincaré in §2(a) (ii)] are wrong on details, but right in principle. They commonly feel ill at ease with model theoretic methods used in formal independence proofs of mathematically definite problems and object to the methods; they suspect a circularity in the argument or a confusion and, presumably, a straight, i.e. formal, contradiction between mathematical definiteness and formal undecidability. These objections are generally quite unfounded; for, this use of model or set theoretic methods is no more, and, of course, no less problematic than a set theoretic proof of any other arithmetic identity. What is suspect is the *significance* of the formal independence proofs for someone who, so to speak, in the same breath uses model theoretic methods. For, as explained above, when doing so he thinks in terms of a notion of set which makes the formally undecided problem mathematically definite. So there is certainly an informal contradiction between the basic *importance* of formal independence and the *acceptance* of the semantic interpretation.

(iii) *Usefulness* of the separation between first order and higher order notions. The mathematical usefulness of first order notions has been mentioned in §0(d); more generally, remarkably general results are valid for all, even infinite, first order axiomatic systems, which do not extend to higher order systems. It is these general results which, so far, have provided the most interesting mathematical applications of logic. And, as for *formal independence results on mathematically definite problems*, they are technically quite essential: we may well be interested in mathematical truth, but we are certainly *also* interested in how to set about discovering it. And then it is certainly useful to know whether the axioms so far found are sufficient to decide a given problem formally. Moreover, in some cases (e.g. Gödel's incompleteness results) the formal independence proof is the most natural way of deciding the mathematically definite problem involved, namely the assertion of the formal undecidability of a certain expression.

What is quite unjustified are the following common claims for special *evidence* of first order notions. (α) First order consequence only needs *denumerable* sets not arbitrary sets, because of the invariance of $V(A)$, p. 254. But, *if* a semantic interpretation is used, what is *intended* is validity for all sets and it is a *theorem* that this is equivalent to validity for denumerable sets. The same point is illustrated even better by the relation between the formulae $V(A)$ and $D(A)$. The latter, involving only quantifiers over hereditarily finite sets, is *invariant* for any universe $\supset C_\omega$, while $V(A)$ is not. This does not show that first order consequence needs only hereditarily finite sets! in fact, $D(A)$ is not equivalent to $V(A)$ if in $V(A)$ the set of quantifiers range over hereditarily finite sets only.[1] (β) Even if second order notions are accepted, any proof only uses certain properties of them, and so the result obtained will hold not only when interpreted in terms of an absolute notion of set, but for all notions of set with the properties used; in fact, the reliability of the result will be increased because one does not need the absolute or privileged notion, but only *some* notion that has the properties. The weakness of the consideration is this (besides the fact that, on the semantic interpretation, the phrases 'the proof uses ... properties', 'the result holds for ...' are themselves interpreted in terms of an absolute notion of set): for the usual formal systems of set theory *the only structure for which we know* (or have reason to believe) *that it has the*

[1] Invariance has a curious proof theoretic interest. Because of confusions about the notion of set (p. 252) one tried to eliminate the axiom of choice (AC, cf. note, p. 224). Several elementary results on first order validity are proved by use of AC. This is eliminated for the following reasons: (i) if an arithmetic formula can be proved from AC by means of the usual methods of set theory, it is also provable without AC by Gödel's work on the ramified hierarchy on p. 217; (ii) reductions to $D(A)$ (proof of invariance) do not use AC.—By note, p. 224 the whole business is a curiosity.

first order properties required also satisfies the second order properties.
An assertion about a class can hardly be said to be more reliable
than about the only member of it that we know.

In other words: though the possibility exists of getting rid of
dubious assumptions by means of axiomatic analysis, cf. p. 218,
this possibility is not realized in the case of set theory. (Note that
the possibility mentioned applies as much to *second* as to *first* order
axiom systems; for instance, second order set theory of Zermelo
would be regarded as more elementary than the first order system
of Zermelo Frankel.

(c) *Meaning and use*

Outright and contextual definitions, proof theoretic reductions.
These notions are needed for a discussion of positivistic accounts
of the meaning of words in terms of their use; a special case of such
an account is in §2(*a*) and §3(*b*) above: of the meaning of mathematical notions in terms of their *formal* use. As already mentioned
(p. 205 and note, p. 230) the distinction between meaning and use is
pointless, unless *restricted uses* only are considered; otherwise, one
use of a word is simply to express its intended meaning.

For an informally rigorous treatment, two things are necessary.
First, to give the technical apparatus for answering questions about
the meaning of a word, a fundamental analysis in the sense of §0(*a*);
in terms of this the *intended* distinction between meaning and use can
be formulated. Second, to see whether, at least in certain contexts,
a *reduction* of meaning to uses (of a limited kind) can be effected:
§3(*a*) provides a typical positive case, §3(*b*) a negative case. In general
one must expect more sophisticated informal arguments than were
needed above.

(i) *Outright definitions* are intended to eliminate a notion in terms
of another without change of meaning. Thus, in §1, granted the
fundamental analysis of notions in terms of *sets*, one answers the
question: what is the structure of the natural numbers, by formulating a (set theoretic) condition $P(\langle N, S \rangle)$ on N (the set of natural
numbers) and S (the successor relation) and showing that a *unique*
$\langle N, S \rangle$ satisfies P up to isomorphism. Generally, we have this:

$P(x)$ is a property formulated in terms of the *definiens* (or: defini-
entes); the definiendum satisfies P, in particular, $P(x)$ is meaningful
for the definiendum; and $\exists ! x P(x)$ holds or, more generally,
$\exists x P(x) \& \forall yz\{[P(y) \& P(z)] \rightarrow y \equiv z\}$ where $\equiv$ means that (the
structures) y and z are isomorphic. (The usefulness of 'purely logical'
conditions $P(x)$ depends on the fact that logical conditions are automatically meaningful for any *definiendum*.)

As long as the fundamental analysis, i.e. our conception of the nature of the subject matter, is not changed, an outright definition is *absolute*; in particular, in contrast to (ii) and (iii) below it is unaffected by extensions of the language or addition of axioms.

A technical point about definability. The notion of outright definition is directly meaningful only if the property P has a well defined sense. For instance, on the conception of §1, one must lay down a range of application of P, i.e. a range X for the variables x and the other variables that occur as quantifiers in P, and subsets of X^{ni} as interpretations of relations symbols $R_i(x_1, \ldots, x_{n_i})$ that occur in P. With trivial exceptions: for any (first order) axiomatic theory T, the notion is highly relative to the particular model considered because any T has many non-isomorphic models. Further, even if each model of T contains the same abstract structure, the conditions above on $P(x)$ are weak: for instance, if T is the theory of commutative fields, take for $P(x)$: $(x = 0 \ \& \ A) \lor (x = 1 \ \& \ \neg A)$, where 0 and 1 denote the (abstract) zero and unity which are the *same* in each commutative field, and for A a formally undecided statement, e.g. 1 has a square root: $\exists x(x^2 + 1 = 0)$. Then $\exists ! \, xP(x)$ holds in each model of T, but in some $P(0)$, in others $P(1)$ holds. I have therefore formulated a notion of *common part* of models (so as to talk of the *same abstract object* in different structures) and *uniform definability* for general axiomatically defined structures. This seems to be the proper refinement of the notion of outright definition for the realist conception of §1. The new notion is of course not needed for categorical (second order) axiomatic theories.

(ii) *Contextual definitions* eliminate a notion in the following sense. Suppose a language L is considered with symbols denoting the definiendum, L' is a part of L not containing these symbols. L is assumed to be understood and sufficiently many truths (axioms) to have been recognized to show the following: For each formula A of L, there is an A' in L' such that $A \leftrightarrow A'$ holds. Then the definiendum has been *eliminated in contexts L* by means of contextual definitions.

In contrast to (iii) below, in the context L a contextual definition is not affected by recognizing more truths about L; but it may be affected by extending L. For example, if L is a language for the theory of natural numbers and functions f of natural numbers, but so restricted that all formulae $P(f)$ denote properties of f which are *continuous* on the product topology. Let L' be the purely number theoretic part of L. Then we have a contextual elimination of function variables since f may be restricted to *finite* functions ($= 0$ ultimately) and the latter can be represented in number theory. But nothing like this holds for an unrestricted language of number theoretic functions.

Since contextual definitions are not stable for extensions of L, they do not generally ensure outright definitions. What they do is to ensure that the *use* of the definiendum (but only: in the limited context L) is reduced to the use of the definiens in a context L'. Since contextual definitions are stable for additions of axioms in terms of L', the elimination is not confined to some particular *formal* use, i.e. not confined to a formal set of rules for L'.

Contextual definitions *are* real eliminations if the additional symbols of L are *intended* as linguistic devices, i.e. manners of speech, such as old-fashioned points of infinity (at a certain phase of geometry). But there is an asymmetry: If a phrase is intended as a merely linguistic device then it must be eliminable by contextual definition (in every given context where it is to be used at all); but the possibility of such elimination in any given context does not ensure that we have to do with a purely linguistic device. For this reason the significance of the elimination of free choice sequences of natural numbers, mentioned on p. 247, is open. (This question is now topical by [13].)

(iii) *Proof theoretic reductions* differ from contextual definitions: given any two systems S and S' and a way of associating A' in S' with A in S, S is said to be *reduced* to S' if, and only if, $(\vdash_S A) \rightarrow (\vdash_{S'} A')$. Thus ($\alpha$) the reduction applies not only to $S' \subset S$, in particular to systems which are both interpreted on the same conception, but S may have a realist and S' an intuitionistic interpretation, (β) the reduction is of no interest unless some restrictions are imposed on the structure of A' in terms of A: if not, one could take for A' some fixed theorem of S'; so the mere idea of proof theoretic reduction is useless, the heart of the matter is to analyse further conditions, in contrast to (i) or (ii), (γ) even if $S' \subset S$, a proof theoretic reduction is not necessarily stable for extensions of S to S_1 (and corresponding S' to S_1') in the language of S, in contrast to (ii).

As a matter of principle: a proof theoretic reduction does no more than connect a strictly limited use of notions (described by rules S) to another limited use of (the same or) other notions, described by S'. This is enough to settle specific questions about S, for instance the consistency of S in terms of the consistency of S' provided the proof theoretic reduction satisfies some obvious conditions, for instance, both S and S' contain symbols for negation denoted by $\neg$ in S and by $\neg'$ in S', and $(\neg A)'$ is $\neg' A'$ or at least $(\neg A)' \vdash_{S'} \neg' A'$.

A commonplace conclusion is that different conditions on reductions are needed for different purposes.

In practice this conclusion is neither here nor there; it leaves open the question whether there are a *few* (realizable) conditions which are sufficient for *many* purposes. If one is positivistically inclined (or merely wants to use positivistic considerations as a guide in the present context) one looks for purely syntactic conditions on proof theoretic reductions. I once tried to do this by use of a notion of interpretation which, roughly speaking, associates with A in S a kind of infinite disjunction A' in S': it turns out that these conditions are sufficient for many applications, but I have not so far been able to express this fact in the form of *general theorems*. To justify these conditions (with informal rigour) one would try to apply the method of §3(*a*), and perhaps show this: if (under suitable conditions, with $S \supset S'$) the reduction A to A' holds for a certain *class $\mathscr{S}$* of extensions of S then there is a contextual elimination for the language L of S in terms of the language of S'. In other words, one does not adopt a doctrinaire formalist position (which rejects the primitive notion of meaning, and hence the difference between meaning and use); but one tries to establish that there are essential *uses*, at least: essential for the meanings expressed in the language L, namely the uses characterized by S. Clearly, this would be a modification of the positivistic position in that the notion of meaning, independent of a particular restricted use, is not rejected; what would remain would be the (possibly refutable) position that in specific contexts meaning *can* be analysed in positivist terms. Trivially, this modified position could not even be stated if the notion of meaning were rejected out of hand.

Marginal Comments. The parallel between philosophy and natural science mentioned in the introduction is quite apt in connection with meaning and use. The meaning involved in the natural sciences is the physical conception; the use is the combination of the formal expression of the conception (the formulation of mathematical laws) and observation, i.e. what is (counted as) given in experience. Meaning is not ignored (whatever positivistic scientists may say!): the moment one asks oneself whether a formulation of a conception is correct, for instance when one says one must not forget the physics in the mathematics! The method of the natural sciences consists in regarding a certain class of uses, namely experimental tests, as essential. But note that this is not a context strictly limited in advance; in fact, a principal problem of physics is to *find* contexts in which two rival theories differ. Proof theoretic reductions, respectively contextual definitions correspond to what are usually called proofs of the *mathematical equivalence* of different physical conceptions (sometimes called: pictures). A point of current interest concerns Heisenberg's and Schrödinger's conceptions of matter: a mathematical equivalence proof was given for contexts of *elementary* quantum mechanical systems, i.e. those describable in a restricted language. The formal development of Schrödinger's conception has led to difficulties. Dirac has recently expressed the hope that the mathematical equivalence will fail when one develops Heisenberg's picture for quantum electrodynamics. This hope is parallel to §2(c) (iii) concerning the (contextual) equivalence of intuitionistic theories with and without free choice sequences; it has been proved in the elementary context of free choice sequences of natural numbers only, but not of other objects.

4. MECHANISTIC THEORIES OF REASONING

In §2 (ii) and throughout §2, 3 a question turned up over and over again, even when there was no doubt that the formulation of a traditional notion was natural. Was it significant? or fruitful? And this in turn leads to the doubts in §0(d). All these questions have to be faced when one seriously wants to find out about the nature of our experience. But there is one area where, roughly speaking, *the significance of a notion consists in the fact that we find it significant*, namely in the study of theory making itself. Examples of this occurred in §1: mathematicians who find the notion of predicative set especially interesting will only use axioms which are valid for predicative sets (even if they try to think of arbitrary sets); once we suspect this psychological 'kink' we quickly discover a predicative formulation of their actual mathematics. Similarly in §2(c), mechanistically minded mathematicians put down only those axioms for constructive functions which are consistent with the assumption that these functions are recursive. Personally I have no doubt of the objective significance of the notion of mechanical procedure, and hence of recursive function, for the analysis of reasoning; but even if one has doubts about *that*, there is no doubt of its significance for the analysis of reasoning actually current.

I wish to point out here a similar significance of this notion for theories outside mathematics itself, in particular to the subject of *molecular biology*. Since this subject is in the process of development (and, in any case, no general formulation has been given) one cannot expect specific counter examples. But there seems to be no doubt about the following points: First, it is to be a *general* schema for the explanation of biological processes, including those of the higher nervous system; second, the basic elements of the explanation (master plan) are of a discrete combinatorial kind, the fitting of shapes into one of a finite number of permitted matrices; third, the complexity of biological phenomena is to be the consequence of the large number of basic objects involved and not of the complexity of the laws governing the basic objects. Certainly, the *attraction* of the subject depends on these three features. *Combinatorial basic steps iterated a (large) number of times are characteristic of recursive processes.* So, if the three properties of (current) molecular biology are to be retained, also the stable macroscopic properties of organisms would be expected to be recursive.[1] So suppose there is an area of macroscopic experience which the theory is intended to cover and which (we have reason to believe) satisfies non-recursive laws: then the theory is defective.

The area of experience which I wish to consider is mathematics itself. The argument is related to Gödel's well known interpretation of his incompleteness theorem: either there are mathematical objects external to ourselves or they are our own constructions and mind is not mechanical. It differs from his in two respects: First I do not make his assumption that, if mathematical objects are our own constructions we must be expected to be able to decide all their properties; for, except under some extravagant restrictions on what one admits as the self I do not see why one should expect so much more control over one's mental products than over one's bodily products—which are sometimes quite surprising. Second, I should like to use an abstract proof of the non-mechanical nature of mind (if I can find such a proof) for the specific purpose of examining a particular biological theory, namely projected molecular biology satisfying the three conditions above. For a difference of emphasis, cf. (*d*) below.

(*a*) *Generalities*

(i) As pointed out on p. 226, (recursive) formalization of mathematics was considered as *positive* evidence for a mechanistic theory of reasoning. It is remarkable how little work was done on this even in areas, such as predicate logic, where the set of valid statements is recursively enumerable. The least one would have to do is to show that there is something mechanical about the *actual* choice of proofs, not only about the set of results: after all, one may ride to work on a camel or a donkey and get there; but this does not mean that a camel is a donkey.

---

[1] At least, we know this: if in a stochastic process (with a finite number of states) the transition probabilities are recursive, any sequence of states with non zero probability is automatically recursive: for, if the process is in the state $f(n)$ at stage n, for non-zero probability, f must be isolated, and so f is the only function which (i) is dominated by some given f_0 (depending on the possible states) and (ii) satisfies a recursive relation $R(f, n)$ for all n. By König's lemma, f is recursive. As long as the macroscopic processes are really stable, mutations should not be important.

(ii) For *negative* results the situation is easier since, if (it is accepted that) the set of valid statements is not recursively enumerable then simply *no* mechanistic process generates them; it is understood that by 'valid statement' one does not here mean something that is necessarily objectively true, but the psycho-physical fact of being accepted. The following points should be noted:

The *first* theory of such psycho-physical phenomena one thinks of is *non*-mechanical. Consider the behaviour of the mathematical community with respect to statements in the language of first order arithmetic. This behaviour seems asymptotically stable. We certainly have no *better* theory at present than this: a statement will be accepted if it is true.

The objection that such a theory could not be checked is fallacious. Of course it could not be checked formally because it is not formulated formally in the sense of §2(*a*): but the whole issue is whether reasoning is mechanistic, and so it is a *petitio principii* to require that only mechanistic theories of reasoning are admitted.

A more serious objection would be this: the statistical principles we use in evaluating information have generally been applied to testing mechanistic theories. Since the whole subject of statistical inference is a bit like cookery, analysis might show that the validity of the principles is tied to the testing of mechanistic theories; cf. (*c*).

(iii) Granted a negative result of the kind described in (ii), *the particular application* to a biological theory proposed above makes the further assumptions:

(α) Mathematical behaviour is regarded as an integral part of the experience to be explained, and not as some corner far removed from the principal activities of the organism.

(β) Mathematical behaviour is to be explained in terms of the basic laws themselves; in particular, one does not assume the influence of some abstract objects such as sets on the organism (by §1, these abstract objects, if they exist, satisfy non-recursive laws!).

(γ) (A technical assumption to be verified mathematically). The basic laws are such that the laws for co-operative phenomena, i.e. interaction of organisms such as involved in mutual teaching of mathematics, are also recursive; cf. footnote 1, p. 267.

A refutation of (β) would be quite interesting! (γ) is a precise technical problem: incidentally, it would be quite interesting to look at corresponding problems in classical statistical mechanics: it is known, from continuity properties of partial differential equations, that discrete classical systems have recursive behaviour; but I do not know corresponding results for co-operative phenomena.

As to (α), if one really rejects it one accepts the division between mental and 'ordinary' biological phenomena. It is foolish to discuss (α) seriously before the hypothetical negative result of (ii) has been established. But I find the following debating point amusing: compare the place of mathematical behaviour among biological phenomena to the place of astronomical behaviour among mechanical phenomena; the former is far removed from ordinary life, exceptionally predictable, exceptional both in the sense that the predictions are precise, and also that they were the first to be noted; since astronomical phenomena played an important part in building up physical theories, should one not expect the analogue too? (I admit I'd be equally prepared to take either side in a debate.)

(b) Gödel's incompleteness theorem

I do not think that it establishes the non-mechanistic character of mathematical activity even under (α)–(γ) above without his assumption that we can decide all properties of our (mental) productions. For, what it establishes is the non-mechanistic character of the laws satisfied by, for instance, the natural numbers: and the theory of the behaviour of arithmeticians mentioned in (a) (ii) above may well be wrong!

In fact, if the description of finitist and predicative mathematics in §2(b) is accepted as a correct description of the behaviour of finitist, respectively predicativist mathematicians, we could mention an arithmetic problem or, at least, an analytic problem which neither can decide, only he'd never know it.

It still seems to me possible, though not probable, that the natural tendency of mathematicians to be finitist or predicativist is significant for the psycho-physical nature of reasoning.

(c) Intuitionistic mathematics (cf. p. 250, assumption ($*$))

Despite the fact that, as shown in §2(c), existing intuitionistic axiom systems are consistent with ($*$), it seems quite probable that ($*$) can be refuted *on the basis of evident assertions about proofs*, in particular, without Gödel's assumption just mentioned in (b). Note that this kind of argument is *not* subject to the criticism of statistical principles given in (a) (ii) above.

At first sight such a refutation seems 'unscientific' because one appeals directly to insights about acceptable proofs (in the 'empirical' sense of p. 268: proofs accepted after reflection). In other words, the argument has an *a priori* character, superficially not unlike arguments about Euclidean space. But it really would be most surprising if there were not *some* respects in which it is easier to find out about ourselves than about planets and galaxies! In other words, there should be procedures of discovery that are reliable for the study of our mathematical activity even though they have failed elsewhere [cf. p. 254, §3(a) etc.].

Note however that we have not yet refuted ($\ast$)!

(d) Mechanism and materialism

To avoid misunderstanding: the hypothesis that reasoning is not mechanistic is by no means anti-materialist or anti-physicalist. *There is no evidence that* even present day *quantum theory is a mechanistic, i.e. recursive theory* in the sense that a recursively described system has recursive behaviour. Specifically, it is not known whether there exists a physical system with a Hamiltonian H such that, for instance, $\sigma(n)$ is the set of possible spins in the nth energy state, $\sigma(n)$ finite for each n, and $\sigma(n)$ not a recursive function of n. (It is not too hard to construct such H which are 'similar' to the Hamiltonians of actual systems, i.e. correspond to laws of force other than the inverse square law.) Naturally, the interest of such a result depends on one's trust in the quantum theory. Note that the classical notion of a *well posed problem* (in the sense of Hadamard) does not apply here. For, even if the unanalysed macroscopic data are approximate, their interpretation by means of the quantum theory may be independent of experimental error. Just as in mathematics: if we know (or assume) that $f(z)$ is analytic inside C then

$$\frac{1}{2\pi i} \int \frac{f'(z)}{f(z)} \, dz$$

is integral, and approximate values of f (and hence of f') on C determine the value exactly.

It would certainly be very interesting if the *size* of the system were connected with recursiveness. This would have a bearing on biological theories because biological molecules are large. If one accepts §0(b), one would expect something of the sort: for, physicists themselves always emphasized the non-mechanistic character of the new physics; at least, I think that is what they meant by: non-materialistic applied to fundamental particles.

It should be remarked that Wigner has considered much more profound difficulties in molecular biological theories than those above. He shows, under certain assumptions (not concerned with mechanistic features), that mere *reproduction* of the systems involved is inconsistent with the laws of (current) quantum theory. I don't feel confident that his assumptions are proper. In any case, he himself says that the experience of consciousness has led him to doubt molecular biological theories. But if this is so, isn't it a bit much to suppose that reproduction is intimately tied to consciousness? So, higher mathematics being traditionally considered as the pinnacle of thought it seems more natural to look for a contradiction between simple minded molecular theories and the phenomena of mathematical experience. (Wigner's paper is Chap. 19 of: *Logic of personal knowledge*, London (1961), Routledge–Kegan Paul.)

Marginal comments. The whole discussion above is carried out in general terms, or, as one says, by use of highly idealized notions. The general reasons given for this in §0(*a*) should perhaps be supplemented as follows. A simplification or idealization is not necessarily a falsification or even imprecise; $1 < 5 < 10$ is perfectly precise and true (though $4 < 5 < 6$ is more informative!). The phenomena considered are complicated: to make them intelligible one has to find general (abstract) features. Particularly in psychological analysis it is necessary to formulate one's ideas in general terms for the sake of objectivity: if the general laws are too close to experience, knowledge of these laws is liable to influence the experience. Finally, at least to me, the use of technically advanced machinery in analysing reasoning is encouraging; after all, Aristotle thought about reasoning; one would like to see clearly what one has that he did not have! (It is no comfort to know that over 2000 years have passed since his time unless one sees just *how* one has used the experience of these 2000 years.)

REFERENCES

1. L. J. B. Brouwer. 'Uber Definitionsbereiche von Funktionen.' *Math. Ann.* 97 (1927), 60–76.
2. S. Feferman. 'Systems of predicative analysis.' *J.S.L.* 29 (1964), 1–30.
3. K. Gödel, 'Russell's mathematical logic,' pp. 123–153, in *The philosophy of Bertrand Russell*, Evanston and Chicago (1944), North-western University Press.
4. K. Gödel. 'Uber eine bisher noch nicht benützte Erweiterung des finiten Standpunktes.' *Dialectica* 12 (1958), 280–287.
5. K. Gödel. 'What is Cantor's continuum problem,' pp. 258–273, in P. Benacerraf and H. Putnam, *Philosophy of Mathematics*, Englewood Cliffs, NJ (1964), Prentice Hall.
6. S. C. Kleene and R. E. Vesley. *The Foundations of Intuitionistic Mathematics*, Amsterdam (1965), North Holland Publishing Co.
7. A. Levy. 'Measurable cardinals and the continuum hypothesis.' *Notices Amer. Math. Soc.* 11 (1964), 769–770.
8. K. Schütte. *Beweistheorie*, Berlin (1960), Springer.
9. W. W. Tait. 'Infinitely long terms of transfinite type,' pp. 176–185, in *Formal Systems and Recursive Functions*, Amsterdam (1965), North Holland Publishing Co.

For additional references:

10. G. Kreisel. 'Mathematical Logic,' pp. 95–195, in *Lectures on Modern Mathematics*, III, New York (1965), Wiley.

>*Errata.* p. 102, l. 3: *replace* ξ, η, $<$ *by* x, y, : *respectively*; p. 104, l. 6: *interchange* range *and* domain; p. 112 (l. 712): ... (though not necessarily more in $R\alpha_{+1}$ than $R\alpha$); p. 118, l. 11: cumulative; p. 169, l. 16: he *for* be.

[10a] concerning [10], p. 103 (l.2), p. 105 (l.52); The structure $\langle O, L \rangle$ consisting of the class O of ordinals and their order L is defined up to isomorphism by the following axioms (analogous to Peano's axioms for arithmetic) in the language of set theory:

> L orders O (totally).
>
> Every initial segment of O in the order L is a well ordered set.
>
> For every well ordered set, i.e. $\langle x, y \rangle$ with $y \subset x^2$ and y a well ordering of x, there is a $z \in O$ such that $\langle x, y \rangle$ is isomorphic to the segment of O preceding z in the order L.
>
> (This proves the conjecture of p. 103, l. 2.)

On the other hand, though by [70] (cf. p. 105, §1.52), the *formal axioms* of the cumulative theory of types can be interpreted in a theory of ordinals, the structure $\langle V, \epsilon \rangle$ consisting of all sets and the membership relation cannot be defined up to isomorphism in the language of the theory of ordinals. Thus there is an *asymmetry* between the reduction of the concept of ordinals to the concept of set and its (formal) converse. (In contrast, for the hereditarily finite sets built up from the empty set, and the natural numbers respectively, the interrelations are completely symmetric.)

[10b] concerning [10], p. 116 bottom. Less hypothetically, validity of *second* order formulae is clearly connected with *axioms of infinity*. Consider the *intended* second order system ([10], pp. 101–102) for *arbitrary* properties Φ; its negation is valid if and only if all ordinals $>\omega$ are accessible.

18

HILARY PUTNAM

The Thesis that Mathematics is Logic

'Russell and Whitehead showed that mathematics is reducible to logic.' This sort of statement is common in the literature of philosophy; but all too rarely nowadays does one see (1) any discussion of what Russell meant by 'logic', or (2) any indication of the impact that studies in the foundations of set theory have had upon sophisticated evaluations of the statement quoted. In this paper I wish to focus on these two matters, leaving regretfully aside a host of interesting topics that would and should be brought into a fuller discussion.

(1) *Russell's notion of 'logic'*

For Russell,[1] 'logic' includes not just the elementary rules of deduction (quantification theory), but also the assumptions Russell wishes to make concerning certain entities—the so-called 'propositional functions'. Thus logic has a (many sorted) universe of discourse of its own: the collection of all individuals (zero level) plus the collection of all propositional functions taking individuals as arguments (level one) plus the collection of all propositional functions taking level one propositional functions as arguments (level two) plus. . . . But what is a 'propositional function'?

Today two simplifications have taken place in Russell's treatment. In the expression $F(x)$, the symbol F is thought of as standing for an arbitrary *predicate* (of appropriate level). Thus $F(x)$ means *not* 'the propositional function $F(\hat{x})$ has the value Truth on the argument x' (or has a true proposition as value on the argument x), but more simply 'x *has* the property F'. Thus Russell's 'propositional functions' came to be identified simply with *predicates*. Secondly, it came to be assumed that two predicates are *identical* if they have the same extension (the so-called 'Axiom of Extensionality'). This assumption, or axiom, is simply false on the classical interpretation of 'predicate' as 'universal taken in intension', since Blue and Square, for example, would be *different* predicates, in the classical sense, even if all squares

[1] In the present paper the contribution of Whitehead will be neglected. It should be noted that all of the foundational ideas in *Principia* were published by Russell *prior* to his collaboration with Whitehead. This includes the theory of types, the axiom of reducibility, etc.

were blue and *only* squares were blue. Thus 'predicate' in turn has come to mean simply 'set'. The net effect of both revisions taken together comes simply to this: $F(x)$ now means 'x belongs to the set F'. Russell's 'propositional functions' have for some time now been taken to be simply sets of individuals, sets of sets of individuals, sets of sets of sets. . . .

This is quite contrary to Russell's explicit statements in *Principia* and elsewhere, however. On the reinterpretation of 'propositional function' just described, Russell's view would have to be that the 'universe of discourse' proper to logic is the system of all *sets* (of arbitrary finite type). 'Logic is set theory.'—But this is a view that Russell explicitly rejects!

Moreover, he surely rejects it with good reason. If we are willing to introduce special mathematical entities, and special axioms governing them (over and above the axioms of quantification theory), then why not just introduce *numbers* outright instead of introducing sets and then reducing numbers to sets? Why not redefine 'logic' to include number theory *by stipulation*? Then 'mathematics' (number theory) would indeed be a part of 'logic'—but only by linguistic stipulation. This would be idle—but it seems equally idle to redefine 'logic' to include set theory, which is what has in effect happened. Thus Russell wished to do something quite different: He wished to reduce number theory to set theory, and set theory *in turn* to 'logic' in his sense—theory of propositional functions.

Whether it is any more justifiable to extend the usage of the word 'logic' to include theory of propositional functions than to extend it *directly* to include set theory or even number theory is not an issue I wish to discuss here. But what is a propositional function?

It seems[1] that a propositional function is just what the name implies: a function whose values (not whose arguments!) are propositions. Propositional functions are thus one-one correlated to predicates (in the sense of universals taken in intension): corresponding to the predicate Blue we have the propositional function $\hat{x}$ *is blue*—i.e. the function whose value applied to any x is the proposition that x is blue. However, there appear to be some conceptual difficulties. Consider the propositional function x *wrote Waverley*. Suppose x happens to be the individual known as Walter Scott, and also known as 'the author of Waverley'. Then what is the value of the propositional function $\hat{x}$ *wrote Waverley* on this particular x as argument? is it the proposition 'Walter Scott wrote Waverley' or the proposition 'The author of Waverley wrote Waverley'? We can

---

[1] Here I am hazarding an interpretation. Russell's own formulations are not completely clear to me.

resolve the difficulty by accepting the first (but not the second) of the simplifications in Russell's treatment mentioned before, and taking the propositional function to be identical with the corresponding predicate. For surely any argument that could be offered for taking 'logic' to be the theory of propositional functions (in Russell's sense) could equally well be offered as an argument for taking logic to be the theory of predicates taken in intension.

(2) *Does Russell's view make logic 'theological'?*

Let us now consider some more-or-less-stock objections to Russell's view of logic.

(i) *The Cantor Diagonal Argument.* Bypassing Russell's well-known construction of the integers, let us consider for a moment statements about propositional functions (or, as I shall henceforth say 'predicates') of integers. According to one of the theorems of classical mathematics (which is, along with many others, proved in *Principia*) *there are non-denumerably many sets of integers.* (This was proved by Cantor, using the famous 'Diagonal Argument'). Since 'sets' are identified with predicates taken in extension[1] in the system of *Principia*, there are then non-denumerably many pair-wise non-coextensive predicates of integers. However, there are only denumerably many well formed formulas in *Principia*. Hence, *the huge majority of all predicates of integers must be indefinable* (in the system of *Principia*, and indeed in any human language or constructed system). This reveals something about the way in which 'predicate' (or 'propositional function') is being used by Russell: 'consider the class of all predicates of integers', means consider an alleged totality which includes not only the predicates of integers that can be defined, but, allegedly, all the predicates of integers that can 'exist' in some absolute sense of 'exist'. Is it any wonder that

---

[1] Actually, the famous 'no-class' theory of *Principia* is formally unsatisfactory. What Russell and Whitehead really needed was an interpretation of set theory, based on the simple theory of types, in *Principia* (or a relative consistency proof of *Principia plus* the Axiom of Extensionality relative to Principia). This has been supplied by Gandy (cf. his papers on the Axiom of Extensionality in the *Journal of Symbolic Logic*). Their own procedure was to define classes 'in use'; but the suggested definition has the annoying consequence that there are two truths which are respectively of the forms P and not-P in *abbreviated* notation. Thus *Principia plus the definition of class* is inconsistent! Gandy's definition of 'class' is more complicated than Russell and Whitehead's, but intuitively (as well as formally) more satisfactory. The definition is inductive: at level one, every propositional function is a 'class'; at level $n + 1$, every *extensional* function whose arguments are all 'classes' is a 'class'. An *extensional* function is one which applies to an argument if and only if it applies to every function coextensive with that argument. 'Identity' of classes can then be defined simply as *coextensiveness*.

Hermann Weyl has scoffed that this construction is *theology* rather than mathematics?

(ii) *The Löwenheim–Skolem Theorem*. According to this celebrated theorem, every consistent theory has a denumerable model (i.e. a true interpretation over a denumerable universe of discourse). In fact, every consistent theory has a denumerable model which is an *elementary submodel* of any given model—i.e. the entities of the sub-model have a property or stand in a relation definable in the theory, when the submodel is used to interpret the theory, if and only if they have that property or stand in that relation when the bigger model is used to interpret the theory. For example, if an entity is 'the successor of zero' in the elementary submodel, that same entity must have been 'the successor of zero' in the bigger model; if an entity is 'the set of all prime numbers' in the elementary submodel, that same entity must have been 'the set of all prime numbers' in the bigger model, etc. In particular, *exactly the same sentences are true* in a model and in any elementary submodel of the given model.

This leads at once to a pseudo-paradox or apparent paradox (it is not a genuine antinomy) that has become known in the literature as the 'Skolem paradox'. Namely, there is a theorem of *Principia* which *says* that there are non-denumerably many sets of integers. Hence there must be non-denumerably many sets of integers (in any model). But this contradicts the Skolem–Löwenheim theorem, which says that *Principia* has a denumerable model! (assuming *Principia* is consistent).

The resolution of the paradox is as follows. The sentence which 'says' that there are non-denumerably many sets of integers runs more exactly as follows:

(S)   There does not exist a two-place predicate *P* such that *P* is a one-to-one correspondence between the set of all sets of integers and the set[1] of all integers.

What happens when we reinterpret *Principia* by taking 'predicate' to mean 'predicate in *M*', where *M* is some denumerable model? The answer is that the *meaning* of the sentence (S) is affected. What (S) *now* says is:

There does not exist a two-place predicate *P in the model M* (i.e. in the appropriate 'level' of the model *M*) such that *P* is a one-to-one correspondence between the set (of the model *M*) which is the set of all sets of integers which exist in the model *M* and the set of all integers.

And this may well be true although *M* is denumerable! In short,

[1] It should be noted in connection with this formula that the 'set of all integers' is reduplicated on every sufficiently high level, in *Principia*.

if M is denumerable, then the set which is 'the set of *all* sets of integers' *from the standpoint of the model M*, is *not* the set of *all* sets of integers 'viewed from outside'. Moreover, the set in question *can* be mapped one-one on to the set of all integers by a certain two-place predicate P, viewing the situation 'from outside'; but the predicate P which is the one-to-one correspondence between the set which is 'the set of all sets of integers' from the standpoint of M, and 'the set of all integers', *is not itself an entity of the model M*.

Let us now re-examine the sentence (S) with all this in mind. What we meant when we said that (S) 'says' that there are non-denumerably many sets of integers is that (S) says this if the model M contains (i) *all* sets of integers, and (ii) *all* two-place predicates (of the appropriate level). But how are we to express these requirements?

The answer is that we cannot, at least not by axiomatic means. Even if, so to speak, God 'gave' us a 'standard' model for *Principia* (one containing *all* sets of integers, *all* sets of sets of integers, etc.), one could find a second model—in fact a submodel of the first—in which the very same sentences would be true! Thus a 'standard' model, if there is such a thing must be distinguished from a non-standard one by properties *other than the ones expressible in Principia (or in any formal language)*. The only such property that suggests itself is the 'property' of containing *all* sets of integers, *all* sets of sets of integers, etc. But just what does 'all' mean here?

It seems that someone who is convinced that he understands what is meant by '*all* sets of integers' can *explain* what he means to the sceptic only by saying '*you* know, I mean *all*'—but that is no explanation at all!

The relevance to Russell's position is immediate. If 'logic' really is the theory of, among other things, the totality of *all* predicates of integers, then just where did we aqcuire this notion (of all non-denumerably many of them)?

(iii) *The Continuum Hypothesis*. Consider the following mathematical assertion, which is known as 'the continuum hypothesis':
(C) If S is any infinite set of sets of integers, and there does not exist a one-to-one correspondence between S and the set of all integers, then there exists a one-to-one correspondence between S and the set of *all* sets of integers.

This asserts that there is no set of real numbers (or, equivalently, of sets of integers) which is properly 'bigger' than N (the set of all integers) but properly 'smaller' than R (the set of all real numbers, or, equivalently, the set of all sets of integers).

Gödel showed in 1939 that given any model M for set theory (or for *Principia*) one can construct a model M' in which this statement holds true. About a month ago (Spring 1963) Paul J. Cohen showed that given any model M one can also construct a model M' in which the *negation* of (C) holds. Moreover, both Gödel's construction and Cohen's construction lead to models which are intuitively 'reasonable'. Thus either (C) or its negation could be adopted as an additional axiom of set theory without forcing a contradiction, or even forcing the models to have intuitively unacceptable properties. Finally, the proofs are relatively 'invariant', in the sense that they would still go through even if further assumptions of an intuitively plausible type (e.g. the existence of inaccessible ordinals) were added to set theory. In short, no axioms for set theory appear even conceivable as of this writing which would close the question of the truth of (C) except by fiat.

I wish to bring this question to bear upon what has been called Russell's 'Platonism'. According to Russell, there is such a well defined totality as the totality of all propositional functions of integers (although we cannot characterize it up to isomorphism by its formal properties, as we know from the Skolem–Löwenheim theorem, and we cannot hope to *list* all the propositional functions in question, even if we were allowed to work for ever, as we know from the non-denumerability proof). Moreover, the other totalities mentioned in (C) are alledgedly well-defined: the totality of all one-to-one correspondences (of the appropriate level), and the totality of all sets of sets (propositional functions of propositional functions) of integers. *Hence* (C) *must be either true or false as a matter of objective fact.*

It is just at this point that the foregoing arguments against Russell's position seem to me to gain 'bite'. We are now dealing with a *bona fide* mathematical assertion (the first problem on Hilbert's famous list of twenty). Russell's position is that universals ('propositional functions') are just as real as tables and chairs, and that statements about them—even statements about *all* of them—are 'objectively' true or false even when we cannot (because of our human limitations) *check* them, just as it might be true that there were between one million three hundred thousand and one million four hundred thousand people in the area now known as North Vietnam six hundred years ago, but we might be utterly unable ever to verify this fact.

It is a matter of sociological fact that Russell's position on this matter seems absurd to most mathematicians and philosophers. *Why* it seems absurd, whereas the statement about North Vietnam does not seem absurd to most people, notwithstanding the apparently equal uncheckability, is a matter for serious philosophical discussion.

The Verificationist answer—that we *might*, after all, find out how many people there were in the area in question six hundred years ago—does not seem adequate (perhaps one could even have a theory of the destruction of information with time from which it would follow that *in principle* it is no longer possible to verify or falsify this statement; yet I, for one, would see no reason to deny that it could be true or false). I would hold that a notion is clear only when it has been adequately explained in terms of notions that we antecedently accept as clear, or when it itself has always been accepted as clear. This is, of course, rough—but it provides at least a rough indication of where the trouble lies: such notions as the notion of a totality of *all* propositional functions of integers, of *all* sets of integers, etc., are relatively novel ones, and they have, as a matter of historical fact, never been explained at all. No one would accept the argument: we know what a language is, in the sense of knowing that English, French, German, are languages: therefore we understand what is meant by the *totality of all languages*, not in the sense of actually spoken languages, but in the sense of an alleged precise and well defined *totality of all possible languages*. Clearly there is no such precise and well defined totality: the notion of a 'language' is much too vague for me to be sure in advance that I can tell under all possible circumstances whether or not some system of sounds (need they be sounds? What about 'dolphinese'? Could there be a language consisting of bee dances?) is or is not, in its actual cultural setting, given the organisms that actually produce it, to be classified as a 'language'. To 'consider the set of all languages' in this 'abstract' sense is to consider no well defined set at all.

Yet just this fallacious argument is what is offered in connection with 'propositional functions' or predicates. Because we know that Blue and Square and Made of Copper are predicates (we have a 'clear notion of predicate' in the sense of *one that is clear in most cases*), we are asked to conclude that there must be a precise and well defined *totality of all predicates*, not in the sense of all actually defined predicates, or in the sense of all predicates which are actually exemplified, or in the sense of all predicates (whether someone has a word for them or not) which *could*, as a matter of physical law, be exemplified, but in the sense of a *totality of all possible predicates*. Clearly there is no such totality. In fact, if we take the 'individuals' of *Principia* to be physical objects, then we boggle at level one: what is meant by the totality of *all possible predicates of physical objects*? Is 'Being Made of Phlogiston' a predicate? And what of 'Being Made of X-on', where 'X-on' is a theoretical term that no scientist ever *did* introduce, but that one *might* have introduced? Indeed, since every *meaningful* theoretical term corresponds to a possible predicate, it would seem that a totality of all possible meaningful theoretical terms (as a precise and well defined totality) is presupposed by the notion of a totality of all predicates of physical objects.

The notion of a totality of all *sets* of physical objects might seem more justifiable than the notion of a totality of all *predicates* (taken in intension), if only because we seem to be sure when a set has been given, and not always sure if a word which has been uttered does or does not correspond to a 'property'. But, if there are infinitely many individuals (and this is postulated by the famous Axiom of Infinity in *Principia*) then this greater sureness is illusory. In the case of infinite sets what we understand is the notion of a *definable* infinite set of things.[1] But the notion of an *undefinable* infinite set—of a *wholly* irregular way of picking out infinitely many things from an infinite collection—has no clear meaning, at least to me, or to many scientists. If it really has a clear meaning, will someone please make it clear to us?

This request is not simple philosophical obstinacy, like the position of the phenomenalist who refuses to understand 'physical object' until and unless it is made clear in *his* terms. I am willing to allow in the clarification of 'arbitrary set' (or 'arbitrary propositional function') any terms which are generally admitted to be clear. It is a matter of historical fact that this new way of speaking—speaking of a totality of *all* subsets of an infinite set—is quite recent (since Cantor), and that Cantor, who introduced it, did so with inconsistencies (sometimes he says a set is all the things 'falling under a rule', and at other times he speaks of wholly *arbitrary* collections— *'beliebige Mengen'*). Surely it is reasonable in science to ask that new technical terms should *eventually* be explained?

(iv) *Remark*. One problem in connection with the foregoing is the so-called problem of 'Impredicative definitions'. Such a definition occurs in *Principia* each time that we, for example, define a predicate of level two using a quantifier over all predicates of level two. The fact that impredicative definitions are permitted makes the problem of defining 'all possible predicates' (even of physical objects) all the more hopeless. For suppose that we had an epistemological theory (of a kind that Russell has sometimes accepted) according to which there exists some finite list of basic predicates (of level one), say $P_1, \ldots, P_n$, such that all *possible* predicates of physical objects are

---

[1] It seems to me that the Diagonal Argument shows that there must be more sets than we can define in any one language, or in any well defined sequence of languages, but not that there must be sets which are 'undefinable' in some *absolute* sense. Of course, the 'totality of all languages' is not a well-defined totality at all.

allegedly definable in terms of these. Then we could make the notion of a 'predicate of physical objects' precise by taking it to mean 'predicate definable (by specified means) from $P_1, P_2, \ldots, P_n$'. However, if the 'specified means' include *impredicative definition* then some of the predicates included in the totality will presuppose the whole totality. The question whether a given individual has such a predicate will then reduce to a question about the whole totality which may in turn depend on the very question with which we started—whether the individual with which we began has the property with which we began.

Another difficulty is the non-denumerability. The predicates of individuals definable in *Principia* from any finite list of basic predicates $P_1, \ldots, P_n$ are only denumerably infinite in number. This is also related to impredicativity in that the Cantor Diagonal Argument depends upon the fact that 'all sets of integers' includes sets of integers defined by reference to this very totality. If impredicative definitions are excluded from *Principia* (as recommended by Weyl) then it is no longer possible to prove that any set is (absolutely) non-denumerable; but, unfortunately, many sets needed in mathematics—e.g. the set of *all* real numbers—are then not definable! (I omit the well-known discussion of the Axiom of Reducibility here, since formally speaking that axiom is equivalent to the allowing of impredicative definitions.)

(3) *'If-Thenism' as a Philosophy of Mathematics*

Before he espoused Logicism, Russell advocated a view of mathematics which he somewhat misleadingly expressed by the formula that mathematics consists of 'if-then' assertions. What he meant was not, of course, that all well formed formulas in mathematics have a horseshoe as the main connective! but that mathematicians are in the business of showing that *if* there is any structure which satisfies such-and-such axioms (e.g. the axioms of group theory), *then* that structure satisfies such-and-such further statements (some theorems of group theory or other). In the remainder of this paper I wish to make a modest attempt to rehabilitate this point of view. What are the difficulties?

(i) *The study of Finite Structures.* One difficulty is this: when we derive consequences from a set of axioms we are determining the properties *not* just of all *finite* structures which satisfy those axioms, but of *all* structures (including the infinite ones) which satisfy those axioms. But there are certain branches of mathematics which limit their inquiry to finite structures of a certain kind. For example, there is a whole literature dealing with the properties of finite groups.

Clearly the theorist here is not just deriving consequences from the axioms of group theory, for in that case he would be proving theorems about *all* groups. He would never prove a statement of the form 'All finite groups have the property *P*' unless indeed the stronger statement were true: 'All groups have the property *P*.' But the whole object of this branch of mathematics is to obtain properties of all finite groups which are *not* properties of all groups!

This objection may be dealt with in two ways. First of all, one may distinguish the thesis that mathematics studies the properties of all structures of a specified kind (groups, finite groups, fields, etc.), without asserting the *existence* of any such structures (except within a well-understood context: e.g. 'existence of an identity', in group theory, means *if* there is given any group *G*, *then* there exists an element *e* in *G* with the property of being the identity of *G*), from the thesis that mathematics is the derivation of consequences from axioms by means of logic (in the sense of quantification theory). We may say, for example, that when we wish to prove that all *finite* models for an axiom-set have certain properties, then we have in general to admit *a primitive mode of proof* over and above 'logic'; namely *mathematical induction*. On this view, the use of mathematical induction as a valid way of proving theorems about all structures of interest in a given domain *is* our way of expressing the fact that those structures are all finite, as well as we can.[1]

---

[1] Strictly speaking, the situation is this. If we accept the notion of a 'totality of all predicates' (of the structures in question), then we can say that the *finite* structures are *completely characterized* by the fact that mathematical induction holds for an *arbitrary* predicate: i.e. if the empty structure has a property, and the property is preserved under adjoining a single element to a structure, then every *finite* structure has it. The finite structures form the *largest* class with respect to which this mode of reasoning is valid. As remarked below, however, every formalized theory admits of models in which 'all predicates' does not really mean *all* predicates. In such models, a class may satisfy the formal definition of the 'class of all finite structures', but contain some structures which are infinite 'viewed from outside' (or viewed from a different model). This will happen because *for every predicate which 'exists' from the standpoint of that model*, it is true that if the empty structure has the predicate and the predicate is preserved under adjoining single elements, then every structure in the class *F* has it, where *F* is the class which is taken to be the 'class of all finite structures' in that model. If *F* has a member which is an infinite structure, viewed from outside, then there will be a predicate—say *not being infinite* (in the sense of the 'outside' model) which does *not* obey mathematical induction with respect to the whole class *F*; but this predicate is no predicate at all from the standpoint of the model in which *F is* the class of all finite structures.

There are thus two standpoints one may take: one may say *either* that the notion of a structure's *really* being finite is a perfectly clear one, but one that cannot be completely formalized; or one may say that the notion *depends essentially* on some totality of predicates, and thus partakes of the same unclarity

Alternatively, we may imbed the axiom-set in question in a richer axiom set (including a portion of set theory) within which the notion of a 'finite model' for the axiom-set in question is explicitly definable, and within which mathematical induction is formally derivable. Then theorems about all 'finite groups', say, are just a subclass of the theorems about all structures of a larger kind—say all 'models for T', where T is a certain system of set theory. (Of course, T might be left unformalized, in actual practice, or might be a large class of 'acceptable' set theories.)

(ii) *The restriction to Standard Models.* A more important difficulty is this: number theory, for example, is usually held to be concerned not with *all* models for, say the Peano Axioms, but solely with all standard models—i.e. all models in which every element is either 'zero' (the unique element with no predecessor), or 'the successor of zero', or 'the successor of the successor of zero', or.... In short, we are concerned, as number theorists, with those models in which every element bears a finite power of the successor relation to 'zero'.

This is, in principle, the same difficulty as (i). The view I am suggesting is that *standardness should be viewed as a relation between models*, rather than as an absolute property of a given model. In other words, when we say that such-and-such (some construction defined in set theory) is a standard model for Peano Arithmetic, this should be interpreted as meaning that *if M* is any model for the set theory in question, *then* such-and-such entities in M form a model for Peano Arithmetic, *and* that model is standard relative to M. In any usual set theory it can easily be proved that any two standard models for Peano Arithmetic are isomorphic; thus for each model M of the set theory, those entities u of M which are standard models for Peano Arithmetic relative to M will be isomorphic to one another. A 'standard model' is here defined as above: one in which each element bears a *finite* power of the successor relation to 'zero', *where the*

as the notion of the 'totality of all predicates' (of a given level). The latter view is the one taken here. I am aware that it is counterintuitive. I believe that it will seem *less* counterintuitive, however, if one fixes it in one's mind that *from the mathematical standpoint* what is *essential* and *all* that is essential about the totality of all finite structures is that this totality obeys mathematical induction *with respect to an arbitrary predicate*, and no larger collection does. Whereas 'intuitively' a finite structure is one that one could 'get through counting' (and thus the intuitive notion of finitude is connected with our experience of space and time), in *mathematics* the finite structures are the ones with respect to which a certain mode of reasoning is valid. If the two notions turn out to be non-coextensive, then it will be the 'intuitive' notion that will have turned out to be wrong!—because time does not have the properties that we intuitively think it to have.

meaning of 'finite' may vary with the model selected for the set theory.

To complete this, we introduce the convention that a model which is *non-standard* relative to any model *M* shall be called 'non-standard' (absolutely) even if it is standard relative to some other model *M'*. We do not introduce a parallel *absolute* use of 'standard' because we do not wish to presuppose a totality of *all* models (this would put us right back in 'theology'). The point is that if I define a model *M'* for a set theory as a function of an arbitrary given model *M*, and then define a model *M''* for Peano arithmetic in terms of *M'* in such a way that *M''* is standard relative to *M'* but *non*-standard relative to the bigger model *M*, then we may say simply that '*M'''* is a non-standard model for Peano Arithmetic'—meaning that there is some model (really a class of hypothetical models, of course) relative to which *M''* has been defined, and relative to which *M''* is non-standard. None of this really presupposes the *existence*, in a non-hypothetical sense, of any models at all for anything, of course!

One common objection is as follows: 'Why not restrict models for *set theory* to be such that all "finite" sets (in the sense of the usual definitions) are *really* finite? Then standard models for Peano Arithmetic are models which are standard relative to *such* models for set theory.' My reply, in a nutshell, is that I have no need for the alleged concept of a set being *really* finite. But this needs a little unpacking.

First of all, notice that this added restriction cannot possibly be of *use* in mathematics. The only way we *ever*, in fact, know that a model for number theory is non-standard is by showing that it is non-standard *relative* to some model for set theory relative to which it has been defined. If the alleged concept of a *really standard* model, in an absolute sense, makes sense at all, then it is *still* a concept that we can do completely without in mathematics. In fact, I would not have the faintest conception of how to go about using it!

To make clear what is meant, let us look at a case in which *all* the models of a theory are 'non-standard'. Such a case may arise as follows. There is a term *t* of the theory (call it *T*) such that we can *prove* all of the following sentences:

$$t \text{ is a number}$$
$$t \neq 0$$
$$t \neq 1$$
$$t \neq 2$$
$$\vdots$$

Moreover, the fact that all of these infinitely many sentences of T are provable in T is itself provable in, say Peano Arithmetic. Then T has no standard models! But how do we know this?

The answer is *not* by some mysterious act of 'intuition', as some have urged, but rather that this *theorem*—that T has no standard models—is provable in any normal system of set theory—even in T itself! (and by just the argument that naturally occurs to one).

Thus, what we have really proved, when we prove the theorem that 'T has no standard model', is that *if M is any model for T, and M is itself an entity of M', where M' is any model for the set theory in which the proof is being given, then M is non-standard relative to M'*. What I am contending is that all *uses* of the standard/non-standard distinction in foundational research are uses of this *relational* notion of standardness, in the manner indicated.

Let T_0 be a set theory with some empirical concepts and assertions in which one can express the assertion 'there is a one-to-one correspondence between the sequence of natural numbers and the sequence of successive *minutes* of time, counting from an arbitrary "first minute"'. The intuitive 'definition' of 'finite' is often thought to be this: *a set is finite if one could get through counting it*. There are counter-examples (Zeno's paradox) if one does not require that it should take a minimum time (say, 'one minute') to count out each member of the set: for if I take a half-minute to count 'one', a quarter-minute to count 'two', an eighth-minute ... etc., then I could count out an *infinite* collection in a finite time. If the infinite collection has the order type $\omega + 1$ (or any other order type, with a last member) then there could even be a *last* element 'counted' (say, after having counted out the first ω elements in one minute, I take one more half-minute and count out the $\omega + 1$st). Thus an infinite set can be 'counted in a finite time', even if we require that there should be a 'last element counted'. But what if we require that there *should* be a minimum time which it takes to 'count' one element? Have we then captured the alleged notion of 'really finite'?

A little reflection shows that what is being proposed is, in effect, this: *a standard model* for Peano Arithmetic (in the alleged 'absolute' sense) should be one which is *standard relative to T_0* (or some such theory). This proposal has some features which are at first blush attractive. For example, we have the attractive-seeming theorem that any finite set can be mapped one-one on to the minutes in a sequence of successive minutes which is 'finite' *in the sense of possessing a first and last minute*. From the point of view of traditional (psychologically oriented) epistemology, this comes close to capturing the 'natural' notion of a finite set. Why, then, should we not accept this?

There are a host of reasons. We have recently learned that the properties which intuitively belong to *space*—infinitude, unboundedness, etc.—are not necessarily properties of space at all (because space may be non-Euclidean). Similarly, the *chronometrical* properties of *time* are an empircal, not a mathematical question. And the proposed definition of 'finite', however 'traditional' and 'epistemologically correct' is riddled with empirical (cosmological) assumptions about time: that there is an infinitude of future time, for example; that the sequence of successive minutes (counting from an arbitrary 'first minute') is *well ordered*; that the sequence has the order type ω. Every one of these assumptions may be false! even if it seems strange to think that, for example, there may be *more than* ω future minutes! No mathematician can consent to let the properties of the *mathematical* notion of finiteness depend upon cosmological hypotheses concerning the true chronometry (= 'time geometry').

This brief discussion, may, however, point to the origin of the widespread belief that we *have* an absolute notion of 'finite'. It is a fact that for a long time the principles of intuitive chronometry, like those of Euclidean geometry, were regarded as synthetic *a priori*. And as long as the usual chronemtry (which assigns the order type $\omega^* + \omega$ to the sequence of all *minutes*—from negative to positive infinity) is thought to be *a priori*, then it seems that we *have* (physically) a standard model for Peano Arithmetic—for the sequence of minutes from some arbitrary first minute is itself such a model (assuming 'plus' and 'times' to be inductively defined in the usual way). And we can *fix* the notion of 'standard model' by taking this model to be *the* model. This is in effect what Kant did; but it is erroneous for just the reason that Kant's views on geometry are erroneous: because the cosmological properties of time in the large are no more *a priori* than those of space in the large.

To recapitulate: we cannot fix any precise notion of an 'absolutely standard' model even for Peano Arithmetic, except *relative* to some other model. We might take some empirically given model and define it to be *the* standard model, but such a course is useless in pure mathematics. Thus if I am wrong, and there is indeed some 'absolute' notion of a '*really* standard' model for Peano Arithmetic, I am anxious to know just where in mathematics we could use it. Similar remarks hold with respect to the notion of a 'standard model' in set theory. Such a model is usually taken to be one in which the power set of a given set *really* contains *all* the subsets of the given set. Once again, this makes perfect sense as a *relation between models*; and if it has any further 'absolute' sense, that absolute sense seems totally unusable and irrelevant from the standpoint of mathematics. I conclude, thus, that an 'if-thenist' view of mathematics *can* do justice to talk of 'standard' and 'non-standard' models *in so far as such talk does any work*.

(iii) *Gödelian arguments.* Suppose I 'accept' a set theory T as 'correct' in the sense that all the number-theoretic statements provable in T are *true* (in *the* standard model, assuming, for the moment, the 'Platonistic' attitude towards standard models which we just criticized). Then the further statement $Con(T)$ which expresses the consistency of T is one that I should *also* accept, since it must be true if T is consistent. But Gödel showed that $Con(T)$ is not provable in T if T is consistent. Thus we have found a sentence—namely $Con(T)$ —which I have as good grounds for accepting as I have for accepting T itself, but which cannot be proved in T.

It has sometimes been urged that the fact that we can 'see' in this way that we should accept $Con(T)$, although $Con(T)$ cannot be formally proved (in T) shows that we *have* and are able to *use* the alleged Platonistic notion of 'truth'—i.e. of truth in *the* standard model for Peano Arithmetic. But this is simply a mistake. If T becomes inconsistent when $Con(T)$ is adjoined—i.e. if $Con(T)$ is *refutable* in T—then T has no standard model, as is easily proved (even in T itself, in most cases). Thus I have as good grounds for accepting the added axiom $Con(T)$ as preserving consistency as I have for expecting that it will not turn out to be provable that T has no standard models. If I 'accept T' in the sense of having this very strong expectation (which may easily be unreasonable in the case of some of the extant systems of set theory), then I should also be willing to accept this added axiom; but this argument does *not* turn on the existence of a non-relational notion of 'standardness'.

(iv) *The problem of Application.* We now come to the difficulty that caused Russell himself to abandon 'if-thenism'. This is, in my view, a far more serious one than the ones we have discussed so far (although the ones we have discussed so far tend to worry mathematicians more). In my opinion, the great strength of logicism as compared to other positions in the philosophy of mathematics is its ability to handle the problem of the *application of mathematical methods to empirical subject matters*; and this is just what Russell himself has always stressed.

Let us review briefly this aspect of the logicist account. Consider first the application of logic itself to empirical premises to derive an empirical conclusion. A simple syllogism will do, say

> All timid persons fear hungry lions
> All bankers are timid
> _____
> (*therefore*) All bankers fear hungry lions

The principle: (for all *A*, *B*, *C*) if all *A* are *B* and all *B* are *C* then all *A* are *C*, is itself a principle of pure logic. But when we assert that the principle is *valid* we are thereby saying that the principle holds even when empirical subject matter terms are 'plugged in' for the capital letters *A*, *B*, *C*; not just when subject matter terms from formal logic and mathematics are 'plugged in'. (In my opinion the Intuitionist account of logic fails to give an adequate account of just this fact; however this falls outside the scope of the present paper.)

Now consider an inference from (applied) arithmetic rather than from logic, say

There are two apples on the desk
There are two apples on the table
The apples on the desk and table are all the ones in this room
No apple is both on the desk and on the table
Two plus two equals four

(*therefore*) There are four apples in this room

The logicist account of such an inference is well known. The logicist definitions of 'there are two *A*s' and 'there are four *A*s' are such that one can *prove* that 'There are two *A*s' is equivalent to a statement of pure quantification theory (with identity) namely: 'There is an *x* and there is a *y* such that *x* is an *A* and *y* is an *A* and $x \neq y$ and such that for every *z*, if *z* is an *A* then either $z = x$ or else $z = y$.' Similarly, 'There are four *A*s' is equivalent to a formula in quantification theory with identity. Thus the entire inference above is equivalent, line by line (except for 'two plus two equals four') to an inference in pure logic, by the narrowest standard—quantification theory with identity. What of the line 'two plus two equals four'? The answer is that the above inference is still valid with that line omitted! Moreover, the logicist translation of 'two plus two equals four' is equivalent, not to a formula of first order logic (quantification theory), but to a formula of second order logic; in fact, to the formula

For every *A*, *B*, *C*, if *C is the union of A and B* and *A and B are disjoint* and *A has two members* and *B has two members* then *C has four members*

where the italicized clauses are all expressible in first order logic with identity. And what this formula says is that the above inference is valid!

Thus we see the role of the formula 'two plus two equals four' in the above inference: it is not an added *premiss* (the inference is valid without it); it is rather the *principle* by which the conclusion is derived from the (other) premisses. Moreover, the principle is essentially a first order principle: since the initial universal quantifiers 'for every A, B, C' can be inserted in front of every valid first order principle. Thus the above inference is tantamount to an inference in pure logic even by narrow standards of what constitutes pure logic; and the fact that the principle 'two plus two equals four' can be used to derive empirical conclusions from empirical premisses is simply an instance of the fact that we noted before: the fact that when we assert that a principle of pure logic is 'valid' we thereby assert that the principle is good under all substitutions for the predicate letters A, B, C, etc.; even substitutions of empirical subject matter terms. What has confused people about 'two plus two equals four' is that *unlike* '(for all A, B, C) if all A are B and all B are C then all A are C' it does not *explicitly* contain 'A, B, C' which can have empirical subject matter terms 'plugged in' for them; but it is demonstrably equivalent to a principle which *does* explicitly contain 'A, B, C'.

This discussion contains what is of permanent value in logicism, I think. This account of the application of (discrete) mathematics is neat and intellectually satisfying. Moreover it *does*, I think, show that there is no sharp line (at least) between mathematics and logic; just the principles that Kant took to be 'synthetic *a priori*' (e.g. 'five plus seven equals twelve') turn out to be expressible in the notation of what even Kant would probably have conceded to be logic. Of course, the logicists did *not* show that *all* of mathematics— not even all of number theory—is expressible by means of first order formulas in the manner in which 'two plus two equals four' is. We have already noted that the Continuum Hypothesis, for example, is expressed in *Principia* by a higher order formula which presupposes propositional functions of propositional functions of . . . of individuals, and that such quantifications over an alleged totality of *all* propositional functions (of a given level)—including the ones defined in terms of the alleged totality itself—pose some real problems of interpretation. But there is an unfortunate tendency in philosophy of mathematics to overlook the fact that the logicist translations of *some* mathematical propositions in fact, just those propositions about specific integers ('five plus seven equals twelve') which figured in Kant's discussion—do *not* presuppose higher order logic, and thus do not depend on the notion of a totality of 'all' propositional functions except in the harmless way in which even first order logic does: via the idea that we can state principles which contain 'dummy letters' *A, B, C* for which one can plug in any propositional function one likes. But this use of schematic letters does *not*, I think, require that we suppose the totality of all permissible values of the letters to be a well defined one, as does the explicit definition of a propositional function in terms of the alleged totality in question.

In more formal language, what I am drawing is a distinction between those principles of Second Order Logic whose predicate quantifiers (in prenex form) are all universal (and precede all first level quantifiers), and the remaining principles (which involve existential second level quantifiers). The former principles are simply first order formulas; the function of the second level quantifiers is merely to express the notion that the formula holds for all *A, B, C*, i.e. the notion that the formula is *valid*. On the other hand, a formula which contains '(EP)'—*there exists a propositional function P* must be regarded as presupposing that the totality of *all* propositional functions is a well defined one (unless the bound variable *P* can somehow be restricted to a special class of propositional functions which anyone would admit to be well defined). Since the 'translations' of *some* number theoretic utterances are formulas of the first kind, I am arguing that Russell *has* shown that *some* mathematical truths are part of logic (or that part of logic is identical with part of mathematics), and hence that the line between the two subjects is not sharp, even if one boggles at counting formulas of the second kind (ones which assert that 'there exists a *P*') as part of 'logic'. To have shown that the 'line' between 'logic' and 'mathematics' is somewhat arbitrary was a great achievement; and it *was* the achievement of *Principia*, I contend.

Consider now such a statement as 'the number of the planets is nine'. What this 'means', according to *Principia*, is that a certain *set*, the set of planets, belong to a certain other set (intuitively, the set of all nine-tuples, although it is definable in pure logical notation, in the fashion illustrated in connection with 'two'—i.e. it is definable without using the term 'nine'). If propositional functions and sets are entities which can be understood only *relative to models*—if a 'set', for example, is any entity in a model which bears a certain relation (the converse of the 'epsilon relation' of the model) to certain other entities of the model—then mathematics, *so understood*, does not assert the *existence* of any sets at all (except in the way in which it asserts the 'existence' of an identity in group theory—that is, it asserts that certain sets exist *in each model*). In particular, then, although it may be a theorem of *Principia* that there is such a set as 'the set of planets', all this means is that *if M* is any model for *Principia, then* there is an entity *u* of *M* which bears the converse of the 'epsilon relation' of M to each planet and only to the planets. Similarly, 'the number of the planets is nine', if asserted in this 'if–then' spirit, could only mean: *if* M is any model for *Principia*, *then* the entity of M which is 'the set of planets' belongs to the entity v which is 'the number nine'. So far I have skirted the dangerous question: what does it mean to suppose that a model 'exists'? Does a model have to be a system of *physical objects* (in which case the mathematical theories we have been discussing concern the properties of hypothetical *physically infinite* structures), or can it be a system of *abstract* objects? And what would an 'abstract object' *be* anyway? But one thing is clear: if 'existence of a model' is so interpreted that models for, say, *Principia might* in fact exist, but do not necessarily exist (in whichever sense of 'exist'), then we seem to be in trouble. For, if the sentence '*M* is a model for *Principia*' is *false*, then any 'if–then' sentence with this antecedent is vacuously true. Then for every number n, 'The number of the planets is n' would be true, on this 'if—then' interpretation!

It is important to notice that this difficulty affects only the problem of understanding *applied* mathematics, not pure mathematics. For, in pure mathematics, the business of the mathematician is not in discovering *materially* true propositions of the form 'If M is a model for T then so-and-so', but in discovering *logically true* propositions of that form. Even if a proposition of the form in question is true, if it is only 'true by accident' (say, because *there is no M* such that *M* is a model for T), then it will not be provable by purely formal means, and hence will not be asserted by the mathematician. But the assertion, 'the number of the planets is nine' cannot be interpreted in the same way—cannot be interpreted as meaning that it is a *logical* truth that, if M is any model for, say, *Principia*, then the entity u which is the set of planets in M belongs to the entity v which is the 'number nine' in M—because it is *not* a logical truth, but only a material truth that the number of the planets *is* nine. And if we attempt to interpret the assertion, 'the number of the planets is nine', as the assertion of the *empirical* truth of a material implication, then the familiar paradoxes of material implication arise to plague us.

For this reason, Russell took the view that since we regard various groups of things as actually having a cardinal number (independently of whether any one ever counts those groups, and ascertains that cardinal number, or not) then the corresponding sets must be accepted by us as actually 'existing' (or rather, the corresponding predicates must be—'sets' are construed as special kinds of predicates in *Principia*), and so must all the predicates of these predicates (since that is what numbers are, on the *Principia* view), and so on. In short, even if *pure* mathematics does not presuppose that a model for *Principia* actually exists, *applied* mathematics does. Indeed, since the truth-value of these applied statements must be well defined, a particular model—*the* standard model—must be fixed once and for all, as the one to be used in interpreting *Principia*.

This argument does not appear to me to be decisive, as it did to Russell forty-five years ago. Consider, first of all, a single empirical statement involving a number-word, say, 'there are two apples on the desk'. Russell himself has provided us with not one but *two* ways of rendering this statement in *Principia* notation: the one we reviewed before, which requires only quantification theory with identity, and the one involving the existence of sets. The former way of saying 'there are two apples on the desk' can always be used, whether we assume that models for *Principia* exist or not, and it expresses an objective factual claim which is true or false independently of the existence of anything but the apples on the desk (as it should be). Thus we do not *have* to render 'the number of the planets is nine' by an elaborate assertion about a relation between two highly defined sets, which in turn becomes interpreted (on the 'if-thenist' view) as a hypothetical assertion about models for *Principia*. Even if we accept the 'if-thenist' view, the statement in question can be regarded as a simple first order assertion about the planets. The puzzle is how mathematics then ever becomes useful in empirical investigation.

In order to solve this problem, let us abbreviate the statement 'the set of planets belongs to the number nine' as P_1, and the statement 'there is an x and there is a y and . . . such that x is a planet and y is a planet and . . . and $x \neq y$ and . . . and such that for every z if z is a planet then $z = x$ or $z = y$ or . . .', which expresses 'the number of the planets is nine' in a purely first order way, as P^*. The equivalence, $P \equiv P^*$, is a theorem of *Principia*, and hence holds in all models. Thus, *if we assume Principia has a model*, it does not matter whether we assert P or P^*. Otherwise, as we have just seen, it is necessary to use P^* to express what we wish to say without committing ourselves to sets, models, etc.

In a similar way, let Q be the statement 'the set of all suns (in the solar system) belongs to the number one', and let Q^* be the statement, 'there is an x such that x is a sun (in the solar system) and such that for every z, if z is a sun then $z = x$' [which expresses 'there is exactly one sun (in the solar system)']. Let R be the statement, 'something is a major body in the solar system if and only if it is either a planet or a sun', let S be the statement, 'nothing is both a planet and a sun', let T be the statement, 'the set of major bodies in the solar system belongs to the number ten', and let T^* be the corresponding statement in quantification theory with identity ('there is an x and there is a y and . . . such that x is a major body in the solar system and y is a major body in the solar system and . . . etc.'). Now, we may visualize the following as happening: someone accepts 'the number of planets is nine', which he renders indifferently by P or P^*; he accepts 'there is exactly one sun (in the solar system)', which he renders indifferently by either Q or Q^*; and, of course, he accepts R and S. In *Principia*, he then carries out the deduction 'P & Q & R & S, therefore T', and accordingly accepts T. Finally, since $T \equiv T^*$ (in *Principia*) he treats T and T^* as equivalent, and also accepts T^*. He has been led to the correct conclusion: but virtually all of the 'in between steps' in his reasoning 'make sense' only *given* some model for *Principia*. Or is this true?

Well, let us ask: what would happen if someone some day came to an *incorrect* conclusion in this fashion? Let U be the statement, 'the set of major bodies in the solar system belongs to the number *eleven*', let U^* be the corresponding statement in quantification theory with identity, and suppose that someone some day found a deduction of 'P & Q & R & S, therefore U' in *Principia*. What would this mean? Since a deduction remains valid no matter *what* constants are 'plugged in' for A, B, C, etc., one could replace 'the set of planets belongs to the number nine' by 'the set of natural numbers from one through nine belongs to the number nine', replace 'the set of suns belongs to the number one' by 'the set of natural numbers from ten through ten belongs to the number one', etc. In short, from the premisses 'there are nine numbers from one to nine', 'there is exactly one number ten', 'nothing is both a number from one to nine and the number ten', 'every number from one to ten is either a number from one to nine or the number ten', all of which are theorems of *Principia*, one could deduce 'there are *eleven* numbers from one to ten', which is the *negation* of a theorem of *Principia*. Thus *Principia* would be formally inconsistent, and hence *could have* no models at all!

In short, if I find a proof of, say, 'P & Q & R & S, therefore T' in *Principia*, I can rely on the corresponding first order statement, 'P^* & Q^* & R & S, therefore T^*', *provided* I am confident that *Principia could have* models. Since any discovery of a mistaken inference of this kind would be *ipso facto* a discovery of an inconsistency in *Principia*, I can be as confident in such inferences as I am that no inconsistency will turn up in *Principia*. There is a clear difference between believing in the actual existence of something, and believing in its *possible* existence: and I am contending that the employment of *Principia*, at least in deriving such statements as we have been discussing from each other, does *not* presuppose 'Platonism', i.e. belief in the *actual* existence of sets, predicates, models for *Principia*, etc., but only presuppose a belief that a structure satisfying the axioms of *Principia* is *possible*. What it is to believe that the existence of something is possible, is a philosophical issue which will not be entered into here; however, this much is clear: to think that *there could be* a structure satisfying the axioms of *Principia*, in any sense of 'could', is *at least* to be confident that no contradictions will turn up in *Principia*. And that is all we need to employ *Principia* in the manner which I have been describing.

In sum, I am suggesting that pure mathematics consists of assertions to the affect that *if* anything is a model for a certain system of axioms, *then* it has certain properties, while applied mathematics consists of assertions to the affect that *if* anything is a model for a certain system of axioms, *then* certain statements 'if *A* then *B*' hold, where *A* and *B* are first order statements *not* about the hypothetical model, but about real things. If such a statement turned out to be false, then it would have turned out that the set of axioms in question could have no model. Thus applied mathematics does *not* presuppose that models for our mathematical axiom-sets ('standard' or 'nonstandard') actually do exist, but only that they *could* exist.

(v) *Consistency*. On the view just presented, and indeed on *any* view, the application of mathematics to 'the real world' presupposes the *consistency* of the mathematical theory applied. If we do not wish to assume the consistency of as 'strong' a system as *Principia*, then we may try to get by with weaker systems—but the consistency of at least elementary number theory is presupposed by every school in the foundations of mathematics (the relative consistency of Intuitionist and 'classical' elementary number theory is easily demonstrated). On what does this presupposition rest?

This question does not seem to me to pose any *especial* difficulty for the view proposed here. Our confidence in the possible existence of a model for at least Peano Arithmetic reduces to our belief that there is nothing contradictory in the notion of an ordinary infinite sequence. *That* belief is shared by all philosophies of mathematics: the Intuitionists may *say* that they 'only presuppose the potential infinite', but this is only terminologically different from saying that they too reject the idea that a contradiction could ever be found in the idea of a sequence proceeding for ever. On my view, such framework assumptions[1] in science neither have nor require any 'justifica-

---

[1] Cf. my paper 'The Analytic and the Synthetic', in *Minnesota Studies in the Philosophy of Science*, vol. III, ed. H. Feigl and G. Maxwell, 1962, pp. 358-397.

tion'; it is only that we require a justification if we ever propose to *revise* them.

With respect to mathematical systems stronger than Peano Arithmetic the situation (*vis à vis* consistency proofs) today appears problematical. Hilbert hoped to show the consistency of all the standard systems (including *Principia*) relative to number theory; but Gödel dashed this hope in his Second Incompleteness Theorem. What is still not clear is whether the consistency of, say, *Principia* can be demonstrated *relative to* some system whose consistency is more 'intuitively evident' than that of *Principia*. As long as this is not done, we have to admit that classical mathematics, pure and applied, rests upon foundations which *might* someday turn out to be inconsistent. But so what? That is what the situation is; and we have constantly to put up with much more pressing risks in life and in science. If the 'philosophy of mathematics' proposed here offers no more 'justification' than *our intuitive conviction that certain kinds of structures are possible* for our assuming the consistency of 'strong' systems of mathematics, what 'philosophy of mathematics' *does* offer more justification than this?

(4) *Hilbert's 'Formalism'*

The position just defended, although substantially that of Russell in *The Principles of Mathematics*, has a certain relation to Hilbert's position, as expounded, for example in the famous article on the Infinite.[1] Our first order statements about planets, apples on desks, etc., correspond to the statements that, on Hilbert's view, figure in the ultimate *application* of mathematics in empirical science. It was essential to Hilbert's view that *ultimately* the statements we are concerned with when we *apply* mathematics should be simple assertions of numerical magnitude, such as 'there are two apples on the desk'. The corresponding assertions of pure mathematics—e.g., 'two plus two equals four', which can, as I noted, be expressed either as first order formulas, or (by prefixing predicate quantifiers binding '*A, B, C, ...*') as second order formulas, correspond to Hilbert's 'real statements'. Thus, in the example I gave some paragraphs back, '*P* & Q* & R & S*, therefore *T**' was a *real* statement. (In fact, it was equivalent to the real statement 'nine plus one equals ten'.) The remaining statements in mathematics are called 'ideal statements' by Hilbert. Thus '*P & Q & R & S*, therefore *T*' was an *ideal* statement (from set theory). Hilbert saw just what has been pointed out: that what the passage from the ideal statements to the real statements

[1] An English translation of this article appears in *Philosophy and Mathematics*, ed. P. Benacerraf and H. Putnam, 1964.

implied by those ideal statements requires is the *consistency* of the ideal statements—not in the sense that the ideal statements would *not* imply the real statements even if the ideal statements were inconsistent; of course they would, since an inconsistent statement implies every statement; but that the assumption that all real statements implied by the ideal statements of the mathematical theory T are *true* invokes the consistency of T.

The position I have been defending seems superior to Hilbert's position in several respects, however. First of all, the term 'ideal statement' does not convey very much in itself, beyond the suggestive analogy with 'ideals' in algebraic number theory, which suggested the term to Hilbert. Sometimes, in trying to be more precise, Hilbert said that the ideal statements are *meaningless combinations of signs*; but this does extreme violence to our intuitions. The view taken here —that the 'ideal statements' are *meaningful* and indeed *true* assertions about all structures of certain specified kinds, whether such structures actually exist or not—seems far closer to common sense. And this view is perfectly compatible with Hilbert's further view, that even the possible existence of such structures should not be taken for granted, but should be demonstrated, if possible, by elementary number theoretic means—only that further view appears to have been dashed by the metamathematical results of Gödel. Certain mathematicians appear to gain a sense of security from saying that they are only manipulating meaningless concatenations of signs; but this security is illusory. If the theory we are working in is *consistent*, then there is no reason not to say that we are proving (by pure elementary logic) what properties all structures which obey the axioms of the theory *must* have; and if it is inconsistent, then saying, 'it was all a collection of uninterpreted formulas, anyhow' will not render it mathematically interesting.

Under the term 'real statement' Hilbert included, however, not only the statements 'two plus two equals four', etc., so far discussed, but also certain other statement—for example, 'there is always a prime between x and $2x$'—when proved by 'constructive' means, i.e. means acceptable to the Intuitionists. Here I can follow him only in part. The notion of a statement with 'constructive content'—e.g. there is always a prime between x and $2x$—is clear. 'There is always a prime between x and $2x$', if true (and it is), provides an *effective method* for finding a prime greater than any given prime p. Namely, given p, simply test $p + 1$, $p + 2$, ... up to $2p$, for primacy. At least one of the tests must have an affirmative outcome, and then one will have discovered a prime greater than p. Moreover, it is clearly natural to extend the term 'real statement' to cover statements with constructive content. For, sticking with our example, suppose for some p our computing procedure does not yield a prime greater than p—i.e. it is not possible to find a prime greater than p by simply looking between p and $2p$. Then we will have discovered a contradiction in Peano Arithmetic. Thus we have as good reason to rely on our computing procedure in any actual case (provided it does not take too long to actually carry out the computation) as we do to rely on the 'real statements' discussed before—the basis for our confidence in both cases is our underlying confidence in the consistency of Arithmetic.

Consider, by way of contrast, the 'non-constructive' statement 'there are infinitely many primes'. *In a sense*, this statement too provides a 'computing procedure' for locating a prime greater than p: namely, *hunt through $p + 1$, $p + 2$, $p + 3$, ... until you find a prime*. If the statement is true, this computing procedure (and it is a perfectly feasible one to actually 'programme') must always 'terminate'; and when the procedure 'terminates', we have the desired prime greater than p. However, if the procedure *never* terminates, we cannot conclude that Peano Arithmetic is inconsistent! All we can conclude, if this procedure never terminates in some actual case, is that Peano Arithmetic is at least ω-inconsistent. We can prove (in whatever metatheory we prove that the procedure never terminates) that Peano Arithmetic has no 'standard model'. (The nature of such *relative* 'non-standardness' was discussed above.) But we cannot say: 'if the procedure never terminates, you will obtain an inconsistency in Peano Arithmetic.' For, if the procedure never terminates in a particular case, I will not *find this out* (save by proof in a more powerful theory); all I will find out is that I 'run out of computer time'. And since no bound was given in advance on the length of *this* computation, my 'running out of computer time' does not at all establish that the termination of this computation will never come.

Thus, I can agree with Hilbert that there is a clear difference between relying on theorems of Peano Arithmetic which say that a certain computation will terminate in less than some specified number of steps, and relying on theorems which only say that a computation will 'eventually' terminate, or which don't provide an effective procedure at all. But I see *no* reason to agree with Hilbert that it matters in the least, to a statement's counting as a 'real' statement in the sense we have been discussing, whether it has been proved by Intuitionist means or not! Consider again 'there is always a prime between x and $2x$'. Even if this were proved using the Law of the Excluded Middle, or some other principle that Brouwer rejects, it would *still* provide a way of finding a prime greater than any number x, in a predetermined number of trials (in fact, x trials).

Moreover, if this procedure ever failed, then *both* 'classical' arithmetic and Intuitionist arithmetic would be inconsistent.

In sum: *my*, so to speak, 'real statements', 'two plus two equals four', etc., are all 'essentially' first order (since, when written as second order statements in the fashion indicated before, all second order quantifiers are prenex and universal); and the predicate variable A, B, C, etc., correspond to just the empirical subject matter terms that one would naturally 'plug in' in an application. Hilbert's 'real statements' 'there is always a prime between x and $2x$', are not of this simple character. However, the statement that something is a Turing Machine with a specified machine table T is easily written in first order terms, provided we have appropriate predicates to serve as the 'states' (these are now 'empirical subject matter terms', although in the pure theory of the Turing Machine in question they would be replaced by dummy letters A, B, C, etc.); and for *fixed n*, it is easy enough to write down (again in first order terms) the statement that the machine will 'halt' in n (or however many) steps. Thus the statement that a *particular* empirically given Turing Machine will halt in n steps is a first order statement which presupposes nothing but the machine in question and the various predicates used to describe it; and the 'real statement' 'there is always a prime between x and $2x$', or whatever, serves simply as a device for obtaining predictions of this kind. If the statement is *proved* (and thus hold in all models), all the predictions of this kind obtained from it will hold good (or else Arithmetic will turn out to be inconsistent). Thus we see why Hilbert wished to call such statements (when suitably proved) 'real statements'. For me this is no issue. My 'cut' is different than Hilbert's 'cut'; my distinction is not between *statements with real meaning* and *meaningless concatenations of signs*; and hence I do not have to struggle, as Hilbert did, to include as many statements in the former class as possible without being 'metaphysical'. Instead, I have introduced here a distinction (in the case of such theories as *Principia*) between statements which refer to entities which exist independently of any particular 'model' for the mathematical theory at issue (e.g. the planets, the apples on some desk, a particular Turing Machine), and statements which refer to models, and to what I am construing, as entities within models—sets, propositional functions, etc. Even some of Hilbert's 'real' statements fall in the latter class; however, my account of our confidence in the computing procedures based upon them is roughly similar to Hilbert's.

(5) *Russell's Logical Realism*

Returning now to Russell's views, we are struck by two differences between the 'if–thenist' position, which he first espoused, and the later position. First, he seems to have come to the conclusion that the application of mathematics presupposes a restriction to *standard* models; and secondly, he seems to have come to the conclusion that it is necessary and possible to select a *particular* standard model (for *Principia*). What led him to the *second* of these views? (The first has already been discussed.) A number of considerations seem to have been operative. Linguistic considerations may have played a role. We do not speak of *a* number two, but of *the* number two. This is in agreement with the idea that there is some one definite model which is presupposed in number theory, and that even the substitution of an *isomorphic* model would be a change of subject matter. On this view it is a perfectly genuine theoretical question: 'is the number two the set of all pairs, or is it the set consisting of the null set and the unit set of the null set (as in von Neumann's theory), or some third set, or not a set at all?' I do not think that any mathematician would or should be impressed by this linguistic point. Secondly, both Frege and Russell sometimes write as if the logicist analysis of 'there are two *A*s' (reviewed above) *depended* upon 'two' being defined as 'the set of all pairs'. This is a mistake (as Quine has pointed out). Even if we took the numbers *one, two, three, . . .* as *primitive* (in direct violation of the Frege–Russell spirit), it would suffice to define '*A* has *n* members' (where *n* is a *variable* over integers) to mean '*A* can be put in one-to-one correspondence with the set of natural numbers less than *n*' (or, alternatively, 'with the set of natural numbers from one *through n*'). Then the equivalences $P \equiv P^*$ discussed before would be forthcoming as theorems. It is these equivalences that underlie the logicist account of the application of mathematics; how exactly the numbers are defined, or whether they are taken as primitive is immaterial as long as these equivalences can be derived.

Let us shift attention, however, to the question: how and why did Russell think it was *possible* to single out a standard model for *Principia*? The answer, in broad outlines, is well known. Russell is a 'realist' with respect to universals; and he believed that these (universals, or predicates, or 'propositional functions') provide a model, and in fact the *intended* model, for *Principia*. His critics reply 'theology' (as we saw above), and the battle rages. But there is something curiously unsatisfying here.

What is unsatisfying is that at least three different issues have been blurred together. There is the hoary issue of 'the existence of universals'. There is the quite different issue of the existence of a hierarchy of propositional functions satisfying the axioms of *Principia*. And, unnoticed since Hume, but connecting the other two issues, there is the question of the relation between the 'natural' and 'philosophical' notions of a predicate or property.

Let us take this third issue to start with. Hume remarked that 'relation' (two place predicate) is used in two senses: in the 'natural' sense, *father of* and *to the left of* are 'relations', but *a thousand miles away from* is not what we ordinarily think of as a relation. This is a 'relation' only in the 'philosophical' sense (i.e. the logician's sense). A similar point can be made about *properties*. *Being either green or a human being or a doughnut* is a 'property' in the logician's sense, but not in the 'natural' sense.

This distinction between the 'natural' and 'philosophical' senses of 'property', 'relation', etc., bears also on the first issue—the 'existence of universals'. Let us review this issue for a moment. Realists insist that universals—colours, shapes, etc.—*exist*. Nominalists insist that they do not. Ordinary language, I note in passing, appears to have a blithe disregard for both positions. Realists should be troubled by the fact that 'the colour red *exists*' is such an extraordinary thing to say (but they are not); Nominalists should be equally troubled by the fact that '*there is* a shade of green which is as intense as scarlet' is not at all extraordinary in ordinary English.[1] The traditional argument of the Nominalist is that assuming the existence of universals is otiose: whatever we want to say by saying 'the colour red exists' can just as well be said by saying 'there are red things'. The traditional argument of the Realist proceeds in stages. First a distinction is drawn between classes (like Red) whose members have, intuitively 'something in common', and *arbitrary* collections (whose members need not have anything in common). Then it is argued (correctly, I believe) that the Nominalist has no satisfactory way of analysing this distinction, i.e. of rendering the simple assertions that red things, for example, have something in common. This cannot be rendered by 'red things are all red' because of the 'for example'. What is wanted is a general analysis of the predicate (as a predicate of a number of things) 'having something in common'. The Nominalist might propose to meet the Realist half way by admitting *extensional* universals (classes), and then taking 'the members of x have something in common', where x is a class, as a *primitive* predicate. But then he still would not be able to

---

[1] These 'idiosyncrasies' of ordinary language, as some view them, fit rather well with Carnap's well-known distinction between 'external' existence questions (which purport to question the existence of a whole 'framework', e.g. colours, numbers, physical objects) and 'internal' existence questions, which presuppose some such framework. Ordinary language accepts the latter quite cheerfully, but not the former.

analyse 'the members of x_1 have something *different* in common from the members of x_2'.

What is interesting about this argument is that it rests the existence of universals upon the intuitive notion of a 'something in common'. Intuitively 'red' and 'square' are universals in *this* sense: all red things and all squares have, intuitively, 'something in common', although what they have in common is different in the two cases. But there is not the slightest reason to believe that 'universals' in *this* sense[1] are closed under logical operations, or obey any of the axioms of *Principia*.

In particular, consider the familiar proof that the number of propositional functions is non-denumerable. Let us try to adapt this so that it becomes a proof that 'properties', in the intuitive sense, are non denumerable. Let x_1, x_2, x_3, be some denumerably infinite list of things. (The argument assumes the Axiom of Infinity.) Suppose there were only denumerably many properties, say P_1, P_2, ..., where each P_i is a 'natural' property, i.e. a 'something in common'. Define a predicate Q as follows: x has Q if and only if x is x_n for some n and x does not have P_n. Then Q is a property and must be different from each property P_i in the list P_1, P_2, ... But this was supposed to be an enumeration of *all* properties. Thus we have a contradiction.

This argument is fallacious, on the 'natural' notion of 'property', because we should hardly say that x and y, for example, have 'something in common', *merely* because in some *arbitrary* listing x is the seventeenth element (or x_{17}), y is the onehundredth (or x_{100}) and neither does x have the seventeenth property in some list of properties nor does y have the onehundredth. Even if P_1, P_2, ... are all properties in the 'natural' sense, Q would clearly be a 'property' only in the 'philosophical' sense.

I conclude that the traditional debate between Nominalists and Realists, whatever its status, is irrelevant to the philosophy of mathematics. 'Properties' in any 'natural' sense no more form a model for *Principia* than physical objects do. And properties in the 'philosophical' sense are simply *predicates*. I think, myself, that by a 'predicate' what is normally meant is a *predicate in some language*, and that the diagonal argument simply shows that there is no well defined totality of all *languages*. But be that as it may, we have already seen that it is one thing to suppose that we have a *usable* notion of a 'predicate' and quite another to suppose that there is a well defined totality of all predicates (including predicates defined only in terms of that totality and predicates which cannot apparently be defined at all). The latter supposition is tantamount to the supposition that

---

[1] Obviously the sense in question has not at all been made clear.

301

there exists a standard model for *Principia* in some absolute sense of 'standard': but no traditional argument to the effect that 'all red things have something in common' will support *that* supposition. And, indeed, what argument could?

I have already contended that the question, whether a model for *Principia* (or any mathematical theory) actually exists lies outside of mathematics altogether. I would now go further and say the same for the question, whether only physical objects exist (in which case a model for *Principia* could only exist if it were physically realized, i.e. each 'propositional function' of the model would have in reality to be a physical object, and the relation of 'applying to' which connects propositional functions with their arguments would have to be a suitable relation among these physical objects), or whether 'universals exist'. If this is a question at all, and not a pseudo-question, it is a question for philosophers; but not, thank God! for philosophers of *mathematics*. Mathematics tells us that if anything is a 'group' then it has certain properties: but it does not matter whether the group is a set of physical objects, or a set of *colours*, or whatever. Similarly, mathematics tell us that if anything is a 'model for *Principia*' then it has certain properties: but it does not matter whether the model is a set of physical objects, or of colours, or whatever. If assuming the 'existence of universals' *ipso facto* guaranteed the existence of models for theories such as *Principia*, then the traditional question of the existence of universals might have some bearing on the philosophy of mathematics; but, as far as I can see, it doesn't.

(6) *Mathematics as Logic?*

In summary, I have rejected the thesis that mathematics is logic in the sense outlined in *Principia*, for the reasons given in the second section of this paper. I have proposed instead to revive Russell's earlier view (the 'if–thenist' view). This view too makes mathematics 'logic', *in a sense*. For the essential business of the pure mathematician may be viewed as deriving logical consequences from sets of axioms. (Although mathematical induction may be viewed *either* as an 'extra-logical' method of proof, or as a 'logical' method in a richer theory, when we are studying *finite* models, as I noted). However, mathematics is not *just* logic. For our intuitive conviction that certain kinds of infinite structures *could* exist plays an essential role in the *application* of mathematics. It is a part, and an important part, of the *total* mathematical picture that certain sets of axioms are taken to describe *presumably possible* structures. It is only *such* sets of axioms that are used in *applied* mathematics. Thus there is a question which remains irreducibly a question is the philosophy of mathematics over and above the 'philosophy of logic': the question of illuminating and clarifying our acceptance of mathematical structures as 'presumably possible', or of mathematical axiom sets as 'presumably consistent'. Today this seems largely arbitrary; but no one can exclude that new results in the foundations of mathematics will radically alter the picture.

19

W. V. QUINE

Russell's Ontological Development

The twentieth century began, as many of you know, in 1901. Russell was 28 and had published three books: one on politics, one on mathematics, and one on philosophy. Late next summer the century will be two-thirds over. Russell's books have run to forty, and his philosophical influence, direct and indirect, over this long period has been unequalled.

Russell's name is inseparable from mathematical logic, which owes him much, and it was above all Russell who made that subject an inspiration to philosophers. The new logic played a part in the philosophical doctrines that Russell propounded during the second decade of this century—doctrines of unsensed sensa and perspectives, logical constructions and atomic facts. These doctrines affect our thinking today both directly and through supervening schools of thought. The impact of logical empiricism upon present-day philosophy is to an important degree Russell's impact at one remove, as the references in Carnap and elsewhere generously attest. Moreover, Wittgenstein's philosophy was an evolution from views that Russell and the young Wittgenstein had shared. The Oxford philosophy of ordinary language must admit, however bleakly, to a strong strain of Russell in its origins.

I think many of us were drawn to our profession by Russell's books. He wrote a spectrum of books for a graduated public, layman to specialist. We were beguiled by the wit and a sense of new-found clarity with respect to central traits of reality. We got memorable first lessons in relativity, elementary particles, infinite numbers, and the foundations of arithmetic. At the same time we were inducted into traditional philosophical problems, such as that of the reality of matter and that of the reality of minds other than our own. For all this emergence of problems the over-riding sense of new-found clarity was more than a match. In sophisticated retrospect we have had at points to reassess that clarity, but this was a sophistication that we acquired only after we were hooked.

Russell spoke not only to a broad public, but to a broad subject matter. The scatter of his first three books set a precedent to which his books of the next six decades conformed. Some treat of education, marriage, morals, and, as in the beginning, politics. I shall not venture to guess whether the world is better for having heeded Russell in these farther matters to the degree that it has, or whether it is better for not having heeded him more. Or both.

Instead I shall talk of Russell's ontological development. For I must narrow my scope somehow, and ontology has the virtue of being central and not unduly narrow. Moreover Russell's ontology was conditioned conspicuously by both his theory of knowledge and his logic.

In *Principles of Mathematics*, 1903, Russell's ontology was unrestrained. Every word referred to something. If the word was a proper name, in Russell's somewhat deviant sense of that phrase, its object was a *thing*; otherwise a *concept*. He limited the term 'existence' to things, but reckoned things liberally, even including instants and points of empty space. And then, beyond existence, there were the rest of the entities: 'numbers, the Homeric gods, relations, chimeras, and four-dimensional spaces' (pp. 44, 449). The word 'concept', which Russell applied to these non-existents, connotes mereness; but let us not be put off. The point to notice, epithets aside, is that gods and chimeras are as real for Russell as numbers. Now this is an intolerably indiscriminate ontology. For, take impossible numbers: prime numbers divisible by 6. It must in some sense be false that there are such; and this must be false in some sense in which it is true that there are prime numbers. In *this* sense are there chimeras? Are chimeras then as firm as the good prime numbers and firmer than the primes divisible by 6?

Russell may have meant to admit certain chimeras (the possible ones) to the realm of being, and still exclude the primes divisible by 6 as impossibles. Or he may, like Meinong, have intended a place even for impossible objects. I do not see that in *Principles of Mathematics* Russell faced that question.

Russell's long article on Meinong came out in *Mind* in instalments the following year.[1] In it he criticized details of Meinong's system, but still protested none against the exuberance of Meinong's realm of being. In the same quarterly three issues later, however, a reformed Russell emerges: the Russell of 'On denoting' (1905), fed up with Meinong's impossible objects. The reform was no simple change of heart; it hinged on his discovery of a means of dispensing with the unwelcome objects. The device was Russell's theory of singular descriptions, that paradigm, as Ramsey has said, of philosophical analysis. It involved defining a term not by presenting a direct equivalent of it, but by what Bentham called *paraphrasis*: by

[1] 'Meinong's theory of complexes and assumptions', *Mind*, 1904, pp. 204–19, 33–54, 509–24.

providing equivalents of all desired sentences containing the term. In this way, reference to fictitious objects can be simulated in meaningful sentences without our being committed to the objects.

The new freedom that paraphrasis confers is our reward for recognizing that the unit of communication is the sentence and not the word. This point of semantical theory was long obscured by the undeniable primacy, in one respect, of words. Sentences being limitless in number and words limited, we necessarily understand most sentences by construction from antecedently familiar words. Actually there is no conflict here. We can allow the sentences a monopoly of full 'meaning', in some sense, without denying that the meaning must be worked out. Then we can say that knowing words is knowing how to work out the meanings of sentences containing them. Dictionary definitions of words are mere clauses in a recursive definition of the meanings of sentences.

Bentham was perhaps the first to see the sentence thus as the primary vehicle of meaning. Frege took up the tale.[1] But Russell, in his theory of singular description, was the first to put this insight to precise and effective use. Frege and Peano had allowed singular description the status of a primitive notation; only with Russell did it become an 'incomplete symbol defined in use'. What suggested the expedient to Russell was not in fact Bentham's work, it seems, but a use of operators in the differential calculus.[2]

Russell's preoccupation with incomplete symbols began with his theory of singular descriptions in 1905. But it continued and spread, notably to classes. For background on classes we must slip back a few years. Classes were an evident source of discomfort to Russell when he was writing *Principles of Mathematics*. There was, for one thing, his epoch-making paradox. Burali-Forti had found a paradox of classes as early as 1897, but it concerned infinite ordinal numbers, and could be accommodated, one hoped, by some local adjustment of theory. On the other hand, Russell's simple paradox of the class of all classes not belonging to themselves struck at the roots. It dates from 1901, when, as Frege is said to have said, arithmetic tottered.

Russell's accommodation of the paradoxes, his theory of types, came only in 1908. In *Principles*, 1903, we find no more than tentative gropings in that direction. But *Principles* evinces much discomfort over classes also apart from the paradoxes. The further source of discomfort is the ancient problem of the one and the many. It seems strange now that Russell saw a problem in the fact that a single class might have many members, since he evidently saw no

[1] *Grundlagen der Arithmetik*, §60.   [2] Cf. *Principia Mathematica*, I, p. 24.

problem in the corresponding fact that a single attribute, or what he then called a class-concept, might apply to many things. What made the difference was that, in the bipartite ontology of *Principles of Mathematics*, classes counted as things rather than as concepts; classes existed. Russell observed against Peano that 'we must not identify the class with the class-concept', because of extensionality: classes with the same members are the same (p. 68). Since the class was not the class-concept, Russell took it not to be a concept at all; hence it has to be a thing. But then, he felt, it ought to be no more than the sum of the things in it; and here was his problem of the one and the many.

We saw that in 1905 Russell freed himself of Meinong's impossibles and the like by a doctrine of incomplete symbols. Classes were next. In his 1908 paper, 'Mathematical logic as based on the theory of types', there emerges not only the theory of types but also a doctrine of incomplete symbols for explaining classes away. This latter doctrine is designed precisely to take care of the point Russell had made against Peano in connection with extensionality. Russell's contextual definition of class notation gave the benefit of classes, namely extensionality, without assuming more than class-concepts after all.

Seeing Russell's perplexities over classes, we can understand his gratification at accommodating classes under a theory of incomplete symbols. But the paradoxes, which were the most significant of these perplexities, were not solved by his theory of incomplete symbols; they were solved, or parried, by his theory of types. One is therefore startled when Russell declares in 'My mental development' that his expedient of incomplete symbols 'made it possible to see, in a general way, how a solution of the contradictions might be possible'.[1] If the paradoxes had invested only classes and not class concepts, then Russell's elimination of classes would indeed have eliminated the paradoxes and there would have been no call for the theory of types. But the paradoxes apply likewise, as Russell knew, to class concepts, or propositional functions. And thus it was that the theory of types, in this its first full version of 1908, was developed expressly and primarily for propositional functions and then transmitted to classes only through the contextual definitions.

The startling statement that I quoted can be accounted for. It is linked to the preference that Russell was evincing, by 1908, for the phrase 'propositional function' over 'class concept'. Both phrases were current in *Principles of Mathematics*; mostly the phrase 'propositional function' was visibly meant to refer to notational forms,

---

[1] P. A. Schilpp, ed., *The Philosophy of Bertrand Russell*, p. 14.

namely open sentences, while concepts were emphatically not notational. But after laying waste Meinong's realm of being in 1905, Russell trusted concepts less and favoured the more nominalistic tone of the phrase 'propositional function', which bore the double burden. If we try to be as casual about the difference between use and mention as Russell was fifty and sixty years ago, we can see how he might feel that whereas a theory of types of real classes would be ontological, his theory of types of propositional functions had a notational cast. In so far, his withdrawal of classes would be felt as part of his solution of the paradoxes. This feeling could linger to 1943, when he wrote 'My mental development', even if its basis had lapsed.

We, careful about use and mention, can tell when Russell's so-called propositional functions must be taken as concepts, more specifically as attributes and relations, and when they may be taken as mere open sentences or predicates. It is when he quantifies over them that he reifies them, however unwittingly, as concepts. This is why no more can be claimed for his elimination of classes than I claimed for it above: a derivation of classes from attributes, or concepts, by a contextual definition framed to supply the missing extensionality. On later occasions Russell writes as if he thought that his 1908 theory, which reappeared in *Principia Mathematica*, disposed of classes in some more sweeping sense than reduction to attributes.

Just how much more sweeping a reduction he was prepared to claim may have varied over the years. Readers have credited him with explaining classes away in favour of nothing more than a nominalistic world of particulars and notations.[1] But Russell early and late has expressly doubted the dispensability of universals. Even if we were ingeniously to paraphrase all talk of qualities, for instance, into an idiom in which we talk rather of similarity to chosen particulars instancing those qualities, still, Russell more than once remarked, we should be left with one universal, the relation of similarity. Now here, in contrast to the class matter, I think Russell even concedes the Platonists too much; retention of the two-place predicate 'is similar to' is no evidence of assuming a corresponding abstract entity, the similarity relation, as long as that relation is not invoked as a value of a bound variable. A moral of all this is that inattention to referential semantics works two ways, obscuring some ontological assumptions and creating an illusion of others.

What I have ascribed to confusion can be ascribed to indifference; for we are apt to take pains over a distinction only to the degree that we think it matters. Questions as to what there is were for Russell of

[1] Hans Hahn, 'Ueberflüssige Wesenheiten', Vienna, 1928.

308

two sorts, questions of existence in his restricted sense of the term and residual questions of being—questions of what he came to call subsistence. The questions as to what subsists evidently struck him as less substantial, more idly verbal perhaps, than questions as to what exists. This bias toward the existential would explain his indiscriminate bestowal of subsistence in *Principles of Mathematics*. True, he called a halt in 1905 with his theory of descriptions; but on that occasion he was provoked by the impossibility of Meinong's impossibles. And he had even put up with those for a time. Moreover, Russell continued to be very prodigal with subsistence even after propounding his theory of descriptions. We find him saying still in 1912 that 'nearly all the words to be found in the dictionary stand for universals'.[1]

I am suggesting that through his fourth decade Russell took a critical interest in existential questions but was relatively offhand about subsistential ones. This bias explains his glee over eliminating classes, and his indifference over the status of the surviving propositional functions; for we noted that in *Principles* the classes occupied, however uneasily, the existential zone of being. To hold that classes, if there be any, must exist, while attributes at best subsist, does strike me as arbitrary; but such was Russell's attitude.

Russell's relative indifference to subsistence shows again in his treatment of meaning. Frege's three-way distinction between the expression, what it means, and what if anything it refers to, did not come naturally to Russell. In 'On denoting', 1905, he even argued against it. His argument is hard to follow; at points it seems to turn on a confusion of expressions with their meanings, and at points it seems to turn on a confusion of the expression with the mention of it, while elsewhere in the same pages Russell seems clear on both distinctions. The upshot is that 'the relation of "C" to C remains wholly mysterious; and where are we to find the denoting complex "C" which is supposed to denote C? . . . This is an inextricable tangle, and seems to prove that the whole distinction between meaning and denotation has been wrongly conceived' (p. 50).[2]

In other writings Russell commonly uses the word 'meaning' in the sense of 'reference'; thus ' "Napoleon" means a certain individual' and ' "Man" means a whole class of such particulars as have proper names'.[3] What matters more than terminology is that Russell seldom seems heedful, under any head, of a subsistent entity such as *we* might call the meaning, over and above the existent object of reference. He tends, as in the 1905 paper 'On denoting', to blur that

---

[1] *Problems of Philosophy*, p. 146.   [2] Pagination of *Logic and Knowledge*.
[3] *Analysis of Mind*, pp. 191, 194.

entity with the expression itself. Such was his general tendency with subsistents.

For my own part, I am chary of the idea of meaning and further-more I think Russell too prodigal with subsistent entities. So it would be odd of me to criticize Russell for not recognizing meanings as subsistent entities. However, the outcome that wants criticizing is just that for want of distinctions Russell tended to blur meaningless-ness with failure of reference. This was why he could not banish the king of France without first inventing the theory of descriptions. To make sense is to have a meaning, and the meaning is the reference; so 'the king of France' is meaningless, and 'The king of France is bald' is meaningful only by being short for a sentence not containing 'the king of France'. Well, even if the theory of descriptions was not needed in quite this way, it brought major clarifications and we are thankful for it.

Russell's tendency to blur subsistent entities with expressions was noticed in his talk of propositional functions. It is equally noticeable in what he says of propositions. In *Principles of Mathematics* he describes propositions as expressions, but then he speaks also of the unity of propositions (p. 50), and of the possibility of infinite pro-positions (p. 145), in ways ill suited to such a version. In 'Meinong's theory', 1904, he speaks of propositions as judgments (p. 523). There is similar oscillation in *Principia Mathematica*.

But by the time of 'The philosophy of logical atomism', 1918, the oscillation has changed direction. At one point in this essay we read, 'a proposition is just a symbol' (p. 185);[1] at a later point we read rather, 'Obviously propositions are nothing. . . . To suppose that in the actual world of nature there is a whole set of false propositions going about is to my mind monstrous' (p. 223). This repudiation is startling. We had come to expect a blur between expressions and subsistent entities, concepts; what we get instead of subsistence is nothingness. The fact is that Russell has stopped talking of sub-sistence. He stopped by 1914. What would once have counted as subsisting has been disposed of in any of three ways: identified with its expression, or repudiated utterly, or elevated to the estate of out-and-out existence. Qualities and relations come to enjoy this elevation; Russell speaks in 'The philosophy of logical atomism' of 'those ultimate simples, out of which the world is built, . . . that . . . have a kind of reality not belonging to anything else. Simples . . . are of an infinite number of sorts. There are particulars and qualities and relations of various orders, a whole hierarchy' (p. 270).

Russell's abandonment of the term 'subsistence' was an improve-

[1] Pagination of *Logic and Knowledge*.

ment. It is a quibbling term; its function is to limit existence verbally to space-time and so divert attention from ontological commitments of other than spatio-temporal kind. Better to acknowledge all posits under an inclusive and familiar heading. Posits too dubious for such recognition will then be dropped, as were propositions in some sense.

As for propositions, in particular, we saw Russell in this essay taking them as expressions part of the time and part of the time simply repudiating them. Dropping then the ambiguous epithet, we might take this to be Russell's net thought: there are no non-linguistic things that are somehow akin to sentences and asserted by them.

But this is not Russell's thought. In the same essay he insists that the world does contain non-linguistic things that are akin to sentences and asserted by them; he merely does not call them propositions. He calls them facts. It turns out that the existence of non-linguistic analogues of sentences offends Russell only where the sentences are false. His facts are what many of us would have been content to call true propositions. Russell himself called them that in 1904,[1] propositions then being judgments; and in the 1918 essay now under discussion he allows them full-fledged existence. 'Facts belong to the objective world' (p. 183). True, he says a page earlier that 'when I speak of a fact I do not mean a particular existing thing'; but he is here distinguishing between fact and thing only as between sorts of existents, paralleling the distinction between sentences and names. Facts you can assert and deny; things you can name (p. 270). Both exist; 'thing' has ceased to be coextensive with 'existent'.

Russell in this 1918 essay acknowledges Wittgenstein's influence. Russell's ontology of facts here is a reminder of Wittgenstein, but a regrettable one. Wittgenstein thought in his *Tractatus* days that true sentences mirrored nature, and this notion led him to posit things in nature for true sentences to mirror; namely, facts.

Not that Wittgenstein started Russell on facts. Russell was urging a correspondence between facts and propositions in 1912,[2] when he first knew Wittgenstein; and he equates facts with true judgments as early, we saw, as 1904. Russell had his own reason for wanting facts as entities, and Wittgenstein abetted him.

Russell was receptive to facts as entities because of his tendency to conflate meaning with reference. Sentences, being meaningful, had to stand to some sort of appropriate entities in something fairly like the relation of naming. Propositions in a non-sentential sense were unavailable, having been repudiated; so facts seemed all the more

[1] 'Meinong's theory', p. 523.   [2] *Problems of Philosophy*, pp. 198 ff.

needed. They do not exactly serve as references of false sentences, but they help. For each true or false sentence there *is* a fact, which the sentence asserts or denies according as the sentence is true or false. This two-to-one variety of reference became for Russell even a central trait distinguishing sentences from names, and so facts from things.[1]

Russell continued to champion facts, right through his *Inquiry into Meaning and Truth* and into *Human Knowledge*, 1948. In *Human Knowledge* the term applies not only to what true statements assert, but to more: 'Everything that there is in the world I call a fact' (p. 143).

Russell's predilection for a fact ontology depended, I suggested, on confusion of meaning with reference. Otherwise I think Russell would have made short shrift of facts. He would have been put off by what strikes a reader of 'The philosophy of logical atomism': how the analysis of facts rests on analysis of language. Anyway Russell does not admit facts as fundamental; atomic facts are atomic as facts go, but they are compound objects.[2] The atoms of Russell's logical atomism are not atomic facts but sense data.

In *Problems of Philosophy*, 1912, Russell had viewed both sense data and external objects as irreducible existents. We are acquainted with sense data beyond peradventure, he held, whereas our belief in external objects is fallible; still, speaking fallibly, both are real. Our belief in external objects is rooted in instinct, but it is rational of us, he held, to accept such dictates of instinct in the absence of counter-evidence (p. 39). This cheerful resignation echoes Hume and harmonizes also with the current Oxford way of justifying scientific method: scientific method is part of what 'rational' means.

Two years later, in *Our Knowledge of the External World*, Russell was more sanguine. Here it was that sense data became logical atoms for the construction of the rest of the world. Already in *Problems* he had talked of private worlds of sense data and the public space of physics, and of their correlations. Now we find him using these correlations as a means of identifying external objects with classes of sense data. He identifies external objects with classes of sense data. He identifies the external object with the class of all the views of it in private worlds, actual and ideal. In so doing he also pin-points each of the private worlds as a point in public space.

It was a great idea. If excuted with all conceivable success, it would afford translation of all discourse about the external world into terms of sense data, set theory, and logic. It would not settle induction, for we should still be in the position of predicting sense data

---

[1] 'The philosophy of logical atomism', pp. 187, 270.
[2] Ibid., pp. 198 f, 270; *Our Knowledge of the External World*, p. 54.

from sense data. But it would settle the existence of external things. It would show that assumption superfluous, or prove it true; we could read the result either way.

It would neatly settle the ontology of the external world, by reducing it to that of the set theory of sense data. In *Our Knowledge of the External World*, moreover, Russell wrote as though he had eliminated classes, and not just reduced them to attributes (cf. pp. 224 f.); so he would have looked upon the project, if successful, as resting on an ontology of sense data alone (cf. p. 153). But by 1918 he thought better of this point, as witness the recognition of 'qualities and relations . . . a whole hierarachy' lately quoted.

In *Our Knowledge of the External World* Russell expressed no confidence that the plan he sketched could be fully realized. In his sketch, as he remarked, he took other minds for granted; moreover he broached none of the vast detail that would be needed for the further constructions, except for a few illustrative steps. But the illustrations gave a vivid sense that the concepts of *Principia Mathematica* could be helpful here and the many ingenious turns and strategies of construction that went into *Principia* could be imitated to advantage. A strategy much in evidence is definition by abstraction —what Whitehead came to call *extensive abstractions*, and Carnap *quasianalysis*.

It was left to Carnap, in 1928, to be inspired to press the plan. Russell's intervening works 'The philosophy of logical atomism', *The Analysis of Matter*, and *The Analysis of Mind* might in view of their titles have been expected to further it, but they did not. The dazzling sequel to *Our Knowledge of the External World* was rather Carnap's *Der Logische Aufbau der Welt*. Carnap achieved remarkable feats of construction, starting with sense data and building explicitly, with full *Principia* techniques and *Principia* ingenuity, toward the external world. One must in the end despair of the full definitional reduction dreamed of in recent paragraphs, and it is one of the merits of the *Aufbau* that we can see from it where the obstacles lie. The worst obstacle seems to be that the assigning of sense qualities to public place-times has to be kept open to revision in the light of later experience, and so cannot be reduced to definition. The empiricist's regard for experience thus impedes the very programme of reducing the world to experience.[1]

Russell meanwhile was warping his logical atomism over from its frankly phenomenalistic form to what, influenced by Perry and Holt, he called neutral monism.[2] Neutrality here has a bias, as it often has

---

[1] This ironic way of putting the matter is due to Burton Dreben.

[2] Cf. *Analysis of Mind* (1921), p. 25; *Analysis of Matter* (1927), Ch. 37.

in politics; Russell's neutral particulars are on the side of sense data. Still, a drift has begun, and it continues. It does not reach the physicalistic pole, even in *Human Knowledge*; but there is an increasing naturalism, an increasing readiness to see philosophy as natural science trained upon itself and permitted free use of scientific findings. Russell had stated the basis for such an attitude already in 1914: 'There is not any superfine brand of knowledge, obtainable by the philosopher, which can give us a standpoint from which to criticize the whole of the knowledge of daily life. The most that can be done is to examine and purify our common knowledge by an internal scrutiny, assuming the canons by which it has been obtained'.[1]

[1] Ibid., p. 71.

ADDENDA TO CONTRIBUTION
BY GEORG KREISEL

Since this paper was written (December 1964) new results have been found which are relevant to some of the issues discussed here, in particular [11], [12], [13] below. For the convenience of readers we give below a list of problems in [10] which have since been solved, and complete some of the references in [10].

[11] Solovay has discovered several remarkable implications of the existence of large ordinals for 'ordinary' mathematics, i.e. for the theory of the continuum and countable ordinals; in particular (i): If there are measurable ordinals then some sets of natural numbers definable in the form $\forall S \exists T \forall U A \, (n, S, T, U)$, where A is arithmetic, are not constructible (note that the notion of constructible set of natural numbers refers only to countable ordinals). In fact, the constructible sets of natural numbers are not only enumerable (as Rowbottom had previously shown, reference [60] of [10]), but they are enumerated by a predicate defined in the form above. This is to appear in *Trans. Amer. Math. Soc.*: A non constructible Δ_3^1 set of integers. Another of his results, perhaps even more surprising, is this: (ii) The (formal) consistency of the assertion 'Every nondenumerable set of real numbers contains a nonempty perfect subset is finitistically equivalent to the consistency of assuming the existence of inaccessible ordinals, where each assertion is added to ZF together with the axiom of dependent choices; cf. also Mycielski, FM 53 (1964), 213.

[12] Tait has developed the theory of definitional equality, applied to several important axiomatic theories T, for constructions of finite type. He associates with each term t a *specific* computation procedure which terminates: if the value of the term is an integer, the final term is α numeral, if not it is itself a term of the axiomatic theory. The final term is the *normal form* of t. Since, in this case, the computation rules are (derived) rules of T, $t = t'$ is derivable in T when t and t' have the same normal form, say $t \equiv t'$. But he also shows that the axioms of T are satisfied if $t = t'$ is interpreted to mean that $t \equiv t'$ and so $t \equiv t' \leftrightarrow \left|\frac{}{T} t = t'\right.$

(in particular, $\left|\frac{}{T} t = t'\right.$ is recursively decidable). Philosophically, the introduction of a *specific* computation procedure is very satisfactory, because intensions are specific. His paper 'Intensional interpretations of functionals of finite type I' is to appear in the *J.S.L.*

[13] The theory of Brouwer's free choice sequences in [6] and [10] imposes strong extensionality conditions on the quantifiers $\forall \alpha \, Ex$, $\forall \alpha \exists \beta$ (by way of continuity axioms). In a sketch of a theory of Brouwer's 'thinking subject' presented at the London Congress for Logic, Methodology and Philosophy of Science (1965) I used relations $A(\alpha, x)$, $A(\alpha, \beta)$ which do not depend extensionally on their arguments, and so, not surprisingly, one asserted $\forall \alpha \exists x \, A(\alpha, x)$ or $\forall \alpha \exists \beta \, A(\alpha, \beta)$ even when neither x nor β depended extensionally on α. Myhill analysed

this situation, and found that, *even for extensional A*, $\forall \alpha \, \exists \, \beta \, A(\alpha, \beta)$ may hold when β is allowed to depend intensionally on α, without there being a continuous F such that $\forall \alpha \, A(\alpha, F\alpha)$: see his (privately circulated) 'Notes on an axiomatisation of intuitionistic analysis', where he sets up a formalism in which this distinction can be developed. The elimination of free choice sequences by contextual definitions requires a new treatment in his wider context.

Additions to [10]

p. 107 (l.536). The open problem was solved negatively by Solovay [11].

p. 109, third paragraph. Solovay and Tennenbaum have shown that Soulsin's hypothesis is consistent with the axioms *ZF*. *Bull. Amer. Math. Soc.* 72 (1966), 980–983.

p. 112, l.3. Tharp has shown that Bernays' reflection principle is even consistent with the assumption that all sets are constructible. *Notices Amer. Math. Soc.* 13 (1966), 138.

p. 114 (l.741). Many more applications to various branches of mathematics can now be found in A. Robinson's book: *Non-standard analysis*, Amsterdam (1966), North Holland Publishing Co.

p. 117 (l.8412). For details, cf. the lecture quoted in [13].

p. 132 (2.422). T_D is even a conservative extension of intuitionistic first order arithmetic by [12]. (It is trivial that T_E is a conservative extension.) pp. 135–141. The proof theoretic results mentioned which concern elementary intuitionistic analysis H, the (first) continuity axiom (2.511), the bar theorem of type 0 (2.6231), and of type 1 (2.6235), have now been published in full: W. A. Howard and G. Kreisel, 'Transfinite induction and bar induction of types 0 and 1, and the role of continuity in intuitionistic analysis', *J.S.L.* 31 (1966).

p. 142 (last paragraph) and p. 146 (2.741). A reduction of the theory of free choice sequences to the theory of absolutely lawless sequences is now available, cf. the lecture quoted in [13]. In this way $\sim[(\alpha)_B \sim \sim(Ex)A(\bar{\alpha}x) \supset (\alpha)_B(Ex)A(\bar{\alpha}x)]$, and thus the incompleteness of Heyting's predicate calculus (for the intuitionistic logic of propositions concerning freely chosen objects) are established with less problematic assumptions than before.

p. 165 (bottom). Tait has obtained a simple completeness proof of Takeuti's 'cut free' rules for analysis (by use of the intended model of analysis): *Bull. Amer. Math. Soc.* 72 (1966).

p. 175 (3.53). Feferman has now formulated a system of predicative set theory which is a conservative extension of his predicative analysis IR; *Bull. Amer. Math. Soc.* 72 (1966), 486–489.

p. 180, l.8. The proof (due to Howard) that the full axiom of choice (4.12) follows from the bar theorem (4.2121) by classical logic, appears in our joint paper l.c.

p. 195 [68] appeared in *J.S.L.* 30 (1965), 175–192; [69] was not submitted for publication.

[73] appeared in *Amer. J. Math.* 87 (1965), 605–648 and *Annals of Maths.* 83 (1966), 437–456.

THE CONTRIBUTORS

PROFESSOR ALFRED JULES AYER, FBA. 1952.

He has been the Wykeham Professor of Logic in the University of Oxford since 1959; he was born on October 29, 1910, and educated at Eton College and Christchurch, Oxford; publications include *Language, Truth and Logic, The Foundations of Empirical Knowledge, Thinking and Meaning, British Empirical Philosophers, Philosophical Essays, The Problem of Knowledge, Logical Positivism, Privacy, Philosophy and Language,* and *The Concept of a Person and Other Essays.*

PROFESSOR WERNER BLOCH

Professor Bloch was born on March 5, 1893, and educated at Freiburg and Strasbourg Universities. He has been Head Physician in the Surgical Department at St Gertrauden Hospital, Berlin, since 1940 and a Professor of the Free University of Berlin since 1951; a member of the Executive Board of the German Surgical Society since 1950; publications include *Die Knochenbruchheilung, Die Durchbhitungsstörungen der Gliedmassen, Misserfolge und Beschwerden nach Gallensteinoperationen, Wundheilungsprobleme* and articles on bone surgery in a variety of German technical magazines.

DR MAX BORN, FRS, 1939; FRSE; MA(Cantab.); DRPHIL(Göttingen); HONSCD(Bristol); HONDRESSC(Bordeaux); HONDSC (Oxford); HONLLD(Edinburgh); HONDRRERNAT(Frieburg i.B.); HONDRING(Stuttgart); HONDSC(Oslo); HONDSC(Bruxelles); HON DRRERNAT(Humbolt Univ., Berlin); Tait Professor of Natural Philosophy, Univ. of Edinburgh, 1936–53; Professor Emeritus, 1953; awarded Nobel Prize for Physics (jointly) 1954.

He was born on December 11, 1882, and educated at the Gymnasium, Breslau and the Universities of Breslau, Heidelberg, Zurich, Göttingen and Cambridge; awarded the Nobel Prize for Physics; principal publications include *Einstein's Theory of Relativity, Problems of Atomic Dynamics, Mechanics of the Atom, Atom Physics, The Restless Universe, Natural Philosophy of Cause and Chance, A General Kinetic Theory of Liquids* (with H. S. Green), *Theory of Crystal Lattices* (with Kun Huang), *Physics in my Generation, Principles of Optics* (with E. Wolf) and *Physics and Politics.*

PROFESSOR C. D. BROAD, MA, LITD(Cantab.); HONLLD(Aberdeen, Bristol, Dublin); Hon. Doctor of Philosophy (Uppsala);

FBA; Knightbridge Professor of Moral Philosophy, Cambridge Univ. 1933–53.

He was born on December 30, 1887, and educated at Dulwich College and Trinity College, Cambridge; publications include *Perception, Physics and Reality, Scientific Thought, Mind and its Place in Nature, The Philosophy of Francis Bacon, Five Types of Ethical Theory, Examination of McTaggart's Philosophy, Ethics and the History of Philosophy, Psychical Research, Religion and Philosophy* and *Lectures on Psychical Research*.

PROFESSOR ERICH FROMM, PHD.

Professor Fromm is a Psychoanalyst and a Professor at New York University. He was born on March 23, 1900, and educated at the University of Heidelberg, the University of Munich and the Psycho-Analytic Institute in Berlin; publications include *Psycho-Analysis and Religion, The Forgotten Language, The Sane Society, Sigmund Freud's Mission* and *The Dogma of Christ and Other Essays on Religion, Psychology and Culture*.

ALDOUS HUXLEY, writer, Companion, Royal Society of Literature (CLIT), 1962.

He was born on July 26, 1894, and died on November 22, 1963. He was educated at Eton and Balliol College, Oxford; publications include *Chrome Yellow, Antic Hay, Those Barren Leaves, Point Counter Point, Brave New World, Beyond the Mexique Bay, Eyeless in Gaza, After Many a Summer, The Perennial Philosophy, Science, Liberty and Peace, Ape and Essence, The Doors of Perception, The Genius and the Goddess, Brave New World Revisited, Island* and *Literature and Science*.

PROFESSOR GEORG KREISEL

Professor Kreisel was born in Austria; educated in Austria, England (Trinity College, Cambridge) and USA (Institute for Advanced Study, Princeton). He was recently Professor of Mathematics at the University of Paris and is now Professor of Logic and the Foundations of Mathematics at Stanford University, California.

LADY CONSTANCE MALLESON (Collette O'Niel)

She was born in October 1895 and educated at Dresden, Paris and R.A.D.A., London; publications include *After Ten Years, Fear in the Heart, In the North: Autobiographical Fragments in Norway, Sweden and Finland, 1936–1946, Queen Margaret of Norway* (translation from Norwegian of Trygve Kielland's historical play), Editor—*As the Sight is Bent*: the unfinished autobiography of Mabel M. Annesley).

PROFESSOR LINUS PAULING, BS, Oregon State College, 1922; HONPHD, Calif. Institute of Technology, 1925; SCD, Univ. of Chicago, 1941; Princeton, 1946; HONLHD, Tampa, 1950; UJD, Univ. New Brunswick, 1950; DSC(Hon.) Cambridge, 1947; London, 1947; Yale, 1947; Oxford, 1948; LLD, Reed College, 1959; Dr honoris causa, Paris, 1948; Toulouse, 1949; Univ. Liege, 1955, Montpellier, 1958; Dr of Fine Arts, Chouinard Art Institute, 1958.

He has been Chairman of the Chemistry Division of the California Institute of Technology since 1931 and Director of the Gates and Crellin Laboratories of Chemistry. He was born on February 28, 1901, and educated at Oregon State College, the California Institute of Technology and the Universities of Munich, Copenhagen and Zurich. He is the holder of two Nobel Prizes; publications include *The Structure of Line Spectra* (with S. Goudinsit), *Introduction of Quantum Mechanics with Applications to Chemistry* (with E. Bright Wilson, Jnr.), *The Nature of the Chemical Bond*, *General Chemistry*, *College Chemistry* and *No More War!*

DR VICTOR PURCELL, CMG, 1946; PHD, LITTD (Cantab.)

He was born on January 26, 1896, and died on January 2, 1965. Before his death he was the lecturer in Far Eastern History at Cambridge University; educated at Bancroft's School and Trinity College, Cambridge. He joined the Malayan Civil Service shortly after World War I and served in China and Malaya for the following 25 years; publications include *The Further Side of No-Man's Land*, *The Spirit of Chinese Poetry*, *An Index to the Chinese Written Language*, *Problems of Chinese Education*, *Chinese Evergreen*, *Cadmus*, *Malaya*, *The Chinese in Malaya*, *The Chinese in South-East Asia*, *The Colonial Period in South-East Asia*, *Malaya: Communist or Free*, *China* (*Nations of the Modern World*), *The Revolution in South-East Asia* and *A Background to the Boxer Uprising*.

PROFESSOR HILARY PUTNAM, BA, PHD

Professor Putnam was born in 1926 and educated at the University of Pennsylvania, Harvard University and the University of California at Los Angeles; now Professor of Philosophy at Harvard University; publications include articles in both Mathematics and Philosophy.

PROFESSOR WILLARD VAN ORMAN QUINE

Professor Quine was born in 1908 and is one of the outstanding philosophers and logicians in the United States. His major works include *From a Logical Point of View*, *Word and Object* and *Set Theory and its Logic*. He is currently a Professor of

Philosophy at Harvard University and is a Fellow of the American Philosophical Society, the American Philosophical Association, the American Academy of Arts and Sciences and a former President of the Association for Symbolic Logic. He graduated with a Ph.D. from Harvard College in 1932.

SIR HERBERT READ, Kt, cr. 1953; DSO, 1918; MC; LITTD(Hon. Leeds); MA(Edin.); Director Routledge & Kegan Paul Ltd., Publishers.

He was born on December 4, 1893, and educated at Crossley's School, Halifax, and the University of Leeds. His publications include *Naked Warriors, Eclogues, Mutations and the Phoenix, In Retreat, Reason and Romanticism, English Prose Style, Phases of English Poetry, The Sense of Glory, The Meaning of Art, Form in Modern Poetry, The Innocent Eye, Art Now, The End of a War, Art and Industry, Poems 1914–1934, The Green Child: In defence of Shelley, Art and Society, Poetry and Anarchism, The Knapsack, The Politics of the Unpolitical, Education through Art, A World Within a War* (poems), *A Coat of Many Colours, The Grass Roots of Art, Education for Peace, The Philosophy of Modern Art, The True Voice of Feeling, Icon and Idea, Moon's Farm* (poems), *The Art of Sculpture, The Tenth Muse, A Concise History of Modern Painting, The Forms of Things Unknown, A Letter to a Young Painter, To Hell with Culture* and *The Contrary Experience*.

HANS REICHENBACH

Hans Reichenbach was a leading philosopher in the inner circle and an outstanding exponent of a scientific philosophy. Reichenbach was a distinguished physicist and an engineer before taking up philosophy and had a great influence both on the Continent and in the United States.

PROFESSOR MARIA REICHENBACH, PHD

Professor Reichenbach is Professor of Philosophy at Los Angeles City College. She was born March 30, 1909, and was educated at the University of Freiberg and University of California, Los Angeles; she is a translator of the *Theory of Probability* and the *Philosophy of Space and Time* and editor of the *Direction of Time*.

PROFESSOR DANA SCOTT

Professor Scott was born in Berkeley, California, on October 11, 1932; educated at the University of California, Berkeley and at Princeton University; now Associate Professor of Logic and Mathematics at Stanford University, California; publications include research papers in Logic and Set Theory.

THE REV. GUTHRIE MICHAEL SCOTT

Fr Scott is Honorary Director of the African Bureau in London and has been an Anglican priest in the diocese of Chichester since 1950. He was born on July 30, 1907, and educated at Kings College, Taunton; St Paul's College, Grahamstown, South Africa, and Chichester Theological College. In 1947 he appealed to the United Nations on behalf of two Tribes of the South West African Mandated Territory; attended sessions of the General Assembly at the Chiefs' request and was granted a hearing by the Fourth Committee in 1949, 1950 and 1955; took part in the formation of the Africa Bureau; publications include *Shadow over Africa, Attitude to Africa, African Episode* and *The Orphans' Heritage.*

I. F. STONE

I. F. Stone, an American writer and newspaperman, was born on December 24, 1907, and educated in schools in Richmond, Indiana, and Haddonfield, New Jersey, and at the University of Pennsylvania. Between 1933 and 1952 he worked on various newspapers, including the *New York Post, The Nation, P.M.,* the *New York Star* and the *Daily Compass.* In 1952 he launched his own newsletter, *I. F. Stone's Weekly,* which fought for civil liberties and peace through the McCarthy and Cold War years; publications include *The Court Disposes, Business as Usual, Underground to Palestine, This is Israel, The Hidden History of the Korean War, The Truman Era* and *The Haunted Fifties.*

JULIAN OTTO TREVELYAN

He is a painter and member of the London Group and engraving tutor at the Royal College of Art. He was born on February 20, 1910, and was educated at Bedales and Trinity College, Cambridge, and studied art in Paris at Atelier 17. His publications include *Indigo Days, The Artist and his World* and *Etching.*

INDEX